A LIFETIME OF INTELLIGENCE

A LIFETIME OF INTELLIGENCE

Follow-Up Studies of the Scottish Mental Surveys of 1932 and 1947

Ian J. Deary, Lawrence J. Whalley, and John M. Starr

American Psychological Association • Washington, DC

Published by
American Psychological Association
750 First Street, NE
Washington, DC 20002
www.apa.org

To order
APA Order Department
P.O. Box 92984
Washington, DC 20090-2984
Tel: (800) 374-2721; Direct: (202) 336-5510
Fax: (202) 336-5502; TDD/TTY: (202) 336-6123
Online: www.apa.org/books/
E-mail: order@apa.org

In the U.K., Europe, Africa, and the Middle East, copies may be ordered from
American Psychological Association
3 Henrietta Street
Covent Garden, London
WC2E 8LU England

Typeset in Goudy by Circle Graphics, Columbia, MD

Printer: Maple-Vail Book Manufacturing Group, Binghamton, NY
Cover Designer: Mercury Publishing Services, Rockville, MD
Technical/Production Editor: Devon Bourexis

The opinions and statements published are the responsibility of the authors, and such opinions and statements do not necessarily represent the policies of the American Psychological Association.

Library of Congress Cataloging-in-Publication Data

Deary, Ian J.
  A lifetime of intelligence : follow-up studies of the Scottish mental surveys of 1932 and 1947 / Ian J. Deary, Lawrence J. Whalley, and John M. Starr.
    p. cm.
  Includes bibliographical references and index.
  ISBN-13: 978-1-4338-0400-7
  ISBN-10: 1-4338-0400-X
  1. Intellect. I. Whalley, Lawrence J. II. Starr, John M. III. Title.

  BF431.D3545 2009
  153.9'309411—dc22

2008016667

British Library Cataloguing-in-Publication Data
A CIP record is available from the British Library.

Printed in the United States of America
First Edition

This book is dedicated to the Scottish Council for Research in Education; Professor Sir Godfrey Hilton Thomson; participants in the Scottish Mental Surveys of 1932 and 1947; the Aberdeen Birth Cohort 1921, the Lothian Birth Cohort 1921, the Aberdeen Birth Cohort 1936, and the Lothian Birth Cohort 1936; and our research teams and collaborators.

CONTENTS

PREFACE

In *The Trend of Scottish Intelligence: A Comparison of the 1947 and 1932 Surveys of the Intelligence of Eleven-Year-Old Pupils* (Scottish Council for Research in Education [SCRE], 1949), Professor Sir Godfrey H. Thomson said,

> I have had for thirty years a very wide experience of making, using, and following up the results of group tests. Few can be more fully aware of their dangers and pitfalls than I am. They are, of course, like all human instruments, far from infallible: but they are less fallible than most other methods of estimating human ability—at any rate, at estimating ability in a comparatively short time, as is often necessary. We must not make the better the enemy of the good. It is a common error of judgment to say (as one can of most things) "this is not perfect," and then to add "so away with it." Of course group intelligence tests are not perfect. But in the absence of any better alternative at present, we must use the group tests and their correlations with the numerous social facts we have collected, while bearing in mind throughout the very many limitations to which these tests are subject. (pp. xiv–xv; see also Figure 1, this volume)

Figure 1. Professor Sir Godfrey H. Thomson, author of the Moray House Test series, member of the Scottish Mental Survey of 1932 Committee, and chairman of the Scottish Mental Survey of 1947 Committee.

REDISCOVERING THE SCOTTISH MENTAL SURVEYS OF 1932 AND 1947

In 1932, Scotland undertook the ambitious task of giving intelligence tests to every 11-year-old child in the country. The aims were to use the data gathered from these 11-year-olds to quantify "mental deficiencies" and the distribution of intelligence in the community. In 1947, Scotland did a similar survey on 11-year-olds again, only this time the aim was to determine whether the country's children were, on average, less intelligent than the previously tested children had been. The data were analyzed and published in a series of monographs, and then no one paid much attention to the data for a long time after that.

Here is how we, the authors of this book, came across the data from the Scottish Mental Surveys (SMSs) of 1932 and 1947 (SMS1932 and SMS 1947). On June 1, 1997,[1] a Sunday, Lawrence Whalley and his wife, Patricia, visited Ian Deary and his wife, Ann, at their home in Edinburgh. Whalley mentioned that there was a cohort of individuals in Aberdeen, born in 1921, on whom there was information about cardiovascular disease. Would they be of interest with regard to any cognitive decrements? Deary replied that they would not because truly estimating a decrement requires a premorbid measure of cognition. The idea was shelved. In the following days, Deary was reading a copy of *Dysgenics* (Lynn, 1996) that had been sent to him by the author. On pages 102 and 103, he read the following:

> In 1932 the intelligence of all Scottish 11-year-olds, numbering 70,805 [Lynn is incorrect; this is the number tested in the SMS1947], was assessed with a group verbal–educational test. The same test was administered again to all Scottish 11-year-olds in 1947. The 1947 children showed a gain of 2.2 IQ points (SCRE, 1949).

---

[1]The date is ironic. It was 65 years to the day since the Scottish Mental Survey of 1932, something that Whalley and Deary knew nothing about at that time.

Figure 2. Ledgers containing the data from the Scottish Mental Surveys of 1932 (SMS1932) and 1947 (SMS1947). The ledgers in the second-top shelf on the left are from the SMS1932. The ledgers on the top shelf on the left and on the third-top shelf on the right are from the SMS1947. There are blue (boys) and pink (girls) folders that contain data from a small number of individual participants from the 6-Day Sample of the SMS1947. The photograph was taken in a temporary, secure storage location shortly after the Scottish Council for Research in Education moved from Edinburgh premises to the University of Glasgow. All SMS materials are now in the Special Collection Archives of the University of Glasgow in Scotland.

He called Whalley back. There might be premorbid cognitive ability data on people born in 1932 after all. The Aberdeen cardiovascular disease sample was forgotten; there were bigger fish to fry. Whalley followed the lead and established the whereabouts of SCRE (Craigie, 1972) and their secure data store. Patricia Whalley visited and was the first of us to view the SMS1932 ledgers (see Figure 2). Whalley recalls what Deary's reply was when he called to tell Deary that the data had been located: "This will change our lives." It is not to Deary's credit that having by then published research on psychometric intelligence for 15 years, he had not been aware of the SMSs previously.

When, in mid-1997, we stumbled on literature mentioning the SMSs, we were excited to learn more. Unlike other intelligence studies, the SMSs had tested an entire population instead of a sample. Furthermore, the availability of childhood test scores of this entire (now aging) population allowed unprecedented opportunities for longitudinal research. We decided to follow up on many of the children (who were now old men and women) to see what had become of them and how they had aged. The aim was to discover the factors—biological and sociobehavioral—that were associated with cognitive aging. What followed over the next 10 years were extensive follow-up studies about the extent to which the original test-takers had aged cognitively and the factors associated with this aging. We used various techniques to study the surviving test-takers, including molecular genetic analyses, brain imaging, interviews, and cognitive testing.

This book is a reasonably full account of the work we have done in 10 years (1997–2007) of following up the SMS1932 and SMS1947. It contains readable, pithy summaries of almost all the published work on the surveys, brought together for the first time as a body of work. Many people we have met want a summary of the work done by the SCRE on the SMSs. More people than we can recall have professed never to have come across this or that study we published from the surveys. We regularly received comments—one is tempted to say *complaints*—that we publish very widely, in journals and disciplines that people never get to or are unaware of. An ensemble of the work was needed.

This book may be considered "Monograph No. 8" from the SMSs. Or perhaps Monograph No. 9, if one counts Hope's (1984) reanalysis, although his volume was not devoted to the SMSs alone.

SCOPES AND METHODS OF OUR FOLLOW-UP STUDIES

The reader will note that the scopes and methods of the studies in this volume vary greatly. For example, sample sizes change from page to page, sometimes from paragraph to paragraph. Certain cohorts are used in certain studies but not in others. This variation results from the pragmatic nature of the longitudinal studies conducted. The studies were not part of an institutionally funded cohort study but instead were dependent on project-type funding. Because the funding bodies wanted to see a specific project for this or that outcome based on this or that predictor, the sample sizes and variables changed from study to study, mostly on the basis of the type of funding that was available at the time.

WHAT THIS BOOK DOES AND DOES NOT INCLUDE

We should explain what sort of book this is and why we constructed it so. Although we have published various findings of our follow-up studies in many different journals, to date these findings have not been compiled into a single volume. This book serves as such a compilation, integrating 10 years (1997–2007) of extensive research with these unique samples of individuals. The research is unlike any other in the field, for two reasons: (a) It captures a lifetime of intelligence, from age 11 to about age 80, and (b) unlike other studies on intelligence and individual differences, many of these studies consider a total population rather than a sample.

The book had to be an account of the work that would not date, or that would date least badly. For this, we had the model of the monographs of the SMS1932 and SMS1947 themselves. They are set in specific times, but as accounts of the surveys they are timeless. The monographs are just as useful now as they were when they were written, because the bulk of each of them describes data: their collection, analysis, and meanings. They abjure, as we have here, two routes to being archaic.

First, there is not too much space devoted to prior literature. That way, the surveys' monographs have not become a useless literature review that stops at the point of their being published. A certain amount of setting is necessary and is provided here. Examples of the main prior studies that led to each of our reports are recorded, but only enough to afford an understanding of why a study was performed. There was nothing to be gained here by relisting all of the introductory references, which may easily be found in our original publications, which are cited. The emphasis here is on what was found in each of our published studies and how they fit together.

Second, there is not too much integration of the findings with other, contemporaneous literature. Again, to devote too much space to this would have the same effect of bringing the account to a cliff edge at the time of any one publication. There is enough by way of discussion to set the findings among other literature, and there are indications of work that was done and is being pursued after the study was published, but the bulk of the account has to be on the findings themselves.

Another decision we made was not to publish, herein, too many of our otherwise-unpublished findings. Most of the data that we think are useful have been reported in peer-reviewed journals. We were aware that any new findings reported here would forever be the objects of suspicion: that they could not be published, that others had not reviewed them, that they exist in a gray literature. As a result of our decision to deal almost entirely with what had already been published, readers can obtain more information about the studies described in this volume from the original journal articles.

ORGANIZATION OF THIS BOOK

Part I of this volume, which consists of chapter 1, provides a historical background by summarizing the work done for the original SMS1932 and

SMS1947. Scope, method, and results for both surveys are provided. The information for this chapter comes directly from the monographs published in the wake of the surveys by the SCRE, which administered the surveys.

Parts II, III, IV, and V summarize the findings of our follow-up research.

In Part II, which consists of chapters 2 through 4, we discuss findings relevant to epidemiology—that is, whether intelligence at age 11 relates to physical and mental illness later in life, or survival to old age. In chapter 2, we discuss the relationship between childhood intelligence and all-cause mortality. In chapter 3, we address the relationship between childhood intelligence and specific causes of death and mortality-related physical factors, and in chapter 4, we discuss the relationship between childhood intelligence and mental illness.

Part III, which consists of chapters 5 through 7, is the heart of our findings. It addresses the original question that we sought to answer: What causes cognitive aging? We looked for correlations between cognitive aging and various biological and health-related factors, including genes, brain structure, smoking, physical fitness, dietary supplements, and so forth. In chapter 5, we describe our process of recruiting the cohorts for this research on cognitive aging, and we report the stability of intelligence differences across almost 70 years. In chapter 6, we discuss the findings on biological factors related to cognitive aging, and in chapter 7 we discuss the findings on health and nutrition-related factors associated with cognitive aging.

Although findings on determinants of cognitive aging (the topic of Part III) are the heart of the research, we first discuss findings on epidemiology (the topic of Part II) because the epidemiology findings also explain how individuals were tracked down to take part in the studies explained in the cognitive aging research.

In Part IV, which consists of chapters 8 and 9, we address other things associated with childhood IQ. In chapter 8, we discuss prior influences of childhood IQ, including sex, birth weight, and being a twin. In chapter 9, we focus on lifetime consequences associated with childhood IQ, including marriage, social mobility, quality of life, and personality.

In Part V, which consists of chapter 10, we discuss the possibility of estimating childhood intelligence without baseline data from early life. Although researchers and clinicians have sought to estimate childhood intelligence using various tests, the tests have lacked longitudinal validity, because not enough data were available to validate them. Using the baseline childhood data from the original SMSs and the data from our follow-up studies, we were able to validate one test, the National Adult Reading Test (Nelson & Willison, 1991).

Finally, in the Postscript we turn our attention to new research that is being conducted on an Edinburgh-based sample of surviving test-takers of the SMS1947: the Lothian Birth Cohort 1936. This sample, which we expect will keep us busy over the next 10 years, is the largest follow-up sample to date.

ACKNOWLEDGMENTS

The directors and employees of the Scottish Council for Research in Education (SCRE) have been wonderful and generous colleagues. We thank the three directors with whom we worked: Wynne Harlen, Valerie Wilson, and Paul Brna, in order of their being in the post. We are also grateful to Graham Thorpe and Rosemary Wake and other SCRE staff with whom we have worked. The SCRE permitted access to the Scottish Mental Surveys (SMSs) of 1932 and 1947 (SMS1932 and SMS1947). Most of all, we are grateful that they conducted the surveys in the first instance and were then far-sighted enough to retain the information for many years and through several changes of location.

The work on the SMSs involved many members of the research teams in Aberdeen and Edinburgh and many specialist collaborators on various projects. The special nature of the samples and the data meant that we benefited from enthusiastic coworkers. First, we thank those who worked with us to trace, recruit, examine, and retain surviving participants of the SMS1932 and SMS1947: Caroline Brett, Margaret Chalmers, Janie Corley, Paula Davies, Helen Fox, Alan Gow, Caroline Graham, Jen Herbert, David Hunter, Steven Leaper, Helen Lemmon, Alison Pattie, Susan Shenkin, Mariesha Struth, Michelle Taylor, and Martha Whiteman. We thank the nurses and other staff at the research clinics in Aberdeen and the Wellcome Trust Clinical Research Facility at the Western General Hospital, Edinburgh. We thank all of our scientific collaborators and coauthors, whose names appear in the asterisked publications listed in the references. John Crawford was important in the design of mental test batteries in Aberdeen and a valued coauthor. Our work is highly collaborative, and without their generous sharing of their expertise there would have been little to tell. In the study of genetic associations of cognition and aging we especially thank Beben Benyamin, Jerome Breen, Andrew Carothers, Sarah Harris, Caroline Hayward, Tia Kachiwala, David Porteous, Paul Shiels, and Pippa Thomson, Jonathan Seckl, David St. Clair, Peter Visscher, and Alan Wright. In our brain imaging work we are indebted to Mark Bastin, Jon Clayden, Alison Murray, Roger Staff, and Joanna Wardlaw. The nutritional work was the result of valuable collaboration with Andrew Collins, Susan Duthie, and Klaus Wahle. In the execution of the epidemiology work we have especially enjoyed working with David Batty, George Davey Smith, Carole Hart, Pauline MacKinnon, Beverly Shipley, and Michelle Taylor. We remember the late David Hole especially fondly. Valuable medical, psychiatric, and ophthalmological collaborations were provided by Richard Athawes, Bal Dhillon, Pauline McConville, Brian McGurn, Niall Patton, and Nicholas Walker. Work on quality of life was completed with the help and expertise of Gillian Bain and Saskia Teunisse. Lindsay Paterson kindly read the manuscript and made many improving suggestions. We are grateful to Joanna Deary for obtaining permissions to reprint tables and figures and for reading the proofs.

During a substantial proportion of the decade's work on the SMSs, Ian J. Deary was the recipient of a Royal Society–Wolfson Research Merit Award, and Lawrence J. Whalley received a Wellcome Trust Career Development Award. We are also grateful to the following bodies that funded important aspects of the research on cognitive aging and cognitive epidemiology: the Alzheimer Research Trust; the Biotechnology and Biological Sciences Research Council; the British Academy; Chest, Heart & Stroke Scotland; the Economic and Social Research Council; Help The Aged; Henry Smith's Charities; the Medical Research Council; Research Into Ageing; the Royal Society; and the Scottish Executive's Health Department's Chief Scientist Office.

The SMSs were not the only remarkable Scottish database used in this research. We are also grateful to Michael Barfoot and his team at the Lothian Health Archive in the University of Edinburgh, James Boyd and his team at the National Health Service Scotland's Information and Statistics Division, the Directors of Public Health in Edinburgh and Aberdeen and their teams working on the respective Community Health Indices, and Carole Hart and the team involved in the Midspan Studies at the University of Glasgow.

I

HISTORICAL OVERVIEW

HISTORICAL OVERVIEW

To understand the context of our follow-up studies, it is necessary to understand the work performed for the original Scottish Mental Surveys of 1932 and 1947. Why were the surveys conducted? How was the content of the surveys chosen and validated? How were the surveys administered? What findings were published, and how were the raw data archived?

Part I provides this basic overview of the original surveys. Because the purpose of this book is to convey the findings of our follow-up studies, we provide only enough detail on the original surveys as is necessary to understand the context for our follow-up studies.

1

THE SCOTTISH MENTAL SURVEYS OF 1932 AND 1947

The body that organized and published the results of the Scottish Mental Surveys of 1932 and 1947 (SMS1932 and SMS1947) was the Scottish Council for Research in Education (SCRE; Craigie, 1972). For most of its history, the SCRE was an autonomous research body, not part of any university, college, or other educational institution. Since 2002, it has been known as the SCRE Centre at the University of Glasgow (Scotland, United Kingdom). Researchers at the SCRE retained the raw data from the SMS1932 and SMS1947 and, in 2007, deposited them in the archives of the University of Glasgow. The SCRE originally published the results of the surveys. Most of the individuals who planned, executed, and wrote up the results of the SMS1932 and SMS1947 were not employed by or primarily affiliated with the SCRE. The SCRE provided the rallying point for the collaboration; it was the nodal point in a network. The salaried staff of the SCRE between its institution in 1928 and 1946 comprised just an honorary director, a secretarial assistant, and a clerkess (SCRE, 1953a).

The SCRE's wide representation was one of the factors in its success. Experts volunteered assistance with studies. For example, very senior academics,

---

The writing of this chapter was supported by research grant RES-000-23-1246 from the UK Economic and Social Research Council.

such as Professor Godfrey H. Thomson (1969), undertook huge design and ana-lytic tasks for the SCRE's research projects. Education authorities gave funding and permitted studies to take place in their geographic areas. Directors of edu-cation helped with the distribution of tests for studies. The Educational Insti-tute of Scotland (EIS), the body representing teachers, provided the SCRE's regular funding, and the EIS's members—the teachers—gathered data and administered and scored thousands of tests. All of this was helped by the fact that Scotland was one of the first countries to have a large proportion of teach-ers with degrees, and its universities were active in teaching educational research.

THE SCOTTISH MENTAL SURVEY OF 1932

The rationale, methods, and results of SMS1932 were reported in a monograph (SCRE, 1933). The monograph itself exemplifies the way in which the SCRE acted as a banner under which many busy, important, and famous individuals rallied and served, without much individual recognition. The dust jacket and book cover of the monograph contain no author, just the title: *The Intelligence of Scottish Children: A National Survey of an Age-Group.* The book's title page (SCRE, 1933, p. iii) and preface (SCRE, 1933, p. viii) have no author listed. Pages ix through x of the monograph list the 23 mem-bers of the Mental Survey Committee, with W. A. F. Hepburn (Director of Education, Ayrshire Education Committee) identified as chairman.

This near-anonymous, quietly reported study was "The most ambitious project which The Scottish Council for Research in Education have so far undertaken" (SCRE, 1933, p. vii). Its scope was comprehensive: Every child born in 1921 was to be included and tested. The cooperation was complete: All of Scotland's 35 Education Committees agreed that schools in their regions might be tested. Teachers and officials undertook the group testing. Schoolteachers and staff and students at the Moray House Training College (Edinburgh's teacher training college) scored the tests and the tabulated these, gratis, in their own time. Some funding was donated by the Carnegie Corporation of America, because the data were to be used by the Interna-tional Examinations Enquiry.

Planning the Scottish Mental Survey of 1932

The Mental Survey Committee of the SCRE comprised SCRE officers, directors of education in Scotland, school rectors (headmasters; they were all men), education committee psychologists, school medical officers, and teacher training college principals. There were two university psychologists, both at the University of Edinburgh: James Drever, Professor of Psychology, and Godfrey H. Thomson, Professor of Education. G. H. Thomson was chairman of the Sub-Committee on Group Testing and of the Statistical Sub-Committee of the SMS1932. He devised and supplied the mental test and oversaw the analysis of the data. Materials in the SCRE archives at the University of Glasgow show large-scale workings in G. H. Thomson's own hand.

The SMS1932 was undertaken at a time when mental testing was a new technology and thought by some to have potential for broad application in school policymaking. The report discussed briefly the massive mental testing of almost 2,000,000 Army recruits in the United States during World War I, which had established the feasibility and utility of group-based cognitive assessment. By the early 1930s, such tests were being used in the United Kingdom for entrance examinations to the Civil Service, and here and there to decide on school scholarships in the move from primary education (up to ages 11 and 12) to secondary school education. Tests were used in some places to identify gifted pupils as well as those whose ability was too low to benefit from the normal school system. The latter purpose was the reason why Binet had devised mental tests originally (Zenderland, 1998). The SCRE had concluded that little was known about the distribution of mental ability in the Scottish community and that there were often "generalisations of an alarmist nature" (SCRE, 1933, pp. 4–5) about the increasing numbers of people with so-called mental deficiency in the population. More empirical information was needed, especially because the 1929 report of the Mental Deficiency Committee in England was perceived to be useful.

> Professor Drever with this in mind made the suggestion that The Scottish Council for Research in Education should undertake a mental survey in Scotland. At the Council Meeting on 16th May 1931 the Council approved of the decision of its Executive Committee to proceed with a survey of mental deficiency in Scotland. (SCRE, 1933, p. 5)

After making the decision, they decided to extend the survey to cover the whole range of intelligence. The Mental Survey Committee decided to test a whole population age group instead of a random sample because the former would be easier, given the problems of recruiting a truly representative sample.

Thought was given to the issues of special types of children. Two types of bilingual child were discussed. The 1931 census recorded 137,149 Gaelic-speaking people among the whole population (2.8%), of whom only 0.15% spoke Gaelic exclusively. Therefore, Gaelic-speaking children were considered to have sufficient English proficiency to take the test in that language. Similarly, groups of Lithuanian pupils in Lanarkshire and its surrounding counties were considered bilingual and with enough proficiency in English to take the test. Blind and deaf children were excluded because of the problems of constructing tests of equal difficulty for these groups. The majority of

Scotland's children were and are educated in state-run schools. These all agreed to take part. Most of the private schools also took part in the study. Children in residential institutions also were tested. Attempts were made to contact children deemed "ineducable," who, by having such a status, fell outside the jurisdiction of the education authorities.

Whom to Test?

The decision to test only those children born in 1921 was a compromise between pupils' being too young fully to understand and follow test instructions, and being older pupils who might already have taken group tests and be more difficult to follow up later. In fact, in one district of Scotland all children born in the years 1921, 1922, and 1923 were tested (SCRE, 1933, p. 67).

When to Test?

School testing typically was done in February, but there was too much illness at this time, and too many pupils were absent from school because roads, especially in rural areas, were impassable because of snow. The school holidays extended from June to September. November was ruled out because too many pupils were ill after the potato-lifting holidays in October. June 1 was chosen.

Which Group Mental Test to Use?

The committee invited tenders for the supply of tests. However, the cost of £700 for the necessary 100,000 tests was considered too great. G. H. Thomson offered one of the group tests he had used for scholarship examinations in England. It was one of the tests from the Moray House Test series (G. H. Thomson, 1940). Hereinafter we call it the *Moray House Test* (MHT). These tests would typically be used to place children from primary to secondary school education. Such school places were considered valuable, and the problem of "wastage" of places—by pupils who failed to complete the courses—was a priority for research (McClelland, 1942). The test was aimed to discriminate among the brighter pupils. At that time, the proportion of people transferring to secondary education for courses that would take them past 14 years was less than the proportion of the Scottish population that now attends university, which keeps them in education until their 20s. The committee devised some nonverbal picture tests to augment the main group test, lest there was insufficient discrimination among the less able pupils. All parts of the test used in the mental survey are described later in this chapter.

Who Should Score the Tests and Tabulate the Results?

The Mental Survey Committee became aware that they did not command enough resources to complete scoring and tabulation of the test results. An appeal was made to the Research Committee of the EIS for help from their local associations. The EIS is nowadays the teachers' trade union and not inclined toward standardized cognitive testing. Things were different in the 1930s. Teachers scored the tests, and in some areas they tabulated the results for the schools and even for the area. Such widespread cooperation and altruism allowed this whole-population survey of psychometric intelligence to run on a small budget. G. H. Thomson either made or checked all calculations on the data. To our much-later benefit, the raw data—known as the *Nominal Rolls*—were retained safely in SCRE's offices. It is these Nominal Rolls that were rediscovered more than 60 years later, when follow-up studies began to revive the SMS1932 (see Figure 1.1).

How to Provide Concurrent Validity for the Moray House Test?

The Mental Survey Committee decided to test 1,000 pupils individually on the Terman revision of the Binet–Simon Test (Terman, 1916). To be as representative as possible, the pupils were to be chosen from people whose birthdays were on or near June 1, 1921, and were drawn from a preplanned, wide geographical distribution.

How to Distribute the Moray House Test to All 1921-Born Scottish Schoolchildren?

The SCRE's 1933 monograph discusses the care with which the printers of the mental test were given instructions about the date on which the parcels were to be distributed, some to individual schools and some to education authorities for distribution to schools. Even before that, all the individuals whose permission and assistance were needed had to be persuaded and recruited. Letters to most of these groups are reproduced in the monograph (SCRE, 1933). The general instructions concerning the survey sent to head teachers noted that "The object of the survey . . . is to obtain data about the whole distribution of the intelligence of Scottish pupils from one end of the scale to the other" (SCRE, 1933, p. 23).

Validation of the Scottish Mental Survey of 1932 Scores

To achieve the Mental Survey Committee's aim to test 1,000 pupils—500 boys and 500 girls—additionally on an individually administered test, they formed the Sub-Committee on Individual Testing. This was chaired by

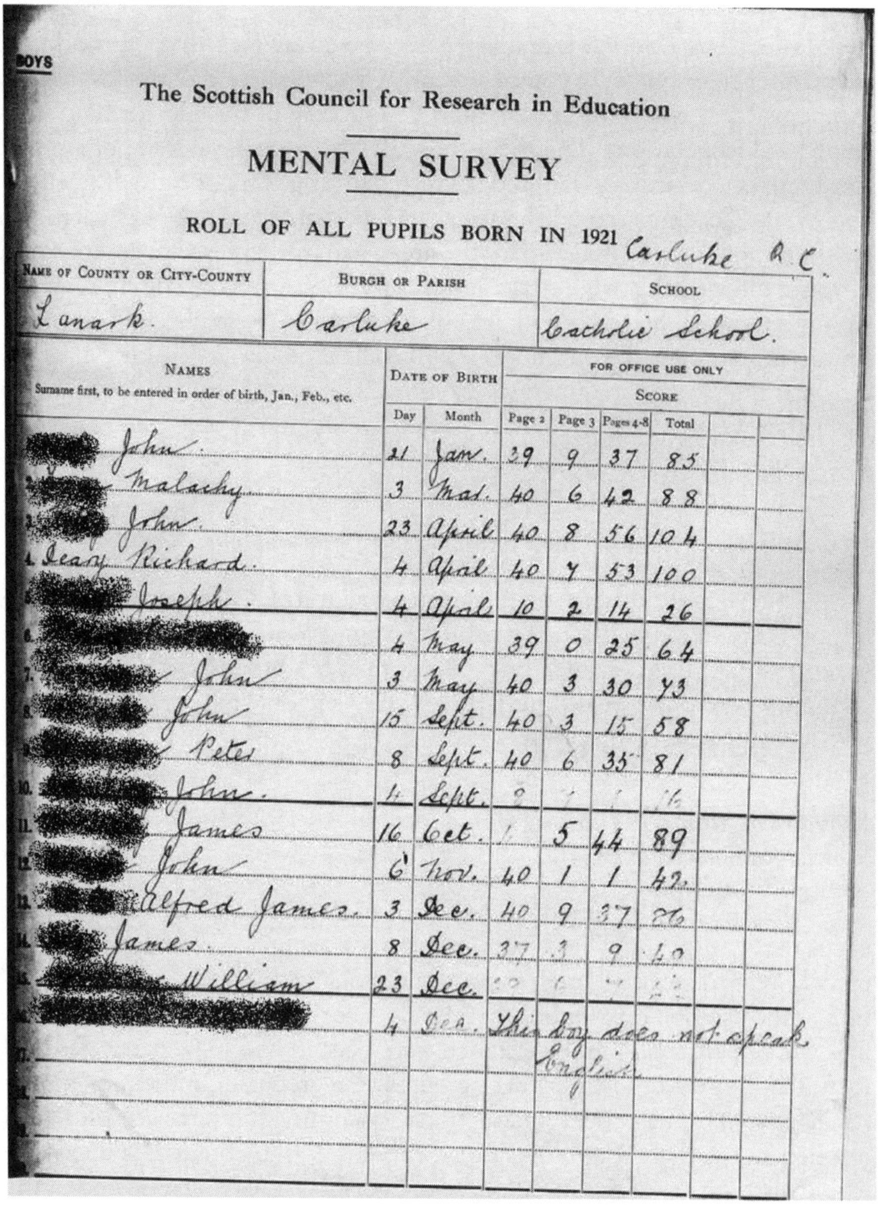

Figure 1.1. An example page from the Nominal Rolls from the Scottish Mental Survey of 1932. Surnames and unusual first names are obliterated. "Page 2" is the score from the First Picture Test (maximum = 40); "Page 3" is the score from the Second Picture Test (maximum = 9); "Pages 4–8" is the score from the Verbal Test, which is the Moray House Test used for follow-up studies (maximum = 76). "Total" is the total score from all three (maximum = 125). Richard Deary, who died in active service at age 21 in World Ward II, is an uncle of Ian J. Deary.

D. Kennedy-Fraser, psychologist to the Glasgow Education Committee. They used Terman's (1916) revision of the Binet–Simon Test. There were some changes from American terminology (listed in SCRE, 1933, p. 51), and an alternative Test 3 at Year XIV was used because of Scottish children's "unfamiliarity with the term *President* [italics added]" (SCRE, 1933, p. 34). Geographical representativeness was sought for the "Binet 1000" but was not fully achieved: The sparsely populated north of Scotland was underrepresented, as were the rural areas. Of the 1,000 students tested, 847 had June birthdays, 101 had May birthdays, 46 had April or July birthdays, and 6 had birthdays in other months.

Trained testers who had a recommendation from a member of the Mental Survey Committee were used. Testing was performed gratis, in their free time. The personnel included "training college lecturers, directors of education, school psychologists, school medical officers, teachers, and students in training, all of whom had special training in mental testing" (SCRE, 1933, p. 37). Testers met, either in Edinburgh or Glasgow, to receive instructions for testing and to receive their allocated areas for testing. Kennedy-Fraser himself tested 187 children and checked the records of all the others. Astonishingly, testers "gave up from one to seven weeks of their holiday time to the work" (SCRE, 1933, p. 38).

No "ascertained mental defectives" (SCRE, 1933, p. 39) were included in the Binet 1000. Overall, they were slightly higher in ability than the whole sample, especially the boys. Nevertheless, the concurrent validity of the SMS1932 Group Test (the MHT, or *Verbal Test*, as they called it) was high. Among the 500 boys, the correlation of the MHT with the Stanford–Binet Scale was .80, and among the 500 girls it was .76 (SCRE, 1933, p. 42). These coefficients are not corrected for the period-free reliability of the tests. The individual testing was done by different examiners, which probably introduced some further unreliability. Among the 99 boys tested by Kennedy-Fraser, the MHT versus Stanford–Binet Scale correlation was .842, and among the 88 girls he tested the correlation was .845. Among the 401 boys not tested by him, the MHT versus Stanford–Binet correlation was .788, and among the 412 girls it was .755. Therefore, the true validity coefficient is probably well above .8.

The actual MHTs completed by the Binet 1000 are still in existence today, bound into ledgers, in the SCRE archives.

The Group Test

The test that was taken by the whole of the SMS1932's participants— 87,498 Scottish pupils born in 1921—had four parts. First, there was a Preliminary Practice Test. The test proper had three parts: (a) the First Picture Test (sometimes called "Page 2" of the test, because it was printed on p. 2 of the test booklet), (b) the Second Picture Test ("Page 3"), and (c) the Verbal Test ("Pages 4–8"). As described earlier in this chapter, the Verbal Test is referred to in this book as the MHT, for reasons we explain later. When referring to the "Group Test," the SCRE 1933 monograph means the whole test booklet, that is, both picture tests and the Verbal Test (i.e., the MHT). The teachers who administered the tests had clear instructions, including exact wordings of their commands to the pupils (SCRE, 1933, pp. 127–129). These precise instructions were used 66 years later in the first follow-up study of the surviving participants of the SMS1932 (Deary, Whalley, Lemmon, Crawford, & Starr, 2000). We now describe the elements of the Group Test in turn.

The Preliminary Practice Test

The Preliminary Practice Test (SCRE, 1933, p. 130) was not scored: It was a short practice for the types of items that would appear in the main MHT (i.e., the Verbal Test). The entire practice test was published in *The Scotsman* newspaper on June 8, 1932. There were eight items. All required reading. One question involved answering a simple instruction, one involved simple knowledge of the alphabet and carrying out an instruction, four were verbal reasoning items (two reasoning-by-analogy items, a three-term series question, and one item that involved reasoning with the alphabet), one question involved general knowledge, and one question was an arithmetic addition sum.

First Picture Test

The First Picture Test is contained on a single page (p. 2 of the Group Test booklet). The SCRE (1933) monograph describes this as a test of Picture–Digit Substitutions. At the top of the page are line drawings of a door, table, chair, wheelbarrow, and a garden roller. Under each, respectively, are the numbers 1, 2, 3, 4, and 5. Below this are 40 further line drawings of these objects in five rows of eight objects each. The pupil's task was to write the correct number under each object. The first four items were used as practice. Thereafter, the pupils were given 1 minute to complete as many items as possible. Most pupils were expected to score perfectly on this test. The task requirements are similar to the processing involved in the Wechsler Digit Symbol-Coding test (Wechsler, 1997) but with different and more concrete stimuli, and the responses are the numbers 1 through 5, inclusive.

Second Picture Test

The Second Picture Test, which had nine items, is also contained on a single page (p. 3 of the Group Test booklet). It is referred to in the SCRE (1933) monograph as *Pictorial Classification*. Each item has three line drawings to the left of a vertical line and five line drawings on the right. For example, the first item, used for practice on the test, contains drawings of snowdrops, daffodils, and crocuses on the left of the vertical line and a bottle, a cup, a rose, a brush, and a pair of scissors to the right. The pupil's task was to find the item on the right hand side of the line "that is most like the first three." This is a classification task. The correct answer to the practice item is the rose. After completing the first two items, pupils were given 2 minutes to complete the remaining seven items. Like the First Picture Test, it was intended to be easy, and most pupils were expected to obtain high or perfect scores.

The Verbal Test or Moray House Test

This is referred to as the "Verbal Test," or "The Verbal Items of the Group Test" (SCRE, 1933, p. 57), because it required literacy and numeracy to understand and complete the items. It is contained in pages 4 through 8 of the Group Test booklet. The test was closely related to Moray House Test No. 12, devised by G. H. Thomson and his team at the Moray House teacher training center.[1] It was used in secondary school selection in England. It had a total possible score of 76 and was administered with a time limit of 45 minutes. Teachers read precise instructions, provided by the SCRE, which may still be consulted (SCRE, 1933, pp. 127–129). The test comprises a variety of item types, as follows: following directions (14 items), same–opposites (11), word classification (10), analogies (8), practical items (6), reasoning (5), proverbs (4), arithmetic (4), spatial items (4), mixed sentences (3), cypher decoding (2), and other items (4). The test has 71 numbered items, 75 items in total. The test, though scored differently and with a maximum score of 98, had been administered to 1,891 nine- to eleven-year-olds in the English town of Ilkeston and to 2,326 candidates for secondary schools in another English county. The revised test was piloted on 11- and 12-year-old children in the English town of Halifax ($N = 1,278$). During all these administrations, there were changes in Moray House Test No. 12 that took out items that were too hard, too easy, or ambiguous. The two picture tests used in SMS1932 were also tested in Ilkeston and Halifax.

Results of the Scottish Mental Survey of 1932

The local associations of the EIS and volunteer parties of students marked and tabulated the tests. Data were checked and cleaned during August through October 1932. The SCRE 1933 monograph gives many tabulated results. For example, the 50th percentile for the 7,048 children born

---

[1] G. H. Thomson was simultaneously the director of Moray House and Bell Professor of Education at the University of Edinburgh, although the two institutions were not merged.

in January (mean age = 136.5 months) was 39.57, and that for the 7,507 children born in December (mean age = 125.5 months) was 31.14. Their growth was about 0.75 marks per month. Among the large amount of descriptive results, much of it aimed at providing conversion from raw scores to percentiles, there arose the interesting finding that boys' scores had more variance than girls' scores. The standard deviations were 17 for boys and 16 for girls. This sex difference in distribution is discussed in more detail in chapter 6 of this volume and by Deary, Thorpe, Wilson, Starr, and Whalley (2003).

A relatively large section of the SCRE 1933 monograph is spent on detailed comparisons of the whole-Scotland survey with the Halifax data and later in attempting to use the Binet 1000–MHT comparisons to gauge the IQs of Scottish boys and girls compared with those in England and the United States. There was discussion about the standard deviation being wider than that found by Terman, meaning that there were more Scottish pupils than expected in the tails of the distributions, with implications for educational provision for these special groups. There was concern that the distribution of mental ability was neither Gaussian nor symmetrical. Another concern was the difficulty of converting MHT scores to IQs, because it was reckoned to have a ceiling effect.

Conclusions of the Scottish Mental Survey of 1932

The massive national survey of Scottish children's intelligence was summed up in four pages. Just over one page was spent stating that the survey had occurred and recapping the fact that the Binet 1000 were not representative of Scottish children as a whole. The principal finding was that the "average I.Q. of Scottish boys born in 1921 may be stated to be 100" (SCRE, 1933, p. 122). The Mental Survey Committee concluded that there was no certain evidence that girls differed from this. Boys' scores had a greater standard deviation, by 1 IQ point. The committee thought that the spread of IQ scores in children of the same age supported the practice of instructing pupils according to their level of ability. Between 1.5% and 3% of the children were in the "mentally defective" category, that is, with an IQ less than 70, with one third more boys than girls categorized thus (SCRE, 1933, p. 123).

Evaluating the Scottish Mental Survey of 1932

For a time, the achievement of having undertaken this massive testing exercise made the SCRE internationally famous. The SCRE's (1937, p. 13) annual report for 1936 to 1937 records permission being granted for the SMS1932 monograph (SCRE, 1933) to be translated into Swedish and Zulu. Some years after SMS1947, when several technical reports devoted to that later survey had emerged, the SCRE wrote a short book that explained its achievements (Maxwell, 1961). The following is Maxwell's (1961) assessment of the SMS1932's explicit aims of discovering the amount of mental deficiency in Scotland and describing the distribution of intelligence in the population:

> Both objectives now appear rather naïve. Since 1932 there have been considerable advances in the techniques of intelligence testing, and very considerable changes in the way of thinking about intelligence and its measurement. It would not now be considered appropriate to use a group intelligence test for ascertainment of the incidence of mental deficiency. It is also now recognised that the distribution of intelligence scores represents as much the method of compiling the test as the distribution of intellectual capacity. Change the way the test is constructed, and the distribution of scores will change correspondingly. Nor would a test, originally constructed to distinguish between pupils suited for an academic grammar school education and those not so suited, be now regarded as the best mode of assessing the intelligence of a whole population. (p. 13)

With regard to the SMS1932's two aims, Maxwell (1961) ultimately concluded that "the information gained about the incidence of mental deficiency and the distribution of intelligence has not been of much lasting value" (p. 14). Instead, the SMS1932 owed any usefulness to matters unforeseen by the members of the 1932 Mental Survey Committee:

> What was important about the 1932 survey was that it was shown possible to test a complete national age-group of children, not just a representative sample. Scotland was the first country to accomplish this, and still remains the only country with records of the intelligence test scores of a complete age-group of school children. Also—and this has turned out to be the most important contribution of the 1932 Survey—there was established a record of the intelligence test scores of all eleven-year-old children in Scotland, boys and girls, classified by education authorities. It is only because such a record was established in 1932 that the later survey in 1947 was worth while, and as a result of this record Scotland was the only country in which at a later date comparison with an earlier investigation on this scale could be made. (p. 14)

Maxwell (1961) was a member of the Mental Survey Committee for the SMS1947, was on the Staff at Edinburgh's Moray House Training College, and was writing under the umbrella of the SCRE when he made the severe judgments about the value of the SMS1932; that is, the SMS1932 contributed little, if anything, toward answering its own questions. The value of the survey instead lay in the fact that it had been conducted and preserved and became useful in answering a question that emerged later. Maxwell (1969a) used the data from the Binet 1000 of the SMS1932, followed up when they were in their 40s, to compare intelligence and marriage in the two surveys (i.e., SMS1932 and SMS1947). Now, we may make a new claim for the usefulness of the SMS1932: In studying the phenomena of old age, especially differences in the mental and physical health of older people, it is very useful to have a record of their mental ability test scores from age 11.

THE SCOTTISH MENTAL SURVEY OF 1947

Fifteen years later, the SCRE did it all again. Sponsored by the Population Investigation Committee and the SCRE, and steered by a Mental Survey Committee under the chairmanship of G. H. Thomson, the Scots undertook another national survey of mental ability: the SMS1947. This appeared as *The Trend of Scottish Intelligence: A Comparison of the 1947 and 1932 Surveys of the Intelligence of Eleven-Year-Old Pupils* (SCRE, 1949).

Whereas the aims of the SMS1932 might have been vague, the SMS1947's aims were stated clearly in the first paragraph of the preface:

> The inquiry reported in this volume was begun in the hope that it might throw light on the causes of a remarkable quantitative social fact, namely, that the results of intelligence tests show that the average score of members of large families is less than that of members of small families. It was feared that this might be leading to a steady fall in the national intelligence, if its cause is that intelligent parents are limiting their families. If, on the other hand, its cause is environmental, it is a duty to discover this, and to strengthen the hand of social reformers. In either case the phenomenon is important, and to show beyond doubt that it really exists would be in itself worthwhile. (SCRE, 1949, p. vii)

As with the SMS1932, the SMS1947 was an example of nationwide cooperation:

> The whole research was an extraordinary example of team work (entirely unpaid); for all the directors of education and their staffs, teachers in all schools, all medical officers of health, all district nurses, students and lecturers in the training colleges, many retired teachers, several university professors, and still others had a share in the project. (SCRE, 1949, p. xvi)

The SCRE had been considering a repeat of the SMS1932 but reckoned that they should wait for about 25 years before doing so. However,

> At the Annual Meeting [of the SCRE] in June 1945 Professor Godfrey Thomson brought to the attention of the Research Council a suggestion made by Dr J. A. Fraser Roberts and conveyed to Professor Thomson by Sir Alexander Carr-Saunders, Chairman of the Population Investigation Committee, that in view of the presumed decline of national intelligence

by reason of the differential birth-rate the Research Council should undertake a repetition of the 1932 mental survey, applying the same test to the corresponding age group, to secure evidence as to whether there had been any change since the original application. (SCRE, 1949, p. 2)

The idea was discussed further at a conference in Edinburgh on March 16, 1946, at which the SCRE's director and Executive Committee met with three members of the Population Investigation Committee: Carr Saunders, Fraser Roberts, and Professor D. V. Glass. They favored a repeat of the SMS1932, because "in no other place was it possible to repeat such a measurement on such a scale" (SCRE, 1949, p. 3). Two possible objections were raised: (a) that the interval between the two surveys might be too short and (b) that the later-tested group's education and mental test performance might have been disrupted by the 6 years of Word War II. An administrative problem was that the new survey would require the cooperation of all of the directors of education and their staffs in Scotland, at a time when they were recovering after the war years and when they were implementing the changes brought in by the 1946 Education (Scotland) Act (Her Majesty's Stationery Office, 1946). It went ahead, however, with the Nuffield Foundation (£2,000) and the Eugenics Society (£2,000) providing grants through the Population Investigation Committee to finance the research. The SCRE's Executive Committee met on May 31, 1946, to appoint the new mental survey committee, and they chose G. H. Thomson as the chairman. The SCRE itself paid for the publication of the 1949 report. In the letters from the Mental Survey Committee to Directors of Education and head teachers it is notable that, in all cases, the "social and national significance" (SCRE, 1949, pp. 13–15) of the possible decline in the nation's intelligence is the main rationale given for the study and the only inducement for them to take part. Eugenics, of this type at least, was alive and active after the years of World War II.

The SCRE decided to add value to the new survey by adding a "sociological survey" to the mental test. Because of the burden this might impose, the Mental Survey Committee decided to administer this extra survey to a random sample rather than the entire population. This extra sociological survey providing a sticking point for some: The directors of education objected, and it took a deputation of G. H. Thomson, Glass, and Fraser Roberts to their association's Executive Committee to persuade them. A few private schools refused to take part because of it. Some idea of the administrative arrangements for the SMS1947 and the contents of the many letters and instructions involved are given in the SCRE's (1949, pp. 7–25) report.

The mental test used was the same as that used in the SMS1932: a version of MHT No. 12. Directors of education were asked not to apply group mental tests to people born in 1936 before the survey's completion, and the fact that the SMS1932 test was to be used again was kept as quiet as possible.

Indeed, before the SMS1947 was finally approved, G. H. Thomson had taken the SMS1932 test out of circulation. Wednesday, June 4, 1947, was the date chosen for the SMS1947 testing.

A short "sociological schedule" was administered to all children born in 1936. A longer schedule was given to all twins and all children born on the first 3 days of each month. This latter sample was called the *36-Day Sample*. Carrying out the longer sociological schedule staggers one's imagination, even beyond that of the mental survey's own extraordinary achievement. The Mental Survey Committee decided that district nurses should carry out the random sample sociological schedule to be given to the 7,000+ members of the 36-Day Sample and the twins in their own homes. Thus, in addition to having coopted the nation's education system to help—gratis—with the survey, members of the Mental Survey Committee wrote to all of the medical officers of health in cities and counties in Scotland and the Queen's Institute of District Nursing for more free help. They got it. Counting the twins and the 36-Day Sample, 8,347 schedules were completed (SCRE, 1949, p. 35). These schedules include information about the children's school, their attendance, their family, height and weight, and their medical history.

On June 4, 1947, the SCRE administered the same mental test—the MHT—to everyone attending school who was born in 1936. The principal rationale was to test a hypothesis about dysgenic trends in the Scottish population; that is, they thought people with lower ability tended to have more children, and there was a worry that the nation's intelligence was declining. Because Scotland had a record of the whole nation's intelligence—at least of its 10.5- to 11.5-year-olds—it was in a good position to readminister the same test to the same age group and discover whether the later population scored worse. In fact, they scored better.

There is much more—and more interesting—detail, however. For individual mental testing—in part to validate the MHT scores again—the Mental Survey Committee chose, in order to obtain as random a sample as possible, to test the children born on the 1st days of the even-numbered months. This is the *6-Day Sample*, and it is, of course, a subsample of the 36-Day Sample. The mental test used was Form L of the Terman–Merrill revision of the Stanford–Binet Scale. Again, this large testing enterprise was carried out by a large, remarkable network of trained testers, who covered most of Scotland (SCRE, 1949, p. 50).

The coverage of this burdensome individual testing was almost total. There were 1,230 pupils who were born on the 1st days of the even-numbered months, and the Mental Survey Committee individually tested 1,215 (98.8%) of them:

> Only fifteen (1.2%) of the children in the six-day sample were not given
> an individual test, and of these, five were in schools where their teachers

or parents refused permission for the test to be applied, two were in hospital medically unfit, four were in relatively inaccessible islands, and four (including one tinker's boy with a group score of P:2, V:0) kept changing so rapidly from school to school and even from county to county that they could not be reached. (SCRE, 1949, p. 52)

Thus, even the missing 15 were relatively well documented, and their omission is forgivable.

The gratis help for the SMS1947 extended even further, to the marking of the 70,000+ test papers. Teachers had marked the SMS1932 scripts, the schools having closed on the afternoon of the test to allow this. For the SMS1947 an assurance was given that the teachers would not be called on, and the general secretary of the Educational Institute of Scotland (i.e., the teachers' union) took responsibility, intending to recruit volunteers to do the work. Even this was too large a task, and eventually the teacher training college directors were called on to enlist their students to do the work. In addition, voluntary workers in many Scottish counties were recruited, and teams of former teachers helped, too. The SCRE (1949) monograph contains much information on the teams' working methods in scoring the mental tests and the methods used to ensure similarity of marking between the SMS1932 and SMS1947.

The sociological schedule, at the scoring stage, caused additional work. There were approximately 8,000 of the 36-Day Sample's schedules and more than 70,000 of the shorter, whole-population schedules. Some had been scored by students in June 1947, and some had been scored by the Mental Survey Committee's office staff in the following year. That still left many to do. The Moray House [teacher] Training College classes were cancelled for 3 days in June 1948 to allow staff, students, and volunteers to code the rest (SCRE, 1949, p. 74).

The SMS1947 collected some data on 75,451 pupils. There were errors and omissions in 240 cases, leaving 75,211 people. Of these, 4,406 were absent on the day of the test, meaning that test scores were available for 70,805 pupils. Tables were constructed that indicated the numbers of boys and girls born in each month of the year and obtaining scores in the tests as follows: 0 to 9, 10 to 19, 20 to 29, and so on up to 60 to 69 and 70 to 76. This was done for both the SMS1932 and the SMS1947. A more concise summary of the SMS1947 and SMS1932, reproduced from the original report, is given in Table 1.1. The Mental Survey Committee noted the increase of 2.284 points between 1932 and 1947, approximately equal to 2 IQ points, with the majority of the increase attributable to the girls' scores. The boys' increase is about 1.4 points, whereas that of the girls is about 3.2 points. The slight shift to the right between the SMS1932 and the SMS1947 is shown in Figure 1.2. The committee also noted that the standard deviation difference between boys and girls had increased over this time. The data illustrate the impact of

TABLE 1.1
Means, Standard Deviations, and Median Scores of the 1947 and 1932 Scottish Mental Surveys

Sex	Year of survey	No. of cases	M	SD	Mdn
Both	1947	70,805	36.741	16.102	38.42
	1932	87,498	34.457	15.481	35.46
Boys	1947	35,809	35.880	16.68	37.54
	1932	44,210	34.503	15.92	35.60
Girls	1947	34.996	37.622	15.44	39.26
	1932	43,288	34.409	15.02	35.32

Note. From *The Trend of Scottish Intelligence: A Comparison of the 1947 and 1932 Surveys of the Intelligence of Eleven-Year-Old Pupils* (p. 85), by the Scottish Council for Research in Education, 1949, London: University of London Press. Copyright 1949 by the SCRE Centre, University of Glasgow (formerly the Scottish Council for Research in Education). Reprinted with permission.

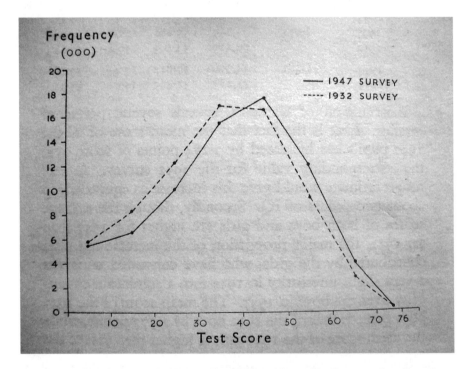

Figure 1.2. Distribution of the Verbal Test (Moray House Test) scores for all pupils from the Scottish Mental Surveys of 1932 and 1947. From *The Trend of Scottish Intelligence: A Comparison of the 1947 and 1932 Surveys of the Intelligence of Eleven-Year-Old Pupils* (p. 86), by the Scottish Council for Research in Education, 1949, London: University of London Press. Copyright 1949 by the SCRE Centre, University of Glasgow (formerly the Scottish Council for Research in Education). Reprinted with permission.

this standard deviation difference by indicating that, although the SMS1947 mean for girls is higher than that for the boys, the percentage of boys who scored 65 (out of 76) or greater is 2.1%, compared with the girls' 1.8%. The greater spread of the boys in the SMS1947 is shown in Figure 1.3. This difference was not symmetrical; the preponderance of the boys at the lowest scores was greater (SCRE, 1949, p. 91).

The SMS1947 monograph (SCRE, 1949) contains many other labor-intensive calculations and tabulations: details on age differences month by month, comparisons of these in the SMS1947 and the SMS1932, the representativeness of the 6-Day Sample, and comparisons of the answer patterns of the SMS1932 and SMS1947. Some of the most detailed calculations and tabulations appear in chapter VII of the monograph, "Intelligence and Family Size" (SCRE, 1949, p. 101). Thus, for each child's position in each size of family, up to family size 19 (!) for the boys and 17 for the girls, the number of children who scored in each 5-point range of the MHT is recorded. The Mental Survey Committee also computed the mean test scores for each

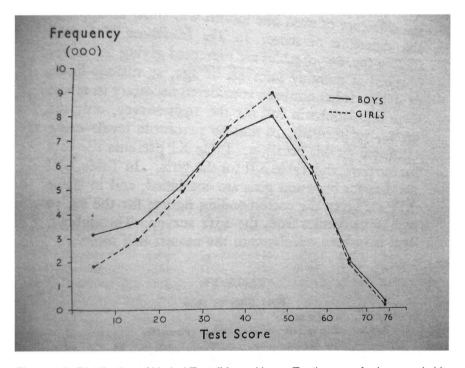

Figure 1.3. Distribution of Verbal Test (Moray House Test) scores for boys and girls from the Scottish Mental Survey of 1947. From *The Trend of Scottish Intelligence: A Comparison of the 1947 and 1932 Surveys of the Intelligence of Eleven-Year-Old Pupils* (p. 87), by the Scottish Council for Research in Education, 1949, London: University of London Press. Copyright 1949 by the SCRE Centre, University of Glasgow (formerly the Scottish Council for Research in Education). Reprinted with permission.

position in each size of family, and Figure 1.4 illustrates the data given in the SMS1947 monograph (SCRE, 1949, p. 107, Table XVII). This shows that although there is a small tendency for the first and later children within family sizes to score better, the far larger effect is that of family size overall. The committee emphasized that they could not discern whether being in a large family led to low scores or whether the children's low scores could be traced back to low scores among the parents (SCRE, 1949, p. 108). The correlation between MHT score and size of family was –.28 (SCRE, 1949, p. 115). One limitation recorded was that because all testing was done at age 11, the first-born children, especially, would come from incomplete families. Thus, for example, the first-born children of some five-children families might eventually turn out to be from larger families.

The correlation between the MHT and Form L of the Terman–Merrill revision of the Stanford–Binet Scale was .81 for both boys and girls (SCRE, 1949, p.123). Although the girls scored better on the MHT than the boys, the boys scored better on the Terman–Merrill revision of the Stanford–Binet Scale.

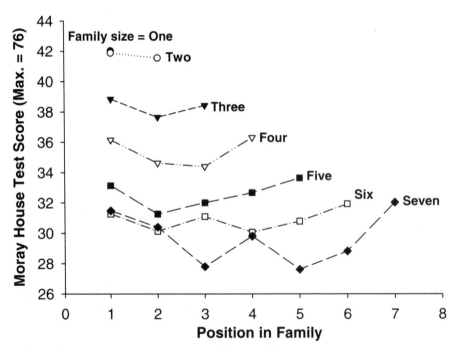

Figure 1.4. Moray House Test score by family size and position in family in the Scottish Mental Survey of 1947. From *The Trend of Scottish Intelligence: A Comparison of the 1947 and 1932 Surveys of the Intelligence of Eleven-Year-Old Pupils* (p. 107), by the Scottish Council for Research in Education, 1949, London: University of London Press. Copyright 1949 by the SCRE Centre, University of Glasgow (formerly the Scottish Council for Research in Education). Adapted with permission.

The SMS1947 was principally conducted to inquire after the possible decline in the nation's intelligence. The strong tenor of the monograph's last chapter was that the issue of the change in the nation's intelligence was unresolved and that more surveys of this type were required. The last chapter also had many suggestions for future analyses, especially tabulations, given that the data had been transferred to Hollerith punched cards. In the last few pages of the monograph, though, the theme changes, and the authors indicate that they saw another possible use for the SMS1947,

> into the factors influencing the way in which individuals possessing various levels of intelligence make use of their intelligence . . . it is of the utmost importance to society to know what happens to individuals with varying degrees of intelligence, and how far obstacles to the full application of that intelligence can be removed by individual or social action. (SCRE, 1949, p. 149)

The authors foresaw how a follow up of the SMS1947 might be more useful than the U.S. "Termites" study (Terman & Ogden, 1947), because the latter included only people with IQs above 135, whereas Scotland had tested a representative sample (SCRE, 1949, p. 150):

> The kind of inquiry suggested would be a difficult one—more difficult to carry out than the California study, which naturally appealed to parents who knew that their children were selected because they were well above average in intelligence. But every effort should be made to overcome the difficulties and to profit from this unique opportunity. Only by undertaking such inquiries can we discover what use the community makes of its personnel, and how to ensure that individuals have adequate scope for employing the abilities they possess. (SCRE, 1949, p. 151)

The present volume is a record of our attempts to meet this challenge and to take up the unique opportunity offered by the SMS1947 and the earlier SMS1932. In the next sections of this chapter, we summarize the five monographs that appeared after the main report of the SMS1947.

Social Implications of the 1947 Scottish Mental Survey

Social Implications of the 1947 Scottish Mental Survey (SCRE, 1953b) was the next publication on the SMS1947. It reported more data on the 36-Day Sample and the twins from the SMS1947. The key to understanding this volume are the data available on the 36-Day Sample that were not available on the whole SMS1947 population. These comprise Questions 18 through 25 of the sociological schedule: The shorter sociological schedule administered to the whole of the SMS1947 sample included only those questions up to and including Question 17. Thus, the 36-Day Sample provides unique information on father's occupation, date of mother's birth, occupancy of the home (i.e., there are questions about the number of rooms and the number of individuals in the home), and height and weight. The majority of the data illustrations concern the relations among these variables and the relations between mental test scores and these variables. There is also a chapter on the twins.

The first analyses in this monograph established that the 36-Day Sample was representative of the whole SMS1947 sample in terms of sex, test score, geographical distribution, and family size. There are associations between intelligence and age of mother, social class of the father, and the occupancy rate of the home (i.e., number of people per room). Thus, for example, children raised in more favorable circumstances tended to have better test scores than those raised in less favorable homes: "But whether this is because the children inherited a high degree of intelligence from their parents, or whether superior performance on the test is the result of good environmental conditions, we have no means of deciding" (SCRE, 1953b, p. 50).

Similar tabulations were performed for height and weight, with similar results. Height and weight correlated negatively with family size and, again, the effect is not accounted for by occupational class, age of mother, or home occupancy rates. When one looks at mental test scores versus height and weight, one notes remarkable congruence in their associations with those of parental occupational class. The correlations were as follows: height with mental test score, boys = .24, girls = .26; weight with test score, boys = .16, girls = .22; height with weight, boys = .68, girls = .67.

There is a reflection, then, on the possible causes of the rise in mean mental test score between the SMS1932 and the SMS1947, an early and very comprehensive occurrence of what later became known as the *Flynn effect*, or *rising IQ*, or *secular rise in IQ scores* (see Flynn, 1999). One suggestion for the cause of the secular changes in mental test scores was test familiarity: the seepage of mental-test-like items into education and popular culture more generally, making succeeding generations more familiar with mental tests. However, if such a secular change also occurred with height and weight, this explanation would not be tenable for those factors: "None of us, by taking thought, can add a cubit to our stature, though we may possibly add a few points to our IQ" (SCRE, 1953b, p. 95).

Using height and weight data from the Education Health Service of Glasgow for 9- and 13-year-olds between 1932 and 1948, the SCRE calculated that, in standard deviation units, the rises in the three variables between 1932 and 1947 were as follows: height = 0.25, weight = 0.30, and mental test score = 0.15. Again, and now in the context of having additional height and weight data, there are reflections on the possible interpretation of the seeming paradox of the rising mean mental test score in the population and the quite strong negative association between mental test score and family size.

It was not definitely accepted that the mean increase in mental test scores meant an increase in intelligence in the population.

As mentioned earlier, the volume contains a chapter on the mental ability of twins. (The topic of twins also is taken up in a later chapter in the present volume.) There are further chapters on the characteristics of low- and high-scorers on the MHT and on the social backgrounds of the 36-Day Sample. We have now provided a short summary of the *Social Implications of the 1947 Scottish Mental Survey*, with some of its major conclusions, but we have not conveyed some remarkable aspects of the volume. For example, the text ends on page 192; however, there are appendix tables that run from page 200 to page 356. Although the SCRE team had a Hollerith machine (i.e., a tabulating machine that used punched cards), the amount of work involved in these tables, mostly compilations and cross-tabulations, was huge. One could argue that the amount and importance of the results hardly warrants all this effort. The principal additions to the original monograph (SCRE, 1949) are the associations between mental test scores and height, weight, occupancy of the home, and the occupational status of the father. It is hard to find any key hypotheses that are tested here, apart from, perhaps, the possibility that twins have lower IQs than singletons, although that is a minor and isolated part of the book.

Educational and Other Aspects of the 1947 Scottish Mental Survey

The next monograph volume, *Educational and Other Aspects of the 1947 Scottish Mental Survey* (SCRE, 1958), appeared 5 years later. By then, G. H. Thomson had died (in February 1955), having been professor of education at the University of Edinburgh since 1925. Norman T. Walker, head of the Department of Education at the University of Aberdeen, was the new chairman of the Mental Survey Committee.

The first analysis presented in this monograph is the geography of Scotland's IQ, possibly the only time this has been done for almost an entire population (see Table 1.2). Noticeable findings of the scores are as follows: The highest mean score occurs in and around Scotland's administrative center and capital, Edinburgh; there is a far lower mean score in the industrial west of Scotland, which contains Glasgow and its neighboring counties; and the lowest score is found in the far north of Scotland's mainland. The report was coy about the possible causes and interpretation of these differences:

> The obvious inference, that children in the North and West tend to be less intelligent than those in the South and East, may or may not be the true one. Migration, language, educational facilities, occupational opportunities for the parents, and other factors would all require to be taken into consideration, and though we can assess some of these, others we

TABLE 1.2
Regional Groups of Educational Authorities in Scotland, With Scottish Mental Survey 1947 Test Scores for Each Group

Group	Education authorities	No. of children tested	Mean test score	Variance of test score
I	Orkney Zetland	506	37.39	251.09
II	Caithness Inverness Ross and Cromarty Sutherland	2301	33.48	274.54
III	Aberdeen City Aberdeenshire Banff Kincardine Moray and Nairn	6,931	36.42	246.05
IV	Dundee Angus Perth and Kinross	5,397	39.57	245.02
V	Edinburgh East Lothian Fife Midlothian West Lothian	13,486	40.28	239.40
VI	Berwick Peebles Roxburgh Selkirk	1,176	39.26	259.59
VII	Clackmannan Stirling	3,045	37.31	234.99
VIII	Glasgow Dumbarton Lanark Renfrew	30,280	34.66	260.28
IX	Argyll Bute	975	34.98	249.04
X	Ayr Dumfries Kirkcudbright Wigtown	6,575	37.30	250.43
	All Scotland	70,672	36.70	257.36

Note. From *Educational and Other Aspects of the 1947 Scottish Mental Survey* (p. 2), by the Scottish Council on Research in Education, 1958, London: University of London Press. Copyright 1958 by the SCRE Centre, University of Glasgow (formerly the Scottish Council for Research in Education). Reprinted with permission.

cannot. So we leave the findings as stated in table I without further comment. (SCRE, 1958, pp. 2–3)

The monograph includes analyses of migrants versus nonmigrants based on the question "Is the child living in (or near) his birthplace?", which was included in the sociological schedule given to all SMS1947 respondents. Migrants' mean mental test score was 38.20, versus 36.45 for nonmigrants

(SCRE, 1958, p. 7). There follow many pages related to the sizes of schools and classes in the different regions in Scotland and according to whether the schools are in cities or less populated locations.

This is a slim monograph; the data analysis section contains only 54 pages. Pages 64 to 148 contain large numbers of appendixes, which must have required enormous labor. Between pages 55 and 63, the SCRE provides a "Review of 1947 Scottish Mental Survey." The substantive beginning of the summary's reflections evokes a piquant feeling that the SMSs were born of the concerns of a passing age: "Certain topics of interest at the time have now lost some of their urgency" (SCRE, 1958, p. 55). Oddly, given the motivation for the SMS1947, the discussion of intelligence and family size makes no mention of the possible decline in the nation's intelligence; instead, it remarks that the association between family size and intelligence in the SMS1947 confirms what G. H. Thomson had already shown in earlier research and states that there was little further need to replicate the finding. Instead, they thought that efforts were needed to understand it, and one of those efforts should be to test children from the same families as they reach a given age: The SMS1947 had, of course, tested only children from different families. There is also a reflection that the SMS1947 had, of course, no data on the mental abilities of the children's parents. Although it is reflected that the social background data, and their analyses in relation to mental test scores, were valuable, it was also concluded that "The contributions of the Survey in the educational field are not very substantial" (SCRE, 1958, p. 60). The SCRE was more positive about the smallest subsample of all, the 6-Day Sample:

> One further aspect of the 1947 Survey remains. It promises to be possibly the most fruitful of all. The children of the six-day sample are those about whom most information was obtained in the survey. Since then the subsequent careers of these children, about 1,200 in number, have been followed up and recorded. They have all now left school . . . Follow-up of this kind is inevitably difficult and expensive, but it does seem a necessary part of the survey, and it is from the follow-up that the meaning, in personal and social terms, of the survey data becomes clear. The survey data are static, relevant to a given period of time only; the follow-up data are dynamic, showing how the psychological, educational and social factors are operating. (pp. 61–62)

Eleven-Year-Olds Grow Up

In the same year as the last volume in the SMS1947 trilogy there appeared *Eleven-Year-Olds Grow Up* (MacPherson, 1958), the first of the reports on the follow-up studies of the 6-Day Sample of the SMS1947: "This report describes what happened to our 'Miniature Scotland' from 1947 to 1954, that is, between the ages of 11 and 18" (MacPherson, 1958, p. 3). The Nuffield Foundation provided a grant of £1,000 a year for 5 years to follow up the 6-Day Sample ($N = 1,208$). This allowed the SCRE to appoint a Research Officer. The funding proved insufficient, and in 1952 the Rockefeller Foundation provided a special grant of £1,000. The Nuffield Foundation provided, from 1953 onward, another 5-year grant of £1,700 per year. Voluntary workers, including teachers, were used to make home visits to each respondent, and contact was maintained even with those who had left the country.

Because of the method of selecting people born on the first of the even-numbered months, and because the SMS1947 was so comprehensive, the 6-Day Sample proved to be representative of the whole SMS1947 in regard to age, sex, mental test score, geographical distribution, size of family, occupational class of the father, and occupancy rate of the home (MacPherson, 1958, pp. 4–9). The data that were available for analysis in the 1958 report were as follows:

- the MHT score from the SMS1947 and an individually administered Terman–Merrill Form L Intelligence Scale;
- a school schedule and transfer (from primary to secondary schooling) examination schedule from 1950;
- a medical report from 1950;
- a second school schedule obtained when the children left school;
- home visitors' schedules from 1950–1951, 1951–1952, 1953, 1954, and 1955; and
- employment records for each 6-month period from June 1951 to December 1954.

The first school schedule included questions about educational course and included teachers' ratings of the pupils' personality qualities. It is mentioned that there was little use of standardized mental tests in Scotland at that time, in spite of G. H. Thomson's presence and work. The second school schedule recorded, among other factors, the type of educational course followed and the examinations passed at the time the children left school. The home visits were done in many cases by teachers and in others by school nurses. It was the responsibility of the visitor to find out where a family had gone when homes were moved. By 1954, only 7 of the 1,208 respondents had been lost to follow-up. The first schedule for home visits contained the following information: (a) year of parents' marriage; (b) number of younger brothers and sisters born since 1947, with names, dates of birth, and school; (c) occupation of father (with changes of job since 1947); (d) educational level of parents; (e) recreational activities of all members of the family; (f) number of parents' brothers and sisters; (g) parents' ambitions for the pupil;

(h) illnesses of the pupil; and (i) health of parents. The second schedule added the pupil's ambitions, whether he or she had left school, details of and attitudes toward jobs, and interests and activities. The fourth visit (in 1954) was more detailed, with factual and attitudinal questions about marriage, military National Service, occupations, and leisure. Younger siblings were tested on the Terman–Merrill Form L Intelligence Scale as they reached age 11.

MacPherson (1958) provided detailed results on educational outcomes: 31% of the boys and 29.4% of the girls entered 5-year secondary school courses, although only 14.4% of boys and 10.5% of girls completed them. The mean IQ scores for those pupils who took and completed different courses in secondary education are shown in Table 1.3. The report contains much detail on success (or lack thereof) of the different types of secondary education course as well as changes of secondary school course. IQ made some contribution to success or failure in every type of course. The chances of completing a 5-year secondary school education, according to IQ at age 11, were as follows: IQ 136+ = 72%, IQ 126 to 135 = 52%, IQ 116 to 125 = 41%, IQ 106 to 115 = 18%, IQ 96 to 105 = 24%, IQ < 96 = 0%. The report lists, one by one, and ordered by IQ score, the educational outcomes of and careers entered by the 85 boys and 65 girls of the 6-Day Sample (only 12.4%) who completed at least 5 years of secondary school. One quarter of these pupils were from private schools. For example, 6 boys and only 2 girls began a university medical school degree (MBChB [i.e., bachelor of medicine/bachelor of surgery]). There are many additional—and very detailed—tabulations and graphs concerning the likelihood of how IQ scores at age 11 are associated with achieving specific achievements at the secondary school level. There was some evidence that apart from IQ, teachers' ratings (at approximately age 14) of perseverance, conscientiousness, and the will to do well were important, with a recommendation that these might be assessed in addition to IQ to cut down on "wastage" (p. 91). Many case histories are described in terms of the cognitive, personality, and motivational contributions to educational attainment.

TABLE 1.3
Mean IQ for Boys and Girls by Type of School Course

Type of school course	Boys	Girls
5-year course, 2 languages, completed	135.4	133.5
5-year course, 1 language, completed	124.4	126.8
5-year course, 2 languages, not completed	120.8	120.5
5-year course, 1 language, not completed	115.9	112.1
3-year, 1-language course	109.5	105.1
3-year, no-language, technical course	98.1	93.2
3-year, no-language, modified course	86.0	80.5

Note. The IQ scores are based on the Terman–Merrill Form L Intelligence Test, which has a standard deviation of approximately 20. From *Eleven-Year-Olds Grow Up* (p. 35), by J. S. MacPherson, 1958, London: University of London Press. Copyright 1958 by the SCRE Centre, University of Glasgow (formerly the Scottish Council for Research in Education). Adapted with permission.

TABLE 1.4
Occupational Level at Age 18 and IQ Score at Age 11, For Boys Only

Job grade	Job grade description	Mean IQ at age 11
B1	Professional: university students, teacher training, apprentice chartered accountant, and so on	131.4
B2	Higher nonmanual	123.4
B3	Other nonmanual	108.8
B4	Skilled manual	106.0
B6	Unskilled manual	94.0

Note. From Eleven-Year-Olds Grow Up (p. 103), by J. S. MacPherson, 1958, London: University of London Press. Copyright 1958 by the SCRE Centre, University of Glasgow (formerly the Scottish Council for Research in Education). Adapted with permission.

The presentations of occupational destinations and their relation to IQ scores in Eleven-Year-Olds Grow Up once again reflect the available analytic technology of the time: the punched cards and the ability to sort these; that is, there are huge numbers of tabulations, with many minor variations. The occupations can be followed only to about age 18, so the data are far from conclusive. However, most people at that time left school at 15 and so had occupational destinations, often quite a few. It was also a time when women's occupational destinations often bore little relation to their cognitive abilities. One clear finding was an association between a boy's occupational level at age 18 and IQ at age 11 (see Table 1.4). Table 1.4 shows, for example, a 12-point gap in IQ between skilled and unskilled manual workers. This was for the last job recorded, at age 18. The gap was only 7.8 IQ points when people's first jobs were considered, and MacPherson (1958) considered that this "would indicate that the gap is widening and that the young men are being sorted out by ability" (p. 104). We show in later chapters that with modern analyses of the SMS1932 data, this trend continued into more mature adulthood. Eleven-Year-Olds Grow Up includes many more tabulations, minutely summarizing numbers of jobs, changes in jobs, how people heard about jobs, job preferences, and further education.

The next chapter (VI) of Eleven-Year-Olds Grow Up concerns social aspects of the 6-Day Sample, making use of the information in the random sample sociological survey and the questions therein being repeated in the home visits up to 1954, when the participants were about 18 years old. Once more, the tabulations abound, with no statistical tests reported. Still, the occasional remarkable findings emerge; for example, the mean IQs according to occupancy rates of homes changed between 1947 and 1954 (see Table 1.5). There is a shift toward, overall, less overcrowding[2] in homes, and the IQ at every level of home occupancy becomes lower when 1947 and 1954 are

---

[2]Overcrowding refers to the number of people in a house relative to the number of rooms. There is no absolute level at which a house is deemed overcrowded; the ratio may be compared across cohorts or used as an individual-difference variable.

TABLE 1.5

Mean IQ at Age 11 in 1947 and Occupancy Rate
(Number of People in the House Divided by
the Number of Rooms) in 1947 and 1954

Occupancy rate	In 1947	In 1954
1	117.6	112.5
2	105.3	103.6
3	99.6	96.4
4	94.5	91.7

Note. From *Eleven-Year-Olds Grow Up* (p. 122), by J. S. MacPherson, 1958, London: University of London Press. Copyright 1958 by the SCRE Centre, University of Glasgow (formerly the Scottish Council for Research in Education). Reprinted with permission.

compared. Along with the secular increase in IQ, this was an improvement in social circumstances in Scotland, with the easing of overcrowding in homes. Other facts that are stated along the way have changed since the 1950s:

Among the 590 boys one or both parents are dead in 16 per cent of the cases, and the parents of over three per cent are separated or divorced. None of the boys who completed five years in secondary school had parents separated or divorced. (MacPherson, 1958, p. 126)

In *Eleven-Year-Olds Grow Up* there was a close examination of the determinants of the completion of a 5-year secondary school course, which was required for entry into higher education. Between IQs of 110 and 150, intelligence had little effect on whether the course was completed; however, within a given band of IQ social factors had a strong influence. For example, in the IQ range of 110 to 150 the chances of completing (having obtained entry to) a 5-year secondary school course were as follows: 80% for Home Occupancy Rate 1 (one person to each room in the house); 50% for Home Occupancy Rate 2; 25% for Home Occupancy Rate 3; and 10% for Home Occupancy Rate 4 (MacPherson, 1958, p. 128).

The concluding analyses of the 6-Day Sample in *Eleven-Year-Olds Grow Up* were illustrative comparisons of high (IQ = 132 or greater; $N = 101$) and low (IQ = 77 or less; $N = 97$) IQ scorers at age 11 years (MacPherson, 1958, pp. 147–158). These comprised approximately the top and bottom 8% of the IQ distribution. On the basis of a nine-category classification of father's occupation, 53% of the high scorers' fathers, but only 6% of the low scorers' fathers, were in the four most professional occupational categories. None of the children of the most professional occupational class appeared in the low-scoring group. Seventy-six percent of the high scorers came from homes with occupancy rates of 1 or 2, and 60% of the low scorers came from homes with occupancy rates of 3 or 4. High scorers were more likely to dwell in cities, and low scorers were more likely to live in rural areas. There is almost no overlap at all in secondary school educational experience for the high and low scorers. Ninety-five percent of the high scorers entered a 5-year secondary school course, with 84% being successful. No low scorer was accepted for a 5-year secondary school course, and more than half did not succeed in the 3-year or special school course they had begun. High scorers were more likely to be rated by teachers as having desirable personality characteristics, to be happier at school, and attended school more consistently: Sixty-four percent of high scorers had 95% or greater attendance records, but only 44% of low scorers did. At age 18, 50% of the high-scoring boys were in the most professional occupational category, but none of the low scorers were, and 73% of the low-scoring boys were in the most manual category, but only 6% of the high scorers were.

This is the first SCRE volume devoted to the 6-Day Sample. The narrowing down of numbers to just around 1,200 brings with it an intimacy not seen in the previous monographs. The reader feels closer to individual stories; no person's identity is ever revealed, but the follow-up social details and the case examples warm up the cold, repetitive porridge of the endless, Hollerith machine–generated tables, relatively few of which are informative. If one is mawkish about it, coming to the end of this volume has the air of a good mother waving goodbye to her child at the school gate for the first time. The pathos is richer, however, because the Cassandras of family background, IQ, and school education have now spoken, nowhere more loudly than in the comparisons of the top and bottom 8% of IQ scorers at age 11. In a departure from anything one has read before from the SCRE on the mental survey data, here is the remarkable, penultimate paragraph of *Eleven-Year-Olds Grow Up*:

> The high [IQ] scorer is likely to come from a family of one, two or three, his father's occupational class is not likely to be lower than that of a skilled tradesman, his home will probably have occupancy rate 1 or 2 and there is a slightly greater chance of his being in a city. By the age of eleven he will almost certainly be in the last or last but one class in the primary school and is most likely to be selected for a five-year secondary school course in which he will be very happy. His attendance at school will probably be at least 95 per cent and his teachers will tend to rate him above average in desirable personality characteristics. He is likely to complete at least five years in the secondary school and on leaving has a fifty–fifty chance of commencing training for a profession. (MacPherson, 1958, p. 158)

We don't see them again until they are 27 years old.

Sixteen Years On: A Follow-Up of the 1949 Scottish Survey

Sixteen Years On: A Follow-Up of the 1949 Scottish Survey (Maxwell, 1969b) describes the further progress of the 6-Day Sample of the SMS1947, to the age of about 27 years. The study was still organized by a committee of the SCRE, chaired by James Maxwell of the Moray House College of Education in Edinburgh. The funding from age 11 to the date of the publication was supplied through three 5-year grants from the Nuffield Foundation. The arrangements show the useful network of voluntary research effort that could be called upon in Scotland at that time:

> The individual testing of the younger sibs was carried out by psychologists from education authorities, hospitals, colleges and universities. Members of the sample were visited regularly in their homes by a corps of teachers, lecturers and others, who have in many cases formed a more personal relationship with the sample members. Latterly, many of the sample members co-operated by keeping the inquiry informed of their own progress. (Maxwell, 1969b, p. 8)

Sixteen Years On comes at the end of a series of 13 annual schedules conducted on the sample members by a home visitor. By 1963, at the time of the last follow-up, the research team had schedules returned on 1,104 (91.4%) of the original 1,208 respondents. Eight were known to have died. Two had been committed to institutions for the "mentally defective" and not followed up. The 1,104 contains schedules from 75 people with whom contact had been lost and were found again thanks to the special effort that was made to contact them for the final schedule. By 1964, more than 1,500 (1,554) siblings of the 6-Day Sample members had been tested on the Terman–Merrill Form L Intelligence Scale as they reached age 11. By the time the final schedule was compiled, 208 of the sample members were living "furth" of Scotland, in 22 different countries: 118 in England, 28 in Canada, 23 in Australia, and 11 in the United States.

The first substantive chapter in *Sixteen Years On* concerns *continuing education*, a term used to capture both higher (mostly university-level) and further (mostly vocational-type, college-level) education. There are summaries of the various types of courses that the boys and girls took and then completed or failed to complete. These are leavened by brief, individual case histories. Completion of further and higher education is tabulated with respect to IQ at age 11, paternal occupation, and parental education. The SCRE found a

> tendency for a considerable number of intelligent pupils to leave prematurely . . . 46 of the pupils of very high intelligence left in 1951, and, what is of more concern, 34 of them took no further courses in education. Reasons for leaving school and education were various—illness, domestic situation, need to earn money, but the dominant one was distaste for school. . . . It appears that one of the necessary steps to be taken to develop the ability of the coming generation is not so much to provide greater facilities for continuing education, as to keep them at school in

the first place. . . . A more powerful influence than intellectual ability appears to be parents' involvement with education. . . . Though it is gratifying to note that the traditional Scottish "lad o' pairts" or his gifted sister, can still make his way from a working class home to professional status, it would be wrong to consider continuing education being used as a broad channel for social mobility. The facilities are there, but are used only exceptionally. The main function seems to be to enable children to continue in the occupational class of their parents. (Maxwell, 1969b, pp. 51–53)

There is a striking mixture of styles in *Sixteen Years On*; tables of data are mixed with more reflection and illuminating idiographic details—quite correctly, because the SCRE researchers were confronting the differentiating of people's experiences as they grew up. Primary school was almost uniform, secondary school brought with it a range of course choices, further and higher educational courses were more varied still, and "When employment is reached, the divergences become almost unmanageable" (Maxwell, 1969b, p. 54). Men and women differed in employment pattern, National Service (in the military) had been a feature of this cohort of men, people changed jobs as many as 14 times in 10 years, and there was the difficult task of classifying the jobs that the 6-Day Sample had done:

> Most of the members entered recognised occupations, but there is the usual range of bizarre-sounding occupations. There is a cutter hackle maker now a bus driver, a tomato grower, a steel bender, a coal picker, a fish curer, a press feeder, a potato dresser, a bonus checker, a leaf stemmer, a board fitter, a bag turner, a ribbon loader, a rivet heater, a bobbin carrier and a bottle labeller. There is a bottler, a greaser, a twister, a heeler, an overhauler, a doubler, a screwer, a ticketer, and a doffer, as well as a horseman, a cardiographer, a doubler screwer, a restaurant owner, an assistant in a doll's hospital, a manager of a tropical fish shop and a member of an Antarctic scientific expedition. (Maxwell, 1969b, pp. 54–55)

The researchers noted a trend at the end of the follow-up period toward greater stability of occupation and for sons and fathers to have similar occupational classes. There are some striking statistics, even among the basic descriptive data. In education, only 62 (10.5%) of the boys and 40 (6.5%) of the girls completed 5 years of secondary education. The percentages for completion of a university or college degree were 6.8% for the boys and 4.7% for the girls. To demonstrate the deterministic nature of not having a 5-year school education for further education, we note that only 3 boys (0.5%) and 3 girls (0.5%) who did not complete a 5-year education course went on later to complete a university or college course. More pages of interesting occupational information reveal the presence of a professional footballer, a professional golfer, and "one athlete of international reputation" (Maxwell, 1969b,

p. 65). One surprising aspect of the long employment section is how little analysis it contains regarding the original IQ measures, though these are often mentioned in relation to individual cases.

At least 24 of the 6-Day Sample were charged with criminal offenses. The average IQ of these 24 at age 11 was 90. Ten were known to have served time in prison, 1 for murder. Even at this sad juncture the SMS1947 authors felt close enough to the sample for whimsy and, literally, gallows humor:

> It is interesting to reflect that they may have been arrested by one of the sample's six police, defended by one of the sample's two lawyers, and put into the custody of the sample's Prison Officer. Fortunately the services of the sample's scaffolder were not required. Nor does the sample contain any social worker for their aftercare. (Maxwell, 1969b, p. 71)

Emigration tells a happier story, though involving a brain drain from Scotland:

> There is a chartered accountant in Peru, a welding inspector, ex Regular Army, last known to be in Iran, a bank manager in the Cameroons, and an accountant who went to Switzerland . . . There is a forester in Nigeria, a journalist in Australia, and of the four members of the sample described as research chemists, one is in Switzerland, one in Canada, one in Australia; and one is in Glasgow. (Maxwell, 1969b, p. 72)

The mean IQs of the emigrants were as follows, according to destination: United Kingdom outwith Scotland = 106.5 (N = 123), Canada = 108.1 (N = 28), United States = 111.6 (N = 11), Australia and New Zealand = 106.6 (N = 25), other = 117.7 (N = 21).

One table from *Sixteen Years On* merits reproduction in this chapter, the one that shows the occupations of the fathers and sons of 513 men in the 6-Day Sample (see Table 1.6). Two things are clear. First, there is a secular shift in employment across the generations toward more nonmanual employment. Second, there is some between-generation stability in types of employment. Almost all of the sons of the professional-class fathers were also in professions, and farming was stable across the generations. Overall, the diagonal line of numbers in the table, which indicates father–son stability of employment type, tended to have the largest numbers in the columns. Exceptions to this tended to be instances of the secular change toward nonmanual work. There is social mobility, too; sons from almost all parental occupational backgrounds reached the professional occupational class. According to the SCRE, "The avenue of such occupational mobility is education, and the determining factors appear to be intelligence and parental education" (Maxwell, 1969b, p. 80).

The discussion of occupations among women is conducted to a large extent in the context of marriage and the effect of illegitimate births. Of the 29 women who successfully ended their education at the university or college

TABLE 1.6

Comparison of the Distributions of the 6-Day Sample's (Men) Occupations, Compared With Their Fathers' Occupations

Father's occupation	6-Day Sample member (men only)									All	All as %
	1	2	3	4	5	6	7	8	9		
1. Professionally qualified and large employers	**14**		2							16	3.1
2. Small employers and self-employed	9	**3**	4	2	3		2		1	24	4.7
3. Salaried employees not professionally qualified	8		**7**	6	3	2			1	27	5.3
4. Nonmanual wage earners	7	2	5	**6**	5	8				33	6.4
5. Skilled manual wage earners	18	3	16	33	**78**	47	8		4	207	40.4
6. Semiskilled manual wage earners	4	2	6	7	21	**29**	17			86	16.8
7. Unskilled manual wage earners	4		4	5	19	22	**16**		3	73	14.2
8. Farmers						3	1	**8**	3	15	2.9
9. Agricultural workers (including crofters)	1	1	4	6	3	7		2	**8**	32	6.2
All	65	11	48	65	132	118	44	10	20	513	
All as %	12.7	2.1	9.4	12.7	25.7	23.0	8.6	1.9	3.9		

Note. Numbers in boldface indicate father–son stability of employment type. From *Sixteen Years On: A Follow-Up of the 1949 Scottish Survey* (p. 78) by J. Maxwell, 1969b, London: University of London Press. Copyright 1969 by the SCRE Centre, University of Glasgow (formerly the Scottish Council for Research in Education). Reprinted with permission.

level, 25 became teachers, and 2 became doctors. The report noted that it was easier for high-ability boys to enter and complete higher education and to progress to corresponding occupations. It was emphatically noted that the future level of employment was mainly determined, at age 15, by the decision to stay on at school or not. The SCRE also noted inertia in occupational classes:

> Intellectual ability and personal preference come into it, but the relation between father's occupational class and the critical educational decision is very strong. Social class also tends to determine the employment chosen where choice is relatively wide. Sons tend to follow their fathers, and

daughters to marry in the same occupational group. This is no cause for serious concern. There is some "wastage," a few cases with rather unhappy consequences, but there is no serious discontent recorded, only some regrets. . . . Like most people, they appear to find life varied, full and interesting, and like most people, probably enjoy their grouses. (Maxwell, 1969b, pp. 97–98)

In *Sixteen Years On* we find that, by 1964, at about age 28, 64% of the men and 82% of the women in the 6-Day Sample were married. There was a small positive association between IQ at age 11 and age at marriage for both men and women. However, there were small differences in opposite directions for the ages of the married and unmarried respondents at age 28: Unmarried women had slightly higher mean IQs than married women (102.0 vs. 100.5), and married men had slightly higher mean IQs than unmarried men (105.1 vs. 103.2). For both men and women, the lowest percentage of married individuals was found at the extremes of IQ scores, and the highest mean IQs were found in those who had their first child 3 years after marriage, compared with having a child earlier. The number of children born to sample members was associated with their IQ scores at age 11, as follows: for zero children, men's IQ = 103.4; for one child, men's IQ = 104.2; for two children, men's IQ = 98.3; for three children, men's IQ = 93.5; for four children, men's IQ = 98.9; and for five or more children, men's IQ = 88.4. Men with very low IQs tended to have few children.

The last data-based chapter in the last monograph of the SMSs is entitled "The Younger Sibs" (siblings). A register was made of each 6-Day Sample member's younger sibs, and brought up to date annually. The SMS1947 committee informed testers in the relevant area about each sib to be tested at the time of his or her birthday. Each was tested on the Terman–Merrill Form L Intelligence Scale. In 1947, one hundred and seven younger sibs were tested. This continued for 16 years, by which time 1,554 had been assessed, about 96% of those who could have been tested (Maxwell, 1969b, p. 174). When the sib testing stopped in 1963, at which time the follow-up of the 6-Day Sample members also ended, only 13 younger sibs had not yet reached 11 years. Some testing took place overseas. The correlation of IQ scores of sibs within families was .44, a number that takes family size into account. That is, within any one family, there is only 70% of the standard deviation that would be found in the relevant population. Thus, although families contained less variance than the population, there were still many, very large differences in IQ scores among sibs of the same family. "This variability makes it very difficult to maintain the view that IQ is largely determined by environmental conditions, especially in the home" (Maxwell, 1969b, p. 183). There was no association between IQ and birth order within a family.

The last chapter—"Review"—reflects that more than 1,000 case histories each provide fascinating information but are hard to capture as a whole. Even 1,000 lives, though, conform to some general rules:

> There is a complex of length of education, occupational class of the parents and level of intelligence, which determines the future course of the members' lives. The three factors, education, occupational class and intelligence, are closely connected. The pupil of high IQ, for instance, is much more likely to continue to some form of higher education if his father is professionally qualified than the pupil of the same level of IQ, whose father is a manual worker. No one of the three factors is independent of the others, and selection by one, length of education for example, implies selection by the others. (Maxwell, 1969b, p. 184)

Sixteen Years On is the SCRE's (Maxwell, 1969b) last major word on the SMS1947. Between this and the SCRE's (1933) report on the SMS1932, 36 years apart, the Mental Survey Committee changed markedly. For SMS1932 (SCRE, 1933), the committee members were all Scottish, with many school representatives. By the end of SMS1947 (Maxwell, 1969b), the SMS1947 Mental Survey Committee of nine people—not counting three who were committee members by virtue of their positions at the SCRE—included C. O. Carter (Director, Clinical Genetics Research Unit, London), J. W. B. Douglas (Director, Medical Research Council Unit, London School of Economics), D. V. Glass (Professor of Sociology, London School of Economics), and J. A. Fraser Roberts (at the Paediatric Research Unit, Guy's Hospital Medical School, London). The chairman was James Maxwell, and the statistician was D. N. Lawley at the University of Edinburgh, formerly with G. H. Thomson at Moray House. That leaves three people: (a) D. M. McIntosh, Principal, Moray House College; (b) J. D. Nisbet, Professor of Education, Aberdeen University; and (c) A. M. Orr, formerly the headmaster at Rothesay Public School. Thus, an original "Scottish school of educational research" was broadened and made more professional as the concerns of the SMS1947 changed, and the English representatives used their experience coming north to look after the SMS1947. Some of the expertise was used to inform the processes and data that were to be gathered in the UK National Survey of Health and Development, also known as the 1946 birth cohort (Wadsworth, Kuh, Richards, & Hardy, 2006).

Here ends the narrative of SCRE's execution of the SMS1932 and SMS1947. It began not very long after the first group tests of intelligence were introduced, and it ends in the notable IQ year of 1969, when Jensen's (1969) *Harvard Educational Review* article started a firestorm of anti-IQ criticism. The SCRE's work on the Mental Surveys accompanies, therefore, huge swings in the use and understanding of mental test scores. It covers eugenics and environment. Some of the work still seems fresh; some of the data and results are still obviously valuable. However, much of the output groans with the effort of massive data management without the use of computers; table follows table of all-but-useless numbers, most without a driving hypothesis. Toward the end of the SMS1947 work, as the personal narratives become more interesting, it was noticeable that there were few empirical reports. The SCRE archives at the University of Glasgow, which retain some of the correspondence—much of it conducted personally by the director of SCRE—concerning the follow up of individual 6-Day Sample respondents and their siblings, record the massive effort required for relatively little scientific return. The end of data collection was recorded in SCRE's (1963) *Twenty-Fifth Annual Report:* "The [Mental Survey] Committee [James Maxwell, Chairman] have recommended that the Survey [SMS1947] follow-up in its present form should be brought to an end this year, and that the 13th Schedule, due for completion this year, should be the final one" (p. 12).

It was suggested in the same report that the SMS1947 members' children might be tested when they reach the age of 11. This was never done. At the time the decision was made to end the data collection on the SMS1947, the director of SCRE was David A. Walker. Thirty-six years after that decision, in his mid-90s, Walker recalled the decision to abandon the SMS1947 because "Visitors were going to homes and not getting any worthwhile information" (D. A. Walker, personal communication to I. J. Deary, August 3, 1999). There were still some reports to come from the SMS1947 after its abandonment but, as the rest of the present volume shows, the main value of the SMS1932 and SMS1947 was to the next generations of researchers.

POSTSCRIPT

The data did not lie idle until we began to use them in 1997. Hope (1984) had the SMS1947 6-Day Sample data transferred to computerized punch cards and published sophisticated path analyses on mental ability, education, and social mobility. Gray, McPherson, and Raffe (1983) conducted reanalyses of the 6-Day Sample of the SMS1947. They concluded that "Scottish secondary education since [World War II] has not been meritocratic" (p. 214) and that "the folk image of the lad o' pairts,"[3] and the accompanying notion of equality, "receive a sharp knock" (p. 226). Later analyses of the SMS1932 found a similar contribution of father's occupational social class to educational attainment, after adjustment for mental ability at age 11 (Deary, Taylor, et al., 2005). That later study also found that the influence of father's

---

[3]*Lad o' pairts* is a Scottish expression that, literally translated, means "boy of parts." An online Scots–English dictionary (http://www.britannia.org/scotland/scotsdictionary) defines it as a youth, particularly one from a humble background, who is considered talented or promising. Godfrey H. Thomson, though not born or educated in Scotland, is often referred to as a lad o' pairts.

occupational social class influenced midlife status attainment (see chap. 5, this volume).

Another SCRE monograph, written by Maxwell (1961), will be of interest and use to readers. However, to include it in the preceding sections, in chronological order, would have disrupted the flow of the story of the SMS1947. Three years after publication of *Eleven-Year-Olds Grow Up*, and 11 years before *Sixteen Years On*, James Maxwell wrote *The Level and Trend of National Intelligence: The Contribution of the Scottish Mental Surveys*. It reviews the SMS1932 and the SMS1947. Pages 9 through 11 summarize the then-headlines of the work from the surveys. The rationales and designs for both SMS1932 and SMS1947 are recounted clearly and briefly, and summaries of data are provided. There is a detailed discussion about the implications of the SMS1932 and SMS1947 mean results with respect to differential fertility. After what seems like a balanced discussion, Maxwell concludes that "to attribute the rise in 1947 group scores solely to greater expertise in tests is probably as naïve an over-simplification as to predict a fall in IQ from differential fertility alone" (pp. 34–35). Neither line of explanation, he thought, accorded with the differences between the group and individual results, and with the results of the boys and the girls. The rest of Maxwell's volume reviews the monographs of the SMS1947.

II

COGNITIVE EPIDEMIOLOGY: DOES CHILDHOOD IQ AFFECT ILLNESS LATER IN LIFE OR SURVIVAL TO OLD AGE?

COGNITIVE EPIDEMIOLOGY: DOES CHILDHOOD IQ AFFECT ILLNESS LATER IN LIFE OR SURVIVAL TO OLD AGE?

To track down individuals from the Scottish Mental Surveys (SMSs) to study cognitive aging (which was the original purpose of our follow-up studies), we first had to find out who was still alive. As we were finding out who might still be alive among the participants of the SMS of 1932 (SMS1932), we realized that we could make a contribution to the field of epidemiology. It was unintended, but we were acquiring data about survival to old age on a population for which we had childhood IQ scores. We could determine whether any associations existed between childhood IQ and the likelihood of surviving to old age. Furthermore, because of the additional death records and National Health Service databases in Scotland, we could determine whether any associations existed between childhood IQ and mortality and illnesses later in life, both physical and mental. We decided that in addition to a program of cognitive aging, there should be a program of research aimed at finding associations between childhood IQ and mortality and morbidity. The latter program was named *cognitive epidemiology*. If the follow-up studies of the SMSs of 1932 and 1947 (SMS1947) can lay claim to having influenced any novel field of study, that field probably is cognitive epidemiology.

A stimulus for our cognitive epidemiology studies—as well as the foundation for our cognitive aging studies—was Scotland's Community Health

Index. The UK National Health Service provides medical care free to all. Each person is registered with a general medical practitioner in his or her local area. This doctor is responsible for people's everyday health care and is the person who refers patients to specialist medical practitioners if that should be required. Scotland's Community Health Index is the list of people who are registered with general medical practitioners. It contains almost the entire Scottish population, because of the universal provision of health care by the National Health Service.

We sought permission to gain access to the Community Health Index to trace and possibly recruit surviving participants of the SMS1932 and SMS1947. These surveys had tested almost everyone who was born in 1921 or 1936. In the Community Health Index, therefore, most of the individuals listed with a birth year of 1921 or 1936—with the exception of people who came to Scotland after age 11—would have taken part in the surveys. With the appropriate ethical approvals and permissions granted, which guaranteed confidentiality of the data, the process of contacting possible surviving participants of the SMSs began. It was during this process of finding surviving participants of the SMS1932 that we realized it would be interesting to investigate possible IQ differences between those who had and had not survived. To complete this task fully, we needed to access additional databases beyond the Community Health Index.

The chapters in Part II relate the findings of our cognitive epidemiology research. In chapter 2, we discuss associations between childhood IQ and mortality in general. In chapter 3, we discuss associations between childhood IQ and specific causes of mortality, physical diseases, and risk factors for physical disease. In chapter 4, we discuss associations between childhood IQ and mental diseases (including both dementia and psychiatric illnesses).

2

CHILDHOOD IQ AND
ALL-CAUSE MORTALITY

This chapter deals with the association between prior cognitive ability and deaths from all causes. We first describe the few previous studies that have found evidence for such an association. Then we describe our studies with samples in the Aberdeen area and west of Scotland, in which we used data from the Scottish Mental Survey (SMS) of 1932 (SMS1932) linked to records of death to establish that lower childhood IQ was significantly associated with earlier mortality. Possible mechanisms of the association are considered and tested. Data from the SMS of 1947 (SMS1947) are used to replicate the IQ–mortality association. Our conclusion is that health and death open up a new area for the predictive validity of IQ tests, that early life IQ matters to health and survival in later life.

IS THERE A RELATIONSHIP BETWEEN CHILDHOOD IQ
AND MORTALITY?

During the process of tracing surviving participants of the SMS1932 via the Community Health Index in Aberdeen for our first planned studies of cognitive aging, we were finding out who was alive. Of those whom we were not able to find, some would have moved away from Aberdeen, some would have moved from Scotland or the United Kingdom as a whole, and some would be dead. This last fact attracted our attention. We could examine IQ scores in the SMS1932 in relation to who had survived. We could examine childhood IQ as a predictor of survival to old age. Had anyone done that previously?

There was much circumstantial evidence to indicate that exploring the IQ–survival relationship would be fruitful. There are well-known health inequalities related to socioeconomic status and education (e.g., see Lawlor, Sterne, Tylenius, Davey Smith, & Rasmussen, 2006). People in less professional jobs, people living in more deprived areas, and people with less education tend to suffer from more diseases and to die younger. It is not just the person's own socioeconomic status that is connected to his or her health; one's parent's socioeconomic status, too, is related to health outcomes. Another well-established set of results concerning education and socioeconomic status is that they are significantly correlated with IQ test scores (Jencks, 1979).

In the web of associations among health, education, socioeconomic status, and IQ, perhaps only the health–IQ association remained to be explored. Researchers had been in this area before: Maller (1933) conducted research at the group level, in a cross-sectional analysis. In Maller's study, New York was divided into 310 health areas. The mean IQ test scores of the areas were correlated with a number of health and social indices. The descriptive data from the study show nearly linear associations between IQ and birth rate, infant mortality, juvenile delinquency, and school progress. Especially interesting was that death rate was higher in areas with lower mean IQs (see Figure 2.1).

More than 50 years later came the first study of which we are aware that reported, prospectively, the association between individually tested IQ scores and mortality. The Malmo study in Sweden examined a cohort that was followed from 1938 to 1979 (Furu, Lingärde, Ljung, Munck, & Kristenson, 1984). Participants had taken the Hallgren Mental Test at age 10 and the Husen Mental Test at age 20. The investigators eventually found 61 deaths among 831 men in the study. Mental test scores of those who had died were lower. These results were obtained from an internal report from the study, and there are no quantitative analyses or available peer-reviewed studies.

The first peer-reviewed report of which we are aware that examined IQ–death associations among individuals was from the Australian Veterans Health Study (O'Toole, Adena, & Jones, 1988). This study examined a cohort of Australian men who served in Vietnam. They were given mental tests at age 18 between 1965 and 1971: the Army General Classification Test, the Army Speed and Accuracy Test, and the Mechanical Comprehension Test. Follow-up continued until 1982, at which time 523 of the 46,166 servicemen

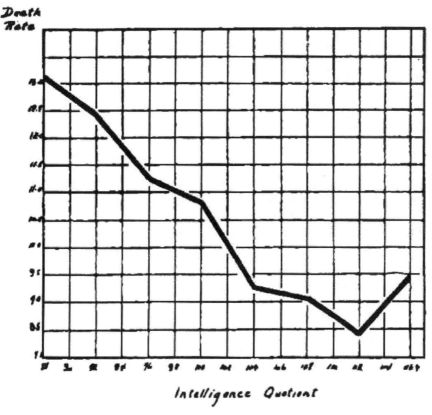

Figure 2.1. The association between population death rate and mean IQ score in 310 health areas in New York. From "Vital Indices and Their Relation to Psychological and Social Factors," by J. B. Maller, 1933, *Human Biology, 5,* p. 106. In the public domain.

had died. Unadjusted analyses revealed significant ($p < .01$) associations between all tests and death. The men with higher test scores at age 18 were more likely to be alive about 15 years later. Analyses adjusted for covariates still indicated a significant association between mental test score and survival. For each unit increase in the Army General Classification Test, the hazard ratio (HR) was reduced by 4% (HR = 0.96, 95% confidence interval [CI]: 0.93, 0.99).

The HR should be explained further because it is used commonly in epidemiology but less frequently in psychology. It is derived from Cox's (1972) proportional hazards regression analysis to estimate the association of a predictor (e.g., intelligence) and an outcome (e.g., mortality by a given date). These analyses produce HRs with accompanying 95% CIs. An HR summarizes the association of an explanatory variable with the risk of an event (Altman, 1991). An HR of exactly 1.0 means that the predictor has no relation with an outcome. An HR greater than 1.0 indicates that the predictor variable is associated with an increase in mortality risk, whereas an HR below this value is evidence of a decrease in risk. For example, an HR of 1.30 means that there is a 30% increase in the hazard per unit of measurement in the predictor; an HR of 0.70 means that there is a 30% decrease in the hazard per unit of measurement in the predictor. CIs that do not span 1.0 (unity) suggest that a relationship is statistically significant at the conventional level ($p < .05$).

In the United States, the researchers working on the Nun Study had found that indices of cognitive functioning were related to survival (Snowdon, Greiner, Kemper, Nanayakkara, & Mortimer, 1999). The nuns were from the School Sisters of Notre Dame. They were followed from between 1931 and 1943 up to 1998. Surveillance of death was based on a period between 1991 and 1998; that is, the investigators studied only those nuns who were still alive in 1991, and each was followed up for vital status until 1998. There were no IQ-type test scores from the nuns' early lives. At entry to the order, the nuns had provided handwritten autobiographies. These were used to provide an indication of their cognitive ability. Idea density and grammatical complexity were used as indicators of mental ability from young adulthood. In the surveillance period, there were 58 deaths among 180 women. The relative rate for survival, for the top versus bottom group, based on idea density scores, was 1.49 (95% CI: 1.17, 1.89). A similar, slightly weaker, association with grammatical complexity was nonsignificant.

Before the first report of any IQ–death association in the SMS1932, therefore, a number of studies had examined the association between IQ, or a cognitive surrogate, in early life and mortality. None had the following features in a single study: a validated IQ-type test, the inclusion of males and females, several decades of follow-up, and a population-representative sample.

CHILDHOOD IQ AND DEATH IN THE CITY OF ABERDEEN: THE SCOTTISH MENTAL SURVEY OF 1932

For the initial investigation to be manageable, we decided to study survival of the SMS1932's participants in the Aberdeen city area (Whalley & Deary, 2001).

We identified children who attended Aberdeen city schools when they took the Moray House Test (MHT) in the SMS1932 (Scottish Council for Research in Education [SCRE], 1933). This included in 2,792 children, born in 1921, for whom there was family name, given name, name of school, date of birth, and MHT score from the SMS1932. Each participant was sought in Scotland's Register of Deaths, starting at 1932 and moving forward to January 1, 1997. Participants who were untraced at this stage were sought in the Aberdeen-area Community Health Index. The SMS1932 had unmarried surnames for females, and the Register of Deaths and the Community Health Index had married names; therefore, any untraced women were sought in the Register of Marriages in Scotland from 1937 onward. When a successful match was found, the woman was again sought in the Register of Deaths and the Community Health Index, using her married surname. Participants who were still untraced at this stage were sought by computer and hand searches in the UK-wide National Health Service Central Register, situated in Southport, England. This database provides additional information about participants who had emigrated from the United Kingdom. After these searches, 2,230 (79.9%) of the 2,792 participants were traced, and their vital status was established. Their MHT scores from the SMS1932 were adjusted for their age in days at the date of the test. The scores were converted to standard IQ scores with a mean of 100 and a standard deviation (SD) of 15.

The numbers of participants who survived, died, moved out of the United Kingdom, and were untraced are shown in Table 2.1. The table shows the mean IQ test scores for each of these groups and divides the samples into males and females. This information provides only a crude indication of any association between IQ and survival, because it does not take account of the time between mental testing and death. For both men and women, those who died up to January 1, 1997, had lower childhood IQ scores.

TABLE 2.1
Mean (SD) IQ Scores From the Scottish Mental Survey of 1932
at Age 11 Years for Participants Who Were Dead, Alive, Untraced,
and Migrant at January 1, 1997

Participants	Total	Dead	Alive	Untraced	Moved away	p^a
All[b]						
N	2,792	1,084	1,101	562	45	
IQ score	100.0	97.7	102.0	100.8	98.9	
	(15.0)	(15.4)	(14.2)	(15.1)	(17.1)	< .0001
Men						
n	1,427	646	507	247	27	
IQ score	100.5	98.9	102.5	101.1	99.0	
	(15.5)	(15.6)	(14.8)	(15.6)	(19.5)	.001
Women						
n	1,365	438	594	315	18	
IQ score	99.4	95.9	101.5	100.5	98.7	
	(14.5)	(14.8)	(13.6)	(14.7)	(13.3)	< .0001

Note. From "Longitudinal Cohort Study of Childhood IQ and Survival Up to Age 76," by L. J. Whalley and I. J. Deary, 2001, BMJ, 322, p. 820. Copyright 2001 by BMJ Publishing Group Ltd. Reprinted with permission. [a]Analysis of variance. [b]Significant post hoc differences between groups (Scheffé tests), as follows. All participants: dead < alive (p = .0001), dead < untraced (p < .0001). Men: dead < untraced (p = .018). Women: dead < alive (p < .0001), dead < untraced (p < .0001).

The appropriate analysis for these data is Cox proportional hazards regression. This form of regression, used mainly in epidemiological analyses, has important characteristics. It is sensitive to the time of the outcome event. In the present case, the date of death was entered. For those who had not died, the information was censored at the chosen census date (January 1, 1997). For participants who had moved out of Scotland, the data were censored at the date of embarkation. There was a significant ($p < .0001$) association between IQ scores at age 11 and survival up to 65 years later (Whalley & Deary, 2001). When all participants are included, the HR of death for each IQ point on the MHT was 0.985 (95% CI: 0.981, 0.989, $p < .0001$). The effect was stronger in women than in men. The HRs were 0.977 for women (95% CI: 0.971, 0.984, $p < .0001$), and 0.989 for men (95% CI: 0.984, 0.994, $p < .0001$).

The figures expressing the Cox regression results that are based on each single point of IQ are somewhat inaccessible. It is useful to illustrate these results by demonstrating the hazard on the basis of a standard deviation difference in IQ score (15 points). Expressed in this way, and including all participants, the HR is 0.79 (95% CI: 0.75, 0.84). This means that a 15-point advantage in IQ score at age 11 is associated with a 21% reduction in the risk (hazard) of dying over the period of the next 65 years. For women, the reduction in risk is 29% (95% CI: 22%, 36%) for a 15-point IQ difference and 49% for a 30-point IQ difference (95% CI: 39%, 58%). For men, the reduction in hazard is 17% (95% CI: 11%, 24%) for a 15-point IQ difference and 32% for a 30-point IQ difference (95% CI: 20%, 42%). Each standard deviation of childhood IQ has a moderate-sized effect on survival to old age.

The reason for the stronger effect in women than men might be cohort specific. The survival curves are shown separately for men and women in Figure 2.2. Among women, there is an early and clear separation of the survival of those in the top and bottom quartiles of IQ. We later found that the middle quartiles fall in between (Deary, Whalley, & Starr, 2003). For men there is a more complex pattern. The female pattern appears in men only in old age. Before that, during the years of World War II (WWII), there is an obvious kink in the association, whereby men in the top IQ-scoring quartile have the greatest risk of dying. Further analysis of individuals' deaths did reveal the higher mean IQs of men who died during active service in the war. This is an interesting warning about associations in humans: They can show such reversals, given different circumstances.

Establishing that there is an association between childhood IQ and survival to old age is merely the first, important step in the long process of explanation. Before we sought an IQ–survival association, there were known associations between parental socioeconomic status; own socioeconomic status; and education and health inequalities, including mortality. IQ provides a third associate of mortality, one that is correlated with those

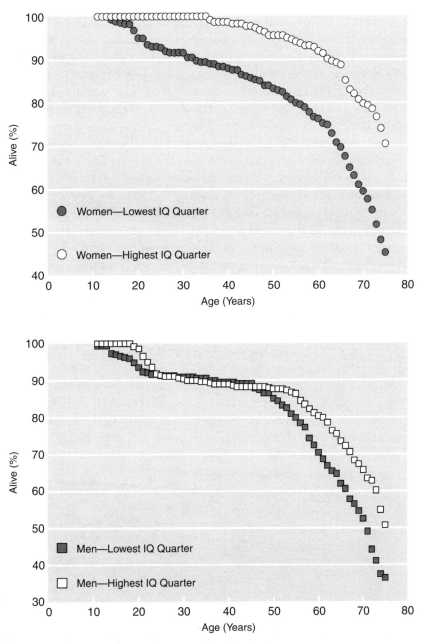

Figure 2.2. Probability of survival at ages 12 through 76 for women and men in the highest and lowest quarters for IQ scores at age 11 in the Scottish Mental Survey of 1932. From "Longitudinal Cohort Study of Childhood IQ and Survival Up to Age 76," by L. J. Whalley and I. J. Deary, 2001, *BMJ, 322,* p. 820. Copyright 2001 by BMJ Publishing Group Ltd. Reprinted with permission.

other associates. Education and socioeconomic status ideally would have been assessed in the original study (Whalley & Deary, 2001), but such data were not available. All that was available was a measure of the mean level of overcrowding in the 1930s in houses in the catchment areas of the schools attended by the children in Aberdeen. These overcrowding levels provide, therefore, neither child-specific data nor specific data about children's own homes. Nevertheless, these overcrowding levels were significantly associated with survival up to January 1, 1997, when the analysis was performed on all participants. There was no significant association when the analyses were done separately in men and women. There was a correlation of −.22 ($p < .001$) between overcrowding in the child's school's catchment area and IQ at age 11. Adjusting the Cox proportional hazard regression models between MHT IQ scores and survival for overcrowding did not significantly alter their effect sizes or significance levels.

Some additional data were available for some study participants. Death certificates contain information about father's occupation; thus, for 722 participants we had data on father's occupational socioeconomic status in addition to IQ, age at death, and school catchment area overcrowding. A structural equation model was performed on the associations among these variables, and the well-fitting model is shown in Figure 2.3. This shows an association between both of the social background factors and childhood IQ, which mediates their effect on age at death.

At this stage in the research on IQ and mortality, one of the unknowns was the form of the relationship. It might be incremental, with ever-higher IQ scores conferring ever-better protection against mortality. There might be a threshold, however, above which higher IQs had little effect on health.

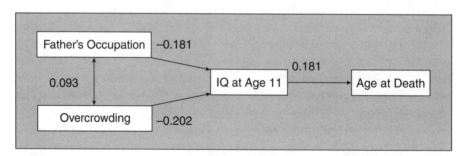

Figure 2.3. Best-fitting structural equation model of associations among paternal occupation, overcrowding, IQ at age 11, and age at death up to age 76. All parameter estimates are significantly greater than zero. Average off-diagonal standardized residuals = .013; $\chi^2(2) = 3.29$, $p = .19$; Bentler–Bonett normed fit index = .965, Bentler–Bonett nonnormed fit index = .956; comparative fit index = .985. All of these indices are indicative of a well-fitting model. From "Longitudinal Cohort Study of Childhood IQ and Survival Up to Age 76," by L. J. Whalley and I. J. Deary, 2001, *BMJ, 322,* p. 821. Copyright 2001 by BMJ Publishing Group Ltd. Reprinted with permission.

There might mostly be an effect at low IQ levels, with especially low IQ scores being associated with a greater risk of death. This was tested in a further analysis of the Aberdeen SMS1932 sample (Deary, Whalley, & Starr, 2003). The IQs of the boys and girls in the Aberdeen city schools were divided into quartiles. Within each quartile, the number of people alive and dead was recorded. The lowest IQ quartile was used as a reference group, and the odds ratios (with 95% CIs) of the other quartiles was computed, setting the reference group's odds at 1.0. The results for the females show that all quartiles have significantly better survival rates than the lowest IQ quartile (see Table 2.2). The two intermediate IQ quartiles have similar odds ratios, and that for the highest IQ group is considerably higher. The study, although not sufficiently large to thoroughly examine this question, suggests there is a graded effect between IQ and mortality but might also suggest that there is special risk in the lowest IQs and special protection in the highest IQs. In the males, the three upper IQ quartiles have significantly better survival rates than the lowest IQ quartile (see Table 2.2). There is less difference between the top IQ quartile and the intermediate two quartiles than was seen with the females. This is likely to be caused by the excess deaths among high-IQ men during active service in WWII. Additional samples are required to examine the form of the IQ–mortality association, especially among men.

TABLE 2.2
Odds Ratios (ORs; with ± 95% Confidence Intervals [CIs])
for Death by January 1, 1997, and IQ at Age 11 Years in 1932

Participants	IQ quartile	Mean IQ (SD, range[a])	N dead/alive at 1/1/1997	OR	95% CI
Women	Lowest	79.9 (8.2, 58–90)	150/123	1.0 (Reference)	
	Second lowest	96.7 (3.3, 91–102)	112/155	1.69	1.20, 2.37
	Second highest	106.3 (2.5, 102–111)	110/160	1.77	1.26, 2.50
	Highest	116.9 (5.0, 111–134)	66/156	2.88	1.98, 4.19
Men	Lowest	79.3 (7.8, 60–91)	181/99	1.0 (Reference)	
	Second lowest	96.8 (3.0, 91–102)	153/128	1.52	1.08, 2.14
	Second highest	106.3 (2.6, 102–111)	148/129	1.59	1.13, 2.23
	Highest	118.3 (5.9, 111–139)	151/150	1.81	1.29, 2.52

Note. IQs were grouped as quartiles, and the top three quartiles were compared using the lowest IQ quartile as a reference. From *Brain and Longevity* (p. 158), edited by C. E. Finch, J.-M. Robine, and Y. Christen, 2003, Berlin, Germany: Springer. Copyright 2003 by Springer Science + Business Media. Reprinted with permission.
[a]IQ ranges have been rounded to integers.

IQ, HEALTH, AND SOCIAL FACTORS IN THE WEST OF SCOTLAND: LINKING THE SCOTTISH MENTAL SURVEY OF 1932 WITH THE MIDSPAN STUDIES

It would be fair to criticize the study linking IQ and survival in Aberdeen (Whalley & Deary, 2001) for lacking information from points in the life span between childhood and death and for lacking information about social background. We attempted to make good of some of this deficiency in a linkage between the SMS1932 and Scotland's Midspan Studies.

The Midspan Studies

The Midspan Studies were conceived and started in the 1960s by the pioneering public health physician Victor Hawthorne. The studies were so named because the participants were at about the middle of their life span. Hawthorne's ideas were developments of the post–WWII screening for tuberculosis, which had involved mass X-rays taken in public settings. He realized that the methods of public screening might be extended to chronic diseases in Scotland, such as cardiovascular diseases, respiratory diseases, and cancers. The Midspan Studies comprise a set of related studies, each with its own funding history and population base (Hart, MacKinnon, et al., 2005). Among the ideas pursued in the studies was the notion that reducing high blood pressure in the many people with mild disease—in addition to treating overt disease—might add significantly to relieving the population's illness burden. The studies also attempted to document, in the population, the risk factors for chronic diseases.

Two of the Midspan Studies are of interest here (Hart, MacKinnon, et al., 2005). They began in the 1970s. The Collaborative Study collected its baseline information between 1970 and 1973 from people in the central belt of Scotland. It examined 7,028 people (6,022 men and 1,006 women) of working age in 27 workplaces. The Renfrew–Paisley Study collected its baseline information from 1972 to 1976 from people in the neighboring towns just outside Glasgow. It collected data from 15,402 people (7,048 men and 8,354 women) ages 45 to 64. It was situated in the general population, with a 78% response rate. Both studies, at their baselines, included self-administered questionnaires and screening checks. The questionnaires, not identical in the two studies, included socioeconomic factors, health behavior, cardiorespiratory measures, psychological distress, and (Collaborative Study only) education. The screening check included anthropometric measures, physiological tests, blood samples, and (Collaborative Study only) urine samples. Among the measures were blood pressure, height, weight, cholesterol, forced expiratory volume from the lungs in 1 second, and electrocardiogram. Since their inception, both studies have had ongoing follow-up for mortality (with causes of deaths), cancer incidence, and hospital admissions. These three aspects of the follow-up are possible because of Scotland's remarkable, comprehensive, National Health Service–funded registers for these disease outcomes. Everyone who dies, becomes diagnosed with any cancer, or has a hospital admission is added to these registers, with *International Classification of Diseases* (*ICD*; World Health Organization, 1994) details included in each entry. The Midspan Studies have been very productive, with publications on population screening, blood pressure, cholesterol, smoking, coronary heart disease, stroke, respiratory disease, cancer, alcohol, hemostasis, early origins of adult disease, height, social class and life course influences on illness, stress and psychosocial factors in illness, and hospital admissions. These comprise more than 150 peer-reviewed publications, the details of which can be found at the Midspan Web site (http:// www.gla.ac.uk/faculties/medicine/midspan) and were summarized by Hart, MacKinnon, et al. (2005).

In addition to these rich data are data on social factors for the Midspan participants (Hart, MacKinnon, et al., 2005). People's occupations were coded according to the United Kingdom's six-level classification from most professional (I = professional) to least professional (V = unskilled) jobs, with II (intermediate), IIINM (skilled nonmanual), IIIM (skilled manual), and IV (semiskilled) in between. Scotland also affords the possibility of deriving a measure of the affluence–deprivation of the small area in which each person lives. The measure is called the *Carstairs–Morris Index* (Carstairs & Morris, 1991). Each person's residence has an area postal code. On the basis of census data, four variables are combined to give an indication of the degree of affluence–deprivation in the area: (a) male unemployment, (b) overcrowding, (c) car ownership, and (d) proportion of heads of household in occupational social classes IV and V. These scores range from 1 (*least deprived*) to 7 (*most deprived*).

Consider the data held on members of the Midspan Studies. At mid-life, in the early to mid-1970s, there were rich anthropometric, demographic, psychosocial, physiological, and medical data. From then onward there were steadily collected data on illnesses and deaths. A perusal of the ages of the Midspan participants made it clear that some of them would have been born in 1921. This made it conceivable to attempt to replicate the childhood IQ–mortality association that had been found in Aberdeen. In addition, it would be possible to add more, important covariables: possible confounders and mediators of any IQ–mortality association.

Linking the Scottish Mental Survey 1932 to the Midspan Studies

The process of linking the SMS1932 data with the Midspan data was burdensome, in terms of both the permissions required to do so and the procedures that were put in place to achieve accurate matches (Hart, Deary, et al.,

2003). By this stage in the research program, the SMS1932 had been computerized by typing in data from the handwritten, area-based ledgers. The ledgers for Fife, Wigtown, and Angus were missing. Together, the estimated number of people born in these missing-ledger sites in 1921 was 7,542 (SCRE, 1933). Between 1921 and 1933, people would have moved into and out of these areas of Scotland, and some children would not have taken the SMS1932 because of nonattendance at school. The available SMS1932 ledgers contained information about people who did and did not have MHT scores, a total of 86,520. Of these, 81,140 had MHT scores. These then had to be linked with the 1,251 people in the Midspan (i.e., the Renfrew–Paisley and the Collaborative) Studies who had a 1921 birth year.

In the linkage process, the following information was available from the SMS1932: surname (at age 11), forename, date of birth, sex, school, and region (Hart, Deary, et al., 2003). The following information was available from the Midspan Studies: surname (and maiden name, for women who had married), forename(s), date of birth, sex, place of birth, and place at time of screening. Linkage between the SMS1932 and Midspan data sets proceeded in three stages. First, exact matches—using surname, forename, and date and day of birth—were found, electronically, between the two data sets. This resulted in 678 matches. In the second stage, the requirement for exact forename was dropped, and sex was added to the criteria for matching. This identified people with multiple forenames (with different names being used in the two studies), abbreviated forenames in one or the other study, and misspellings of forenames. This added another 203 matches between SMS1932 and Midspan. At this stage, there were only 264 people in the Renfrew–Paisley Study, and 108 in the Collaborative Study, who had not been matched to the SMS1932. This reflects the comprehensiveness of the SMS1932. The third stage, therefore, consisted of manually checking all remaining unmatched participants, with reference, at times, to the original handwritten Midspan information. Uncertain matches were discussed by the investigative team. A slight difference in dates of birth between the two studies was a common reason for not matching, and these were accepted as a match if all other information concurred and if the investigators all agreed. This third stage produced another 153 SMS1932–Midspan matches.

There were 1,032 individuals matched between the SMS1932 and the Midspan Studies. Alert readers will note that this is not equal to the total of 1,034 people matched in the three stages; 2 men had taken part in both the Renfrew–Paisley Study and the Collaborative Study. The 1,032 is 82.5% of the 1,251 Midspan participants born in 1921. Of the 1032, 938 (90.9%) were present on the day of the SMS1932 and had an MHT score.

The linked data first afforded an opportunity to examine how IQ at age 11 was related to occupational social class in midlife (Hart, Deary, et al., 2003). This association is shown in Table 2.3. The pattern, though seen in both sexes,

TABLE 2.3

Mean IQ Scores, Corrected for Age at Time of Testing, by Social Class in Adulthood for Men and Women in the Midspan Studies Who Were Matched to a Score on the Scottish Mental Survey of 1932 (SMS1932) Data Set

| Participants | Social class | | | | | | Trend[a] |
	I	II	IIINM	IIIM	IV	V	
Men							
n	41	109	66	211	102	20	
Mean IQ	114.9	111.0	103.7	98.2	96.6	91.9	p < .0001
Women							
n	9	48	101	62	117	36	
Mean IQ	106.0	105.4	104.4	92.9	93.7	93.4	p < .0001
All							
N	50	157	167	273	219	56	
Mean IQ	113.3	108.9	103.3	96.6	94.3	92.1	p < .0001

Note. N = 922, excluding participants with missing social class or deprivation category data. I = professional; II = intermediate; IIINM = skilled nonmanual; IIIM = skilled manual; IV = semiskilled; V = unskilled. From "The Scottish Mental Survey 1932 Linked to the Midspan Studies: A Prospective Investigation of Childhood Intelligence and Future Health," by C. L. Hart, I. J. Deary, M. D. Taylor, P. L. MacKinnon, G. Davey Smith, L. J. Whalley, et al., 2003, *Public Health, 117*, p. 193. Copyright 2003 by Oxford University Press. Adapted with permission.
[a]This is computed from a regression equation in which social class in midlife is the dependent variable and IQ from the SMS1932 is the independent variable.

is clearer in men, perhaps because women's occupational social class was often based on the husband's job. Among men, those in the most professional social class have a mean childhood IQ of 114.9, and those in the most manual have a mean of 91.9, with a graded and significant relationship between these classes of occupation. A similarly graded and significant (p < .0001) relationship exists between childhood IQ and the deprivation of the area in which the person was living in midlife (see Table 2.4). Men living in the most affluent areas had a mean childhood IQ of 110.2, and those living in the most deprived areas had a mean of 92.3. The results for women are very similar. At this stage, no statistical adjustment has been made for parental social class. When the participants within any single social class were divided, using just a binary classification, into whether they lived in a deprived area, those in the nondeprived areas had significantly higher childhood IQs. When the participants within any single deprivation category were divided, using just a binary classification, into whether they had nonmanual or manual occupations, those in the nonmanual occupations had significantly higher childhood IQs.

Childhood IQ and Death in the West of Scotland

The combined SMS1932–Midspan database, with more than 900 participants, was large enough to study epidemiological associations between childhood IQ in 1932 and mortality up to 2002, and it had unusually rich life

TABLE 2.4

Mean IQ Scores, Corrected for Age at Time of Testing, by Deprivation in
Adulthood for Men And Women in the Midspan Studies Who Were Matched
to a Score on the Scottish Mental Survey of 1932 (SMS1932) Data Set

	Deprivation category[a]							
Participants	1	2	3	4	5	6	7	Trend[b]
Men								
n	39	16	81	134	141	101	37	
Mean IQ	110.2	108.7	106.7	102.1	98.5	98.3	92.3	$p < .0001$
Women								
n	27	1	44	74	139	66	22	
Mean IQ	110.8	111.2	101.4	98.3	96.5	95.9	92.7	$p < .0001$
All								
N	66	17	125	208	280	167	59	
Mean IQ	110.5	108.8	104.8	100.8	97.5	97.4	92.4	$p < .0001$

Note. N = 922, excluding participants with missing social class or deprivation category data. From "The Scottish Mental Survey 1932 Linked to the Midspan Studies: A Prospective Investigation of Childhood Intelligence and Future Health," by C. L. Hart, I. J. Deary, M. D. Taylor, P. L. MacKinnon, G. Davey Smith, L. J. Whalley, et al., 2003, *Public Health, 117,* p. 193. Copyright 2003 by Oxford University Press. Adapted with permission.
[a]1 = *least deprived,* 7 = *most deprived.*
[b]This is computed from a regression equation in which deprivation category of the person's area of residence in midlife is the dependent variable and IQ from the SMS1932 is the independent variable.

course data. The next stage was to link this combined data set to the health records held by the National Health Service in Scotland. At that time, various tasks remained for research into early life IQ and health outcomes, including mortality (Hart, Taylor, et al., 2003). First, replication of the IQ–mortality association was required, because there were few peer-reviewed studies. Second, none of the published studies had included the person's adult occupational social class or a measure of the deprivation or affluence of his or her living environment. Third, none had tested the possible mechanisms for the association put forward by Whalley and Deary (2001). The linked SMS1932–Midspan data set would allow at least one hypothesis to be tested: that IQ in childhood acted on survival via an entry to more professional occupations and less deprived environments. Although there was, in the SMS1932–Midspan linkage study, an attempt to replicate the IQ–mortality association found in Aberdeen city, the areas covered by the Midspan Studies were, overall, somewhat more deprived.

People who took part in the Midspan Studies had already been flagged at the Scottish National Health Service's Central Register (Hart, Taylor, et al., 2003). Dates and causes (with *ICD* codes) of death over the 25 years from the Midspan baseline to 2002 were obtained. In chapter 3 of this volume, we discuss specific causes of death. Here, we focus on attempting to replicate our finding of an association between childhood IQ and all-cause mortality (Whalley & Deary, 2001).

There were 922 linked Midspan–SMS1932 participants (549 men and 373 women) with full data: childhood IQ, midlife social class and deprivation information, and follow-up data on morbidity and mortality (Hart, Taylor, et al., 2003). In the 25 or so years since the Midspan baseline data were collected in the 1970s, 422 of the participants (45.8%) had died: 282 men (51%) and 140 women (38%). Cox proportional hazards regression was used to examine the associations between childhood IQ, adult social factors, and the risk of death. In the sex-adjusted model, the risk of dying between the 1970s and 2002 was increased by 17% (95% CI: 7%, 29%) for each standard deviation decrease in IQ. After adjustment for sex and adult occupational social class, this reduced slightly to 13% (95% CI: 2%, 26%), an attenuation of 24%. After adjustment for sex and adult Carstairs–Morris Index, the risk reduced slightly to 14% (95% CI: 3%, 25%), an attenuation of 18%. Therefore, there is a significant association between childhood IQ in the SMS1932 and death between the early to mid-1970s and 2002, and the effect is not substantially accounted for by adult occupational social class or deprivation of the area of residence in midlife.

In a sex-adjusted model, there was an 11% (95% CI: 3%, 19%) increased risk of death in the observation period per category of social class, with higher risk of death for the less professional occupations (Hart, Taylor, et al., 2003). Adjustment for childhood IQ reduced this risk by 45% to a nonsignificant 6% (95% CI: –2%, 15%). In a sex-adjusted model, there was an 11% (95% CI: 4%, 18%), increased risk of death in the observation period per category of deprivation index, with a higher risk of death for people living in the more deprived areas. Adjustment for childhood IQ reduced this risk by 27% to a nonsignificant 8% (95% CI: –1%, 16%). Therefore, there are significant influences of adult occupational social class and deprivation on survival up to age 81, but these are somewhat attenuated and no longer significant after adjustment for childhood IQ.

For the purpose of illustrating the IQ–mortality effect more clearly, the relative rates of death when childhood IQ is divided into quartiles (the three lower quartiles are compared with the top quartile) are shown in Table 2.5 (mean IQ > 110.7; Hart, Taylor, et al., 2003). With only sex added to the model, the lowest IQ quartile had a 47% increased risk of death in the observation period compared with the top IQ quartile. After further adjustment for adult social class and deprivation category, this became a 26% increased risk, a reduction of 45% and no longer significant. It is also evident from Table 2.5 that the two intermediate IQ quartiles have only a little increased risk of death compared with the highest quartile, and this is not significant. Although this does not agree with the Aberdeen SMS1932, in which there appeared to be a graded effect of IQ on mortality (Whalley & Deary, 2001), it suggests that, in this sample, the increased risk occurs below a threshold of IQ. To examine this further, interaction terms were added to the models

TABLE 2.5

Relative Rates (With 95% Confidence Intervals) of All-Cause Mortality
by Quartile of IQ

	IQ quartile				
Variable	1 (≤ 90.6)	2 (90.7–100.5)	3 (100.6–110.6)	4 (> 110.7)	Trend (p)[a]
N	230	231	231	230	
No. deaths	121	101	103	97	
Adjusted for sex	1.47 (1.12, 1.92)	1.14 (0.87, 1.51)	1.13 (0.86, 1.49)	1	.001
Adjusted for sex and social class	1.31 (0.98, 1.76)	1.06 (0.79, 1.42)	1.06 (0.80, 1.41)	1	.019
Adjusted for sex and deprivation category	1.35 (1.02, 1.78)	1.06 (0.80, 1.41)	1.06 (0.80, 1.41)	1	.01
Adjusted for sex, social class, and deprivation category	1.26 (0.94, 1.70)	1.01 (0.76, 1.36)	1.03 (0.77, 1.37)	1	.038

Note. The highest IQ quartile, with risk of death set to 1, is used as a comparator for the other three quartiles. From "Childhood IQ, Social Class, Deprivation, and Their Relationships With Mortality and Morbidity Risk in Later Life: Prospective Observational Study Linking the Scottish Mental Survey 1932 and the Midspan Studies," by C. L. Hart, M. D. Taylor, G. Davey Smith, L. J. Whalley, J. M. Starr, D. J. Hole, et al., 2003, *Psychosomatic Medicine, 65,* p. 880. Copyright 2003 by Lippincott Williams & Wilkins. Adapted with permission.
[a]For this analysis, IQ was computed as a continuous variable.

(Hart, Taylor, et al., 2003). There was a significant interaction between IQ and deprivation category ($p = .026$), but no significant interaction with social class ($p = .73$). The IQ–deprivation interaction with mortality found in this sample is illustrated in Figure 2.4. This suggests that increased risk of death arises when people have the combination of low IQ and high environmental deprivation.

Different analytic methods have their particular strengths. On the one hand, in epidemiology, for outcomes such as death and the onset of illnesses, Cox proportional hazards regression modeling can incorporate the timing of the event, include people who have left the study, and cope with multiple predictors. On the other hand, it does not allow a path analysis explicitly to test hypotheses about mediating effects, such as the hypothesis that social class and deprivation might mediate the effect of IQ on mortality; that is, one may include covariables in the Cox model and observe the effect on the HR, but an actual chain of mediation cannot be stipulated and tested. The research team working on the SMS1932–Midspan collaboration was set up for reasons that included a wish to conduct types of modeling more often conducted by differential psychologists in addition to epidemiological modeling. The hypothesis of mediation by adult social position of the IQ–mortality association was tested using path analysis in the EQS structural equation modeling program (Hart, Taylor, et al., 2003). The principal question asked by this

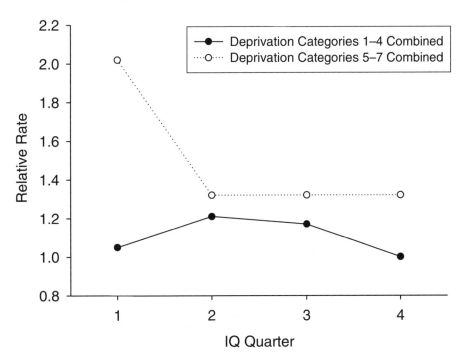

Figure 2.4. Relative rates of all-cause mortality by both IQ and deprivation category. From "Childhood IQ, Social Class, Deprivation, and Their Relationships With Mortality and Morbidity Risk in Later Life: Prospective Observational Study Linking the Scottish Mental Survey 1932 and the Midspan Studies," by C. L. Hart, M. D. Taylor, G. Davey Smith, L. J. Whalley, J. M. Starr, D. J. Hole, et al., 2003, *Psychosomatic Medicine, 65,* p. 880. Copyright 2003 by Lippincott Williams & Wilkins. Adapted with permission.

model was the following: After taking into account mediation by occupational social class and deprivation in middle adulthood, are there direct effects on childhood IQ on mortality? In this analysis, death is modeled as a binary variable (i.e., dead or alive), and so the timing information is lost. The well-fitting (nonsignificant chi-square, and comparative fit index = 1.0) model is shown in Figure 2.5. The model shows that women from the SMS1932 were more likely to be alive in 2002. Higher childhood IQ was associated with more professional occupations at midlife, and both of these were associated with living in a less deprived area. Social class mediated part of the effect of IQ on deprivation category. There was a trend toward people living in more deprived areas in midlife to be dead by the census date in 2002. When all this was taken into account, there was still a remaining, significant direct effect of childhood IQ on survival to 2002. Of course, the term *direct* is used with reference only to the variables examined here; some other set of variables might mediate or otherwise cause the association between IQ and mortality.

Both epidemiological and path analyses conclude that, in this sample, adult social class and deprivation of the area of residence account only in part

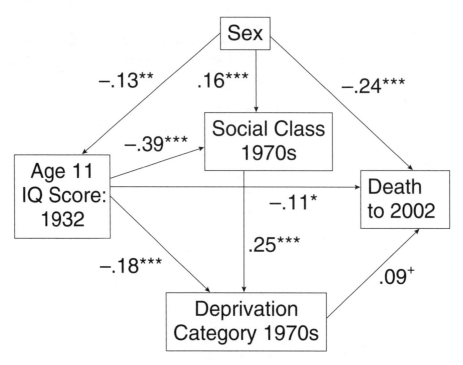

Figure 2.5. Structural equation model of the associations among childhood IQ, sex (1 = male, 2 = female), social class (lower numbers = more professional social class), deprivation category (higher numbers = more deprivation), and mortality (1 = alive, 2 = dead). Coefficients placed beside arrows may be squared to give the variance shared by adjacent variables. $+p \le .1$, $*p \le .05$, $** p \le .01$, $*** p \le .001$. From "Childhood IQ, Social Class, Deprivation, and Their Relationships With Mortality and Morbidity Risk in Later Life: Prospective Observational Study Linking the Scottish Mental Survey 1932 and the Midspan Studies," by C. L. Hart, M. D. Taylor, G. Davey Smith, L. J. Whalley, J. M. Starr, D. J. Hole, et al., 2003, *Psychosomatic Medicine, 65,* p. 881. Copyright 2003 by Lippincott Williams & Wilkins. Reprinted with permission.

for the association between IQ and mortality, and it is not clear whether that partial mediation is a correct interpretation of the data. Occupational social class is correlated with childhood IQ; therefore, when it is placed on a mediation pathway, as is done in Figure 2.5, that does not necessarily mean that social class is an explanatory variable through which IQ acts. It might mean little more than that occupational social class is acting as a proxy variable for adult IQ. If this were true, the apparent mediation would be nothing of the kind, and the interpretation would instead be that childhood IQ leads to higher adult IQ, which is in turn associated—still mysteriously—with mortality.

The association between IQ and mortality was thus replicated in SMS1932 participants in Aberdeen and in the west of Scotland. How do the effect sizes compare? In Aberdeen (Whalley & Deary, 2001), the relative rate for 1 standard deviation of IQ was .79 (95% CI: .75, .84). Higher IQ scorers at age 11 were more likely to be alive at age 76, in 1997, after an observation period of 65 years. In the SMS1932–Midspan linkage study in the west of Scotland, the relative rates were expressed in reverse, with the rate of people with higher IQs being alive at follow-up rather than dead (Hart, Taylor, et al., 2003). When the coefficient is reversed, it provides a relative rate of .85 (95% CI: .75, .84) per standard deviation of IQ; that is, over the observation period of 25 years from the mid-1970s to 2002, the protective effect of higher IQ was similar to that found in the Aberdeen-based study. In addition to the evidence of possible partial mediation of the effects of IQ on mortality by social class and deprivation, the possible interaction of IQ and deprivation warrants further research; that is, in the SMS1932–Midspan Study, high IQ seemed protective in the situation of living in a deprived area; it was people with both low IQ and a deprived living area who died earlier.

Further analyses were carried out on the SMS1932–Midspan linked sample to examine whether the association between IQ and all-cause mortality was found at specific ages. Deaths before and after age 65 were compared (Hart, Taylor, et al., 2005). In this analysis, there were 432 deaths from all causes, 173 of which occurred up to age 65 and 259 of which occurred after age 65 (see Table 2.6). For early deaths—those before and up to age 65—and adjusting for sex, there was a 36% increased risk associated with 1 standard deviation disadvantage in childhood IQ. Further adjustment for occupational social class and deprivation of the area of residence at midlife attenuated the effect by only 19%. However, there was no significant association between childhood IQ and all-cause mortality after age 65. The survival curves (see Figure 2.6) help to illustrate these statistical analyses. The curves show only the top and lowest scoring quarters of childhood IQ. About 5 years after the Midspan baseline examination, the mortality experience of the two groups diverges so that, after about 15 years, at about age 65, they are quite widely separated, having started together—because, of course, all the participants were alive at baseline testing. After 15 years of follow-up the curves of the two extreme childhood IQ groups is more parallel, and a differential level of survival persists.

TABLE 2.6
Relative Rate of All-Cause Mortality (With 95% Confidence Intervals)
Associated With a 1 Standard Deviation Increase in Childhood IQ

Variable	Up to age 65	After age 65
N	173	259
Relative rate adjusted for sex	1.36 (1.18, 1.57)	1.05 (0.93, 1.19)
Relative rate adjusted for sex, occupational social class, and deprivation category	1.29 (1.10, 1.51)	1.01 (0.88, 1.16)

Note. From "Childhood IQ and All-Cause Mortality Before and After Age 65: Prospective Observational Study Linking the Scottish Mental Survey 1932 and the Midspan Studies," by C. L. Hart, M. D. Taylor, G. Davey Smith, L. J. Whalley, J. M. Starr, D. J. Hole, et al., 2005, *British Journal of Health Psychology, 10,* p. 158. Copyright 2005 by the British Psychological Society. Adapted with permission.

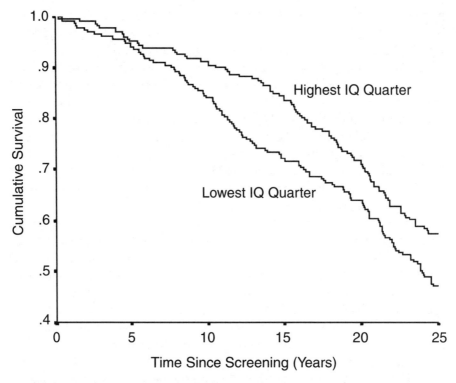

Figure 2.6. Survival in years by highest and lowest quarter of childhood IQ. From "Childhood IQ and All-Cause Mortality Before and After Age 65: Prospective Observational Study Linking the Scottish Mental Survey 1932 and the Midspan Studies," by C. L. Hart, M. D. Taylor, G. Davey Smith, L. J. Whalley, J. M. Starr, D. J. Hole, et al., 2005, *British Journal of Health Psychology, 10,* p. 159. Copyright 2005 by the British Psychological Society. Reprinted with permission.

Until now, the analyses have been conducted by examining the data for associations between childhood IQ and all-cause mortality and then further analyzing the data to discover whether putative mediators and confounders attenuate this effect. Another way to conduct the analyses is to ask whether and how much IQ scores from childhood attenuate the association between known risk factors and all-cause mortality. The extent to which childhood IQ attenuated the association between risk factors and all-cause mortality was examined in the SMS1932–Midspan sample (Hart, Taylor, et al., 2005). The attenuating effect of childhood IQ was examined for mortality up to age 65 and after age 65. In the SMS1932–Midspan sample there were significant all-cause mortality associations with all risk factors that were assessed at baseline in midlife. People were at significantly greater risk of dying if, at midlife, they had higher blood pressure (systolic and diastolic), were shorter, and had a smaller forced expiratory volume in 1 second. The effects of these risk factors for all-cause mortality were very similar, between 21% and 24% increased risk for each standard deviation disadvantage in the measure. Ex-smokers were similar to nonsmokers. Adjusting for childhood IQ had a negligible effect or no effect on the risk factor–mortality associations when deaths at all ages were included. The risk factors differed with regard to where in the life span they had the strongest effect. Height and lung performance were more strongly associated with deaths up to age 65. Smoking and blood pressure had stronger associations with mortality after 65, and there was no attenuating effect of childhood IQ on risk factor–mortality associations for deaths after age 65. Smokers have about double the risk of death compared with nonsmokers. For the deaths up to age 65, adjusting for childhood IQ attenuated these effects by the following percentages: systolic blood pressure = 36%, diastolic blood pressure = 36%, height = 34%, sex- and height-adjusted forced expiratory volume in 1 second = 17%, and smoking = 10%—that is, the attenuating effect of childhood IQ on these risk factors was modest and was specific to deaths up to age 65.

CHILDHOOD IQ AND MORTALITY AT THE NATIONAL LEVEL: THE SCOTTISH MENTAL SURVEY OF 1947

The association between childhood IQ and all-cause mortality and specific causes of death was studied further in the SMS1947, which tested people born in 1936 (Deary, Whiteman, Starr, Whalley, & Fox, 2004). These were the first cognitive epidemiological analyses involving the SMSs that were done at the whole-country level. The 6-Day sample of the SMS1947 was used, which is representative of the whole of Scotland. Of the original 1,208 people in the 6-Day sample, there were remaining records for 908 in the SCRE archives that provided the following information: surname, forename, date of birth, and MHT score at age 11 in the SMS1947.

The Scottish Record Linkage System was used to link these 908 people with illness outcomes (Heasman & Clarke, 1979). This uses name and date of birth information to make probabilistic matches to medical records. Name is used as a Soundex code, which picks up likely misspellings. Records that share information are given a probability weight. This is converted to absolute odds to inform decisions about linkage. An expert in the system then makes a decision about the appropriate threshold above which a linkage is accepted and below which it is not. Whether linkages are accepted is decided by comparison of the putatively linked records. It is a service of the National Health Service Scotland's Information and Statistics Division. Using this service meant that data from the SMS1947 could be linked to all-cause mortality from the Registrar General's death records (1968–2000); all hospital discharges with *ICD*-coded diagnoses from the Scottish Morbidity Records 1 (1968–2000); all psychiatric service discharges from the Scottish Morbidity

Records 4 (1968–2000); all cancer diagnoses from the Scottish Cancer Registry (Scottish Morbidity Records 6/SOCRATES; 1968–1998). Within Scottish Morbidity Records 1, cardiovascular diseases were identified separately on the basis of codes from the ICD.

In the observation period between 1968 and 2000, 125 members of the 6-Day sample died (see Table 2.7; see also Deary, Whiteman, Starr, et al., 2004). Their mean IQ, 97.7 (SD = 13.9), was significantly less than that of the people without linkage to that outcome, which was 104.6 (SD = 17.0). It is expected that few of the SMS1947 participants would have died prior to 1968. Cox proportional hazards regression analysis found that IQ from the MHT score in the SMS1947 was significantly associated with death in the observation period. The HR was 0.975 (95% CI: 0.964, 0.986), meaning that, for each IQ point, there was a 2.5% reduction in risk of being recorded as dead between 1968 and 2000. This replicated the IQ–all-cause mortality association found in the SMS1932 analyses in the Aberdeen area and in the west of Scotland. It generalizes the result to a different cohort, born 15 years later, who did not have WWII active service as a cause of death.

WHY MIGHT CHILDHOOD IQ AND DEATH BE ASSOCIATED?

Correlations have causes and, with the caveat that confounding by social background factors was not ruled out by the previously mentioned studies, there were four nonexclusive suggestions about how childhood IQ and survival might be linked (Whalley & Deary, 2001). These were compiled by reflecting on the known antecedents and outcomes of IQ at age 11. The causes and consequences of IQ must, to some extent, be shared with death.

First, childhood IQ might be a record of bodily insults up to that age. These would include perinatal as well as childhood problems. IQ might in part record the neural tribulations from conception to the date of testing, including any illnesses, nutritional privations, and injuries from birth onward. The 1921-born individuals were born and grew up in a more medically and socially deprived setting than more recent cohorts, so any effects under this cause might not replicate or might be reduced in more recent cohorts. In this model, childhood IQ is a mediator between brain insults and mortality. It is not causal. It acts, at the time of measurement, as an indicator of the ultimate causes.

Second, childhood IQ might be a marker for bodily system integrity. Whereas the previous suggestion construed IQ as a cumulative index of the neurological changes—mostly decrements—incurred by the organism, this idea suggests that there might exist individual differences in how well organisms have been assembled. The emphasis here is on a trait indicator of system integrity rather than on cumulative insults. Certainly, IQ is traitlike, with

TABLE 2.7

Results of Linking the 6-Day Sample of the Scottish Mental Survey of 1947 to Mortality and Morbidity Records

Outcome	n with outcome	n without outcome	IQ of people with outcome		IQ of people without outcome		p	Sex-adjusted HR	Sex-adjusted HR 95% confidence interval
			M	SD	M	SD			
Death	125	783	97.7	13.9	104.6	17.0	< .001	0.975	0.964, 0.986
Cancer	78	830	101.3	16.0	103.9	16.9	.23	0.993	0.979, 1.007
Cardiovascular disease	98	810	100.1	15.1	104.1	17.0	< .05	0.986	0.973, 0.998
SMR 1 hospital discharge	561	347	102.0	16.2	106.3	17.4	.001	0.990	0.985, 0.995
SMR 4 hospital discharge	37	871	100.4	16.8	103.8	16.8	.23	0.987	0.967, 1.007

Note. SMR = Scottish Morbidity Records system. SMR 1 is a records discharge from the hospital for any reason; SMR 4 is a records discharge from psychiatric care. HR = hazard ratio. Adapted from "The Impact of Childhood Intelligence on Later Life: Following Up the Scottish Mental Surveys of 1932 and 1947," by I. J. Deary, M. C. Whiteman, J. M. Starr, L. J. Whalley, and H. C. Fox, 2004, *Journal of Personality and Social Psychology, 86,* p. 141. Copyright 2004 by the American Psychological Association.

high stability of individual differences over several decades (Deary, Whalley, Lemmon, Crawford, & Starr, 2000). The idea of system integrity is linked with two other concepts: (a) Brain or cognitive reserve is often indexed using IQ-type measures, and it is thought that people with more of it are protected against cognitive decline, including dementia (Richards & Deary, 2005), and (b) the common-cause hypothesis of cognitive aging suggests that different bodily systems age in concert, with a decline in any one system tending to happen at the same time to others (H. Christensen, MacKinnon, Korten, & Jorm, 2001). The latter, like the system integrity concept, implies some prior set of causes that can influence the physiological efficiency of multiple organ systems. System integrity, like the bodily insults idea described in the previous paragraph, does not view IQ as causal; it is a marker for something more basic about the organism.

Third, IQ at age 11 might be a predictor of better health behaviors and knowledge over the life span. It is already known that IQ scores are associated with educational and occupational outcomes (Neisser et al., 1996); therefore, it is plausible that IQ might be linked to avoiding risks, becoming more informed about good diets, stopping smoking, engaging in only moderate drinking, finding out about illnesses, managing illnesses, complying with treatment regimens, and so forth (Gottfredson, 2004). In this view, IQ is causal. Health literacy and health behaviors are seen in part as cognitive problems, and persons with better information-processing capacity might be better at resolving them, and so, on average, live longer.

Fourth, IQ might confer an entry to environments that are safer. This idea recognizes that IQ predicts educational and occupational outcomes and reckons that the person with the higher IQ is more likely to become well qualified and to enter a workplace that is associated with lower risk of illness and death. In this view, IQ is causal, but its effects on health are mediated through social and occupational selection processes, based on IQ differences.

CONCLUSION

The studies recounted here, on the SMS1932 and, to a lesser extent, on the SMS1947, provided novel information on how childhood intelligence is associated with mortality. Beyond that, some limited exploration was undertaken into some possible confounders and mediators of the effect, and some possible mechanisms were suggested. All-cause mortality is an important outcome, but it is crude. Clearly, people die from many different causes, and there are many important health outcomes that fall short of death. The next chapter describes the studies using the SMSs' data that began to address this complexity. At the end of chapter 3, there is a broader discussion of the wider prospects for cognitive epidemiology.

3

CHILDHOOD IQ AND SPECIFIC CAUSES OF DEATH AND MORTALITY-RELATED PHYSICAL FACTORS

People die of specific, sometimes multiple causes, but they do die of something. In the Scottish Mental Surveys (SMSs) of 1932 and 1947 (SMS1932 and SMS1947), and in other studies reporting an IQ–mortality relationship, IQ was unlikely to be associated with all individual causes of death. IQ associations with single–disease-based deaths and with individual illnesses and their risk factors might offer tractable paths toward explanations of the IQ–all-cause mortality association. In this chapter, we give detailed examinations of the association between childhood IQ and cancer and then cardiovascular disease, its risk factors, and death. We study childhood IQs in relation to later blood pressure, smoking, smoking-related illnesses, and timing of natural menopause.

CHILDHOOD IQ AND DEATH FROM CANCER

The association between childhood IQ and death from cancer was first examined by further scrutiny of the death records in the Aberdeen SMS1932 sample that formed the basis for our first report in cognitive epidemiology (Whalley & Deary, 2001). Death certificates were examined, and all participants who had died from cancer were compared with those who had not.

Among the women, 159 died of some form of cancer, with a mean IQ of 96.0 (SD = 14.1), which was significantly lower (p < .01) than those who did not (n = 873, mean IQ = 99.7, SD = 14.4; Deary, Whalley, & Starr, 2003). Among the men, 172 died of some form of cancer, with a mean IQ of 97.2 (SD = 16.4), which was significantly lower (p < .01) than those who did not (n = 981, mean IQ = 101.0, SD = 15.1). An analysis of odds ratios by IQ quartile was carried out. With the lowest IQ quartile as the reference group, we noted that there were significantly lower odds of dying from cancer in the second lowest and highest IQ quartiles among women and in the second highest and highest quartiles among men. Cox proportional hazards regression analysis suggested that, for each standard deviation disadvantage in IQ at age 11, the risk of dying of cancer by age 76 was increased by 40% in men and 27% in women (both ps < .01; Deary, Whalley, & Starr, 2003).

There is heterogeneity among cancers. There are many types, with differences in their risk factors. It is unlikely that IQ would be related significantly to all of them, and study of those cancers that did have childhood IQ as a risk factor might provide some understanding of the IQ–death association. The groups who died of stomach and lung cancers, and those whose deaths were from cancer not otherwise specified, had significantly lower IQs than all other traced (alive and dead) participants who had not died of cancer (see Figure 3.1; see also Deary, Whalley, & Starr, 2003). These findings complemented the findings that, among men in the west of Scotland, death from stomach and lung cancers were related to paternal occupational social class (Davey Smith, Hart, Blane, & Hole, 1998). The association with stomach cancer remained significant after adjusting for the person's own occupational social class in adulthood, suggesting that some factor in childhood contributed to the risk.

We also examined the association between childhood IQ and death from cancer in the SMS1932–Midspan sample from the west of Scotland. We described in chapter 2 of this volume how people who took part in the Midspan Studies had been flagged at the Scottish National Health Service's Central Register (Hart, Taylor, et al., 2003). Causes (with *International Classification of Diseases* [ICD] codes; e.g., see World Health Organization, 1994) of death over the 25 years from the Midspan baseline to 2002 were obtained. Some specific ICD codes were combined to give the following categories of deaths: all cardiovascular disease, coronary heart disease, stroke, hemorrhagic stroke, respiratory disease, all cancer, lung cancer, stomach cancer, colorectal cancer, and female breast cancer. Already in place, too, was a computerized linkage for the Midspan participants with the Scottish Morbidity Records system. This gave details of diagnoses (with ICD codes) for all hospital admissions for the Midspan participants from the Midspan baseline to 2002. These latter data were available only to the end of 1995 for participants in the Renfrew–Paisley Study.

The most common causes of death among the SMS1932–Midspan participants were cardiovascular disease, cancer, respiratory disease, and stroke

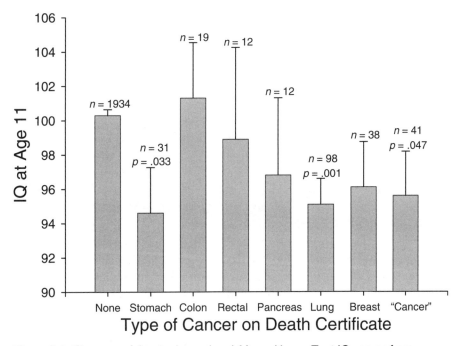

Figure 3.1. The mean (standard error bars) Moray House Test IQ scores from children tested in the Aberdeen area at age 11 from the Scottish Mental Survey of 1932 and later cancer diagnosis on death certificates. Numbers for each diagnosis are shown, as are significant differences from the group marked as having "none." From *Brain and Longevity* (p. 160), edited by C. E. Finch, J.-M. Robine, and Y. Christen, 2003, Berlin, Germany: Springer. Copyright 2003 by Springer Science + Business Media. Reprinted with permission.

(Hart, Taylor, et al., 2003). We discuss the noncancer outcomes later in this chapter. There was a statistically significant association between childhood IQ and deaths from lung cancer (hazard ratio = 1.36, 95% confidence interval [CI]: 1.04, 1.77). There were similar effect sizes between childhood IQ and death from stomach cancer, but this association was nonsignificant because of a smaller number of events. Lung cancer in particular requires further investigations with respect to why it, specifically, is associated with childhood IQ. For example, we examine the association between IQ and one of its major risk factors—smoking—later in this chapter.

CHILDHOOD IQ AND MORTALITY AND MORBIDITY FROM CARDIOVASCULAR DISEASE

In the SMS1932–Midspan sample there were statistically significant associations between childhood IQ and deaths from all cardiovascular disease (relative rate per 1 standard deviation of IQ = 1.12, 95% CI: 1.01, 1.24) and coronary heart disease (1.16, 95% CI: 1.03, 1.32; Hart, Taylor, et al., 2003). There were similar effect sizes between childhood IQ and deaths from stroke and respiratory disease, but these associations were nonsignificant because of smaller numbers of events.

More specific analyses were undertaken for cardiovascular disease, the largest single cause of death among the people studied in the SMS1932–Midspan collaboration (Hart et al., 2004). At about the time of the research, cardiovascular disease, which includes coronary heart disease and stroke, was an underlying cause in 41% of Scottish deaths (Registrar General for Scotland, 2001). To increase the power to examine different cardiovascular events, hospital admissions as well as deaths were considered to be cardiovascular outcome events in the SMS1932–Midspan participants; that is, both morbidity and mortality were included. A number of risk factors for cardiovascular disease were included as well. This permitted the testing of some specific hypotheses about paths of association. Perhaps childhood IQ was associated with risk factors (in midlife) for cardiovascular disease (up to about age 81 in 2002), which in turn mediated the effect of childhood IQ on cardiovascular outcomes.

In the SMS1932–Midspan linked sample there were no significant associations between childhood IQ and blood sugar, plasma cholesterol, and body mass index, all measured at the Midspan baseline in the 1970s (Hart et al., 2004). However, there were significant associations between childhood IQ and the following cardiovascular risk factors measured in midlife in the 1970s (all $ps < .01$): diastolic blood pressure ($r = -.12$), systolic blood pressure ($r = -.16$), height ($r = .24$), and sex- and height-adjusted forced expiratory volume from the lungs in 1 second ($r = .15$). Later in this chapter we discuss smoking, as a risk factor for cardiovascular and other diseases and its relation to childhood IQ, separately.

Among the 938 people in the SMS1932–Midspan sample who had a childhood IQ score, exactly 400 had a cardiovascular disease outcome (death or hospital admission) in the 25-year period between the start of the Midspan Studies and the census date in 2002 (Hart et al., 2004). These 400 people included 238 coronary heart disease episodes and 82 strokes. In sex-adjusted analyses, the additional risk of a cardiovascular disease episode per 1 standard deviation disadvantage in childhood IQ was 11% (95% CI: 1, 23). For coronary heart disease the increased risk was 16% (95% CI: 3, 32). For stroke, the risk was 10% higher but, because of the smaller numbers of stroke events, the result was not significant (95% CI: −12, 36).

For each of the cardiovascular disease outcomes, the associations with IQ scores were adjusted, one at a time, for well-established risk factors (Hart et al., 2004). Here, we omit stroke because it did not have a significant association with childhood IQ. For cardiovascular disease in general (death and hospital admissions), the attenuations of the effect of IQ were 27% or less for social class and deprivation, diastolic blood pressure, height, forced expiratory volume in 1 second, and smoking. For coronary heart disease outcomes, none of that same list of risk factors attenuated the IQ association by more than 25%. Slightly larger attenuation was seen with systolic blood pressure: 45% in the case of cardiovascular disease outcomes, and 31% in the case of coronary heart disease outcomes. Scrutiny of Hart et al.'s (2004) analyses presented in their Table 2 offers some problems of interpretation. Some of the small attenuating effects by the risk factors did reduce the IQ–illness associations to nonsignificant ($p > .05$) levels; therefore, conclusions must be tentative, although the recommendations are clear. First, given the smallish size of the IQ–cardiovascular disease association, the effect needed to be replicated in larger samples. Second, some more formal method was required for deciding whether an attenuation was significant. Third, more formal modeling of possible mediating effects was required, instead of mere statistical adjustment. The interim conclusion is that, apart from systolic blood pressure, the well-known cardiovascular risk factors did not seem to have more than small parts to play in the IQ–cardiovascular disease association.

Age of disease outcome had a large influence on the IQ–cardiovascular disease association. The SMS–Midspan participants who had cardiovascular disease outcomes (mortality or hospital admission) up to 2002 were then divided according to whether the event occurred up to age 65 or after age 65 (Hart et al., 2004). For all cardiovascular disease outcomes, there were 203 events up to age 65 and 197 after that age. For coronary heart disease, there were 108 episodes in the early period and 130 in the later period. For events up to age 65, the increased risk of cardiovascular disease for each standard deviation disadvantage in IQ was 22% (95% CI: 6, 39). For coronary heart disease in the early period, the increased risk was 29% (95% CI: 8, 55). For the events occurring after age 65, for both cardiovascular disease and coronary heart disease, there was no increased risk; the relative rates were very close to 1.0, and the IQ–disease associations were not close to being statistically significant. This sample of individuals, then, has provided an interesting lead to follow up: There is some effect of low IQ on early cardiovascular disease outcomes—they are sometimes called *preventable outcomes*—but not on later outcomes. As in the previous analyses, which included events from all ages, the cardiovascular disease associations with IQ prior to age 65 were adjusted, one at a time, for the risk factors listed earlier. None had an attenuating effect greater than 18%. For coronary heart disease outcomes, none of the risk factors attenuated the association with IQ below age 65 by more than 14%; therefore, the significant association between cardiovascular and coronary heart disease outcomes before age 65 is not accounted for by these risk factors in this sample.

From this division into the two age periods there emerged a novel result on stroke (Hart et al., 2004). Although there was no significant association between childhood IQ and stroke when all deaths and hospital admissions in the 25-year follow-up period were included, there was a significant association between childhood IQ and events occurring up to age 65. Notwithstanding the small number of events in this period ($n = 28$), the increased risk of a stroke event for each standard deviation disadvantage in IQ was 47% (95% CI: 3, 109). There was no significant association between childhood IQ and stroke events ($n = 54$) after age 65.

It is unlikely that the association between IQ at age 11 and cardiovascular events up to but not after age 65 was due to the greater difference in time between IQ measurement and disease observation epoch (Hart et al., 2004). IQ is stable even from age 11 to almost age 80 (Deary, Whalley, Lemmon, Crawford, & Starr, 2000; Deary, Whiteman, Starr, Whalley, & Fox, 2004). Moreover, there is still a large time gap between the IQ measurement and the earlier period of disease observation, between the ages of about 50 and 65. Therefore, it is hardly credible that there is some shared state between IQ and the earlier but not later period of disease assessment. It is possible, given the association between IQ and cardiovascular disease in the age period up to 65, that IQ has played out its effect and that participants with lower IQ have been removed disproportionately, making it unlikely or impossible to observe an effect in the later period. This is found with smoking. Smokers die earlier and are thereby removed from the at-risk population (Marang-van de Mheen, Shipley, Witteman, Marmot, & Gunning-Schepers, 2001). By contrast with this statistical possibility, it might be that the mechanism of the association is different in the two periods, perhaps because the set of risk factors for cardiovascular disease changes with age (Hart et al., 2004).

Another way of looking at the interplay between IQ and risk factors and cardiovascular disease is to turn things around, that is, to ask whether the risk factors measured at baseline in midlife in the 1970s in the Midspan Studies are associated with cardiovascular disease outcomes up to age 81 in 2002 and whether any effects that are found are attenuated after adjusting for childhood IQ. These analyses were done and are shown in Table 3.1 (Hart et al., 2004). Systolic and diastolic blood pressure and adjusted forced expiratory volume in 1 second, but not height, measured at midlife were significantly associated with cardiovascular mortality and hospital admissions over the next 25 years. The strongest effect is for systolic blood pressure, for which the hazard increased by 34% for each standard deviation increase in pressure. There was also, as expected, a detrimental effect of smoking, although ex-smokers seemed to be at no more risk that nonsmokers. Adjusting for childhood IQ had negligible effects on these associations. IQ did not account for the variance shared by these risk factors and cardiovascular disease outcomes.

The association between childhood IQ and cardiovascular disease was examined further in members of the 6-Day Sample of the SMS1947 (Deary, Whiteman, Starr, et al., 2004). There was a significant association between

TABLE 3.1

Relative Rate (and 95% Confidence Interval) of Cardiovascular Disease Hospital Admission or Death Association With a 1 Standard Deviation Change in Risk Factor, and by Smoking Category

	Relative rate adjusted for	
Measure	Sex	Sex and childhood IQ
Diastolic blood pressure[a]	1.27 (1.15, 1.40)	1.25 (1.13, 1.38)
Systolic blood pressure[a]	1.34 (1.22, 1.48)	1.33 (1.21, 1.46)
Height	1.10 (0.96, 1.25)	1.06 (0.93, 1.22)
Adjusted forced expiratory volume in one second[b]	1.15 (1.04, 1.26)	1.13 (1.03, 1.24)
Smoking category		
Never-smoker (reference group)	1	1
Current smoker	1.49 (1.16, 1.93)	1.47 (1.14, 1.90)
Ex-smoker	1.03 (0.74, 1.45)	1.05 (0.74, 1.47)

Note. Direction of association is an increase for systolic and diastolic blood pressure, decrease for height and adjusted forced expiratory volume in 1 second. From "Childhood IQ and Cardiovascular Disease in Adulthood: Prospective Observational Study Linking the Scottish Mental Survey 1932 and the Midspan Studies," by C. L. Hart, M. D. Taylor, G. Davey Smith, L. J. Whalley, J. M. Starr, D. J. Hole, et al., 2004, *Social Science & Medicine, 59,* p. 2135. Copyright 2004 by Elsevier Limited. Adapted with permission. [a]In mmHg. [b]Adjusted for sex and height.

childhood IQ and having been admitted to a hospital for any cause between 1968 and 2000. More specifically, there was a significant association between childhood IQ and having left a hospital with a diagnosis of cardiovascular disease. This more specific association replicates that which was found in the SMS1932–Midspan linkage study (Hart, Taylor, et al., 2003). This provides a guide to possible mechanisms of the IQ–mortality association by identifying a specific pathology for which IQ is a risk factor.

CHILDHOOD IQ AND SMOKING AND LUNG FUNCTION

Smoking is a risk factor for both cardiovascular disease and lung cancer and an important aspect of health behavior in its own right. Participants in the SMS1932–Midspan sample were classified at midlife in the 1970s according to whether they had ever smoked, never smoked, had smoked previously but had given it up, or were still current smokers. *Past smokers* were previous smokers who had not smoked for at least 1 year. The childhood IQs of these different groups were then computed and compared (see Table 3.2; Taylor, Hart, et al., 2003). If one considers men and women together, one notes that there is less than 1 IQ point difference in the means of the ever- and never-smoker groups. Therefore, childhood IQ does not appear to have played a large part in the decision to smoke in this sample. However, there is a sizable and significant difference between current and past smokers, with a difference of

TABLE 3.2
Mental Ability at Age 11 Years According to Smoking Status at Midlife

Participants	Smoking status at midlife			
	Never	Past	Current	Ever[a]
All	100.5 (14.4)	103.7 (14.3)	98.5 (15.3)[b]	99.7 (15.2)
	238 (25.7%)	159 (17.2%)	529 (57.1%)	688 (74.3%)
Men	102.9 (15.7)	103.9 (14.7)	99.6 (15.4)[b]	100.8 (15.3)
	85 (15.7%)	125 (23.1%)	331 (61.2%)	456 (84.3%)
Women	99.2 (13.5)	102.9 (13.1)	96.7 (15.0)	97.6 (14.9)
	153 (39.7%)	34 (8.8%)	198 (51.5%)	232 (60.3%)

Note. N = 926; 541 men and 385 women. Data are mean (*SD*) and number (%). From "Childhood Mental Ability and Smoking Cessation in Adulthood: Prospective Observational Study Linking the Scottish Mental Survey 1932 and the Midspan Studies," by M. D. Taylor, C. L. Hart, G. D. Davey Smith, J. M. Starr, D. J. Hole, L. J. Whalley, et al., 2003, *Journal of Epidemiology and Community Health, 57,* p. 464. Copyright 2003 by BMJ Publishing Group Ltd. Reprinted with permission.
[a]Combination of past and current smokers. [b]Significantly different from past smokers.

more than 5 IQ points between the means. This current-versus-past-smokers difference is also significant when the men are examined in isolation. The result is not significant in women, because of the small number in the past-smokers group. In addition to these simple comparisons of means, regression analyses were performed. Logistic regression, with ever versus never smoking as the outcome and childhood IQ from the SMS1932 as the predictor, found that the risk of ever smoking for each standard deviation increase in IQ was a nonsignificant 0.95 (95% CI: 0.82, 1.10). Cox regression was used to conduct an analysis of giving up smoking within the group who had ever smoked. Cox regression is able to make use of timing information; therefore, for past smokers the time was the number of years from when they starting smoking until they gave it up. For current smokers (at the Midspan baseline, at about age 50 in the 1970s) the time was the duration since they started smoking until their screening visit for the Midspan Studies. There were 667 individuals for this analysis, comprising 516 current smokers, 151 past smokers, and 21 with some missing data were excluded. In sex-adjusted analysis, there was a 33% (95% CI: 13, 57) increase in the rate of giving up smoking for each standard deviation increase in childhood IQ. This fell somewhat to 25%—an attenuation of 24%—but was still significant after adjustment for occupational social class. It fell to 19%—an attenuation of 42%—and was nonsignificant, after adjustment for deprivation of the area of residence in the 1970s.

This association between childhood IQ and giving up smoking, but not with starting smoking, might be cohort specific (Taylor, Hart, et al., 2003). When this group started smoking, there were few messages about the health risks associated with the habit. Health messages about smoking became more widespread in the 1970s; therefore, one interpretation of this effect is that people with higher childhood IQs were more likely to gain access to, understand, or implement health information once it became available.

A further analysis of the SMS1932–Midspan sample followed up on the idea that smoking is a behavior related to (ill) health that is valuable to examine in its own right (Taylor, Hart, Davey Smith, Starr, et al., 2005). Understanding the personal and social associations with smoking might help in its prevention and thereby lessen people's disease burden. A set of smoking-related deaths and hospital admissions was collected from the SMS1932–Midspan sample linkages to health databases in Scotland. These were specific ICD codes that included chronic obstructive pulmonary disease and allied conditions and smoking-related cancers, which comprised mouth, pharynx, esophagus, larynx, lung, pancreas, and bladder. There were 110 smoking-related events among the sample. In a validation of the term, these occurred to 93 current smokers as well as to 9 past smokers and only 8 never-smokers. In sex-adjusted Cox proportional hazards regression analysis the risk of a smoking-related event was 21% greater (95% CI: 1, 45) for each standard deviation disadvantage in childhood IQ. Further adjustment for social class, deprivation, and smoking reduced the risk to a nonsignificant 10% (an attenuation of 52%).

In addition to smoking-related outcomes, an analysis was performed on the amount smoked (including zero) and lung function (measured using forced expiratory volume in 1 second) as outcomes at midlife, because reduced lung function is one route through which smoking affects health (see Figure 3.2; see also Taylor, Hart, Davey Smith, Starr, et al., 2005). The other variables in the model were sex, IQ at age 11, occupational social class at midlife, and deprivation in the area of residence at midlife. Men were more likely to smoke, and there was an additional small effect of deprivation. There was no direct effect of childhood IQ or social class on the number of cigarettes smoked. With regard to lung function, there were significant, independent influences of childhood IQ (partly direct and partly mediated by means of occupational social class), occupational social class, and smoking. The association between childhood IQ and adult lung function is interesting and has been found in the UK National Survey of Health and Development (Birth Cohort 1946; Richards, Strachan, Hardy, Kuh, & Wadsworth, 2005), which we discuss later in this chapter in relation to the Lothian Birth Cohort 1921 (Deary, Whalley, Batty, & Starr, 2006). The association was not found, however, in the Aberdeen Birth Cohort 1921 (Starr, Deary, Lemmon, & Whalley, 2000). Both the Lothian Birth Cohort and the Aberdeen Birth Cohort 1921 are follow-up samples of the SMS1932.

CHILDHOOD IQ AND BLOOD PRESSURE

In addition to smoking, an analysis was conducted of the association between childhood IQ and blood pressure at midlife in the SMS1932–Midspan sample (Starr, Taylor, et al., 2004). Hypertension is a risk factor for

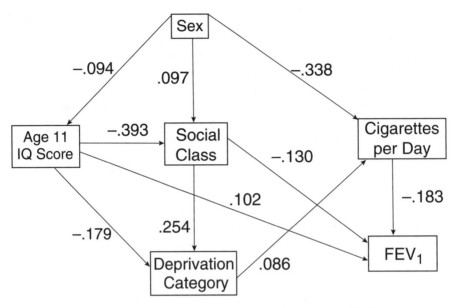

Figure 3.2. Structural equation model of the associations among childhood IQ, sex (1 = male, 2 = female), social class (lower numbers = more professional occupations), deprivation of the area of residence in midlife (higher numbers = more deprivation), cigarettes per day, and forced expiratory volume in 1 second (N = 905 with complete data). Coefficients placed beside arrows may be squared to give the variance shared by adjacent variables. The model has a nonsignificant chi-square value and a comparative fit index of 1.0. FEV_1 = forced expiratory volume from the lungs in 1 second. From "Childhood IQ and Social Factors in Smoking Behavior, Lung Function and Smoking-Related Outcomes in Adulthood," by M. D. Taylor, C. L. Hart, G. D. Davey Smith, J. M. Starr, D. J. Hole, L. J. Whalley, et al., 2005, *British Journal of Health Psychology, 10,* p. 404. Copyright 2005 by the British Psychological Society. Reprinted with permission.

cardiovascular disease and might be one of the mediating variables through which childhood IQ exerts its influence. Another aspect of this analysis is the possible misattribution of causal direction between blood pressure and cognitive aging, which is the basis for many studies (Starr, 1999). Given that hypertension is associated with apparent decline in cognitive ability in old age, and given that childhood and old age cognitive ability are highly correlated, it is possible that the apparent causal link between hypertension and cognitive aging is wholly or partly accounted for by the association of early intelligence with later blood pressure differences.

In midlife, the SMS1932–Midspan sample's mean systolic and diastolic blood pressures were, respectively, 142.8 (SD = 21.5) mmHg and 84.4 (SD = 12.4) mmHg. People with higher childhood IQ scores from the SMS1932 tended to have lower systolic and diastolic blood pressures in midlife (rs = −.16 and −.12, respectively, p < .001; Starr, Taylor, et al., 2004). The correlation coefficients were similar in men and women. These associations were similar in effect size (rs −.13 and −.11, respectively) and still statistically significant ($p < .001$) after adjustment for sex, adult occupational social class, body mass index, height, cholesterol, and smoking consumption. After adjustment for all of these variables, 1 standard deviation increase in IQ at age 11 years in the SMS1932 was associated with 3.15 mmHg lower systolic, and 1.50 mmHg lower diastolic, blood pressure at midlife in the Midspan baseline examination in the 1970s.

These novel results made tenable the idea that some of the association between hypertension and apparent age-related cognitive decline could be caused by lower prior intelligence being associated with the onset of hypertension (Starr, Taylor, et al., 2004). However, it was not clear why this might be the case. It was suggested that intelligence and blood pressure differences might share genes; might both be influenced by events during fetal development; or might both be affected by some of the same environmental insults, including toxins.

CHILDHOOD IQ AND TIMING OF MENOPAUSE

Not all of the epidemiological analyses were conducted by linking data from the SMSs to other stored data sets. Some of the outcomes were collected directly from our follow-up studies of the SMS1932 and SMS1947. An analysis of the association between age at natural menopause and cognition was conducted in the Aberdeen Birth Cohort 1936 (ABC1936), a follow-up sample from the SMS1947 (Whalley, Fox, Starr, & Deary, 2004). It had already been shown that, in participants in the UK National Survey of Health and Development (i.e., the Birth Cohort 1946), higher cognitive test scores in childhood were associated with a later age at menopause (Richards, Kuh, Hardy, & Wadsworth, 1999). The suggestion was that gonadal steroids might influence both neurodevelopment and the timing of menopause. However, there was also dispute about the role of female sex hormones and cognitive aging. The ABC1936 provided novel data by having childhood cognitive test scores and mental test scores from the mid-60s, in addition to information about the timing of menopause. An analysis was set up that examined hypotheses concerning the association between childhood and age-65 cognition and the timing of natural menopause and whether age at menopause was a mediating factor between cognitive ability at age 11 and age 65.

At the time of the analysis, there were 221 women in the ABC1936 (Whalley, Fox, Starr, & Deary, 2004). Of this number, 159 reported natural menopause, 22 had hormone replacement therapy without hysterectomy, and 40 had had surgical menopause with or without hormone replacement therapy. There were 144 women with natural menopause and data on most of the cognitive tests. Age at menopause was obtained at interview and was defined as the age at which menstruation had not occurred for at least 1 year. This was checked for reliability approximately 1 to 2 years later by asking for the information again, by telephone, from 187 participants. This yielded information on 131 of the 144 women with complete cognitive test data. Of these, 106 repeated the same year of menopause, 12 were different by 1 year, and 13 were different by 2 or more years. The correlation between the two reports was .97.

When participants in the ABC1936 were seen in 2000–2001, at about age 65, they took five mental tests: (a) Raven's Standard Progressive Matrices, (b) the Auditory Verbal Learning Test, (c) Wechsler Block Design, (d) Wechsler Digit Symbol, and (e) Uses of Common Objects (Whalley, Fox, Starr, & Deary, 2004). In the women whose data are examined here, the scores on these tests were subjected to data reduction by principal components analysis. Examination of the scree slope, and applying the eigenvalues greater than one criterion, indicated that a single component should be extracted, accounting for 51.5% of the total variance. The scores from this first unrotated principal component were saved, transformed to an IQ-type score (M = 100, SD = 15), and named "IQ at Age 65."

Age at menopause and Moray House Test (MHT) score at age 11 correlated .22 (p = .008; Whalley, Fox, Starr, & Deary, 2004). Age at menopause and IQ at age 65 correlated .25 (p = .004). Correlations (p values) between age at the natural menopause and individual cognitive tests were as follows: Raven's Standard Progressive Matrices, $r = .21$ (p = .01); Auditory Verbal Learning Test, $r = .16$ (p = .07); Wechsler Block Design, $r = .08$ (p = .35); Wechsler Digit Symbol, $r = .26$ (p = .002); and Uses of Common Objects, $r = .13$ (p = .13). Multiple regression analysis showed that age at menopause did not contribute significant variance to IQ at age 65 after MHT IQ score at age 11 had been added. Moreover, a Cox proportional hazards regression model showed that MHT IQ score at age 11 was a significant predictor of age at menopause (p = .036).

A structural equation model of cognitive ability at age 11 and age 65, and the timing of the natural menopause, was constructed (Whalley, Fox, Starr, & Deary, 2004). Cognitive ability at age 65 was a latent trait of the five measured tests. The model shown in Figure 3.3 had a good fit to the data. The chi-square was 14.5, $df = 14$, $p = .41$. The average of the off-diagonal absolute standardized residuals was .04. The Bentler–Bonett (normed and non-normed) and comparative fit indices were .95, .99, and .99, respectively. The Wald test was applied and suggested that the path between age at menopause and cognition at age 65 (F1 in Figure 3.3) should be dropped; the path weight did not differ significantly from zero. The Lagrange Multiplier Test was applied and indicated that no further paths should be added to improve the fit of the model. The model suggests that there is an association between MHT score at age 11 and age at natural menopause and that this association accounts for the correlation between age at menopause and cognitive ability at age 65. Without the cognitive test score from age 11 we might have

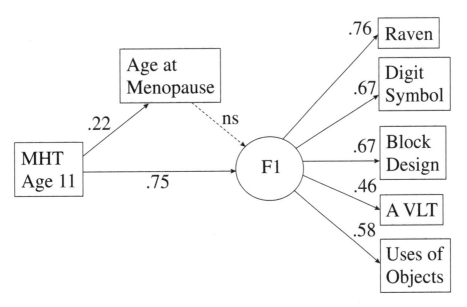

Figure 3.3. Structural equation model of Moray House Test (MHT) IQ score at age 11, the timing of natural menopause, and cognitive ability at age 65 (F1) in the women of the Aberdeen Birth Cohort 1936. IQ at age 11 is significantly associated with the timing of menopause and with cognitive ability at age 65, but the latter two are not significantly associated after age-11 IQ is adjusted for. Cognitive ability at age 65 is assessed by a latent trait from five cognitive tests: (a) Raven's Standard Progressive Matrices (Raven), (b) Wechsler Digit Symbol, (c) Wechsler Block Design, (d) the Auditory Verbal Learning Test (AVLT), and (e) Uses of Common Objects. From "Age at Natural Menopause and Cognition," by L. J. Whalley, H. C. Fox, J. M. Starr, and I. J. Deary, 2004, *Maturitas, 49,* p. 153. Copyright 2004 by Elsevier Limited. Reprinted with permission.

incorrectly concluded that age at menopause was associated with differences in cognitive aging. Therefore, speculations about postmenopausal estrogen depletion affecting cognitive ability are not required. Of course, it is possible that both the timing of menopause and childhood IQ are linked with prior neurodevelopmental factors, some of which might be genetic and some environmental. However, it might be that later menopause is part of the better health we find to be associated with higher childhood IQ. Note the strong association (path weight = .75) between MHT score at age 11 and the general cognitive factor at age 65.

THE BROADER WORLD OF COGNITIVE EPIDEMIOLOGY APPLIED TO PHYSICAL ILLNESS: A BRIEF PROSPECTIVE

Since the reporting of a significant association between childhood IQ and all-cause mortality up to age 76 in the Aberdeen city participants of the SMS1932 (Whalley & Deary, 2001), the field of cognitive epidemiology has grown quickly. There is now a glossary of terms for the research area (Deary & Batty, 2007). A systematic review of the field revealed nine studies—from Scotland, the broader United Kingdom, Sweden, Australia, the United States, and Denmark—and all found that early life IQ was associated significantly with mortality in middle to old age (Batty, Deary, & Gottfredson, 2007). It seemed very unlikely that the results were caused by reverse causality. Mental test scores were available for so many years before the mortality outcomes that it is not plausible that prior illness caused the decline in cognitive ability. Bias of the samples was unlikely too, because many of the studies had high rates of follow-up.

An extension to the explanatory plan laid out by Whalley and Deary (2001) was proposed (see Figure 3.4). Potential confounding effects from early life, such as socioeconomic disadvantage and low birth weight, did not appear to be responsible for the association. With more replications of the IQ–mortality association having appeared from different UK and international locations (e.g., see Hemmingsson, Melin, Allebeck, & Lundberg, 2006; Martin & Kubzansky, 2005; Pearce, Deary, Young, & Parker, 2006), we realized that the field needed to move from association to mechanism. The association was now solid, but still mysterious. The potential mediating factors between IQ and mortality required more intensive study. One approach was to examine whether childhood IQ was associated with further, established

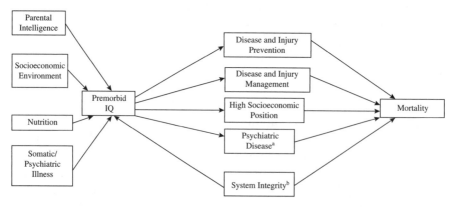

Figure 3.4. Simplified model of influences on premorbid IQ and potential pathways linking premorbid IQ with later mortality. From "Premorbid (Early Life) IQ and Later Mortality Risk: Systematic Review," by G. D. Batty, I. J. Deary, and L. S. Gottfredson, 2007, *Annals of Epidemiology, 17,* p. 284. Copyright 2007 by Elsevier Limited. Reprinted with permission.
[a]Although psychiatric disease is shown as a mediating variable between IQ and mortality, it might also be an antecedent variable if, for example, suboptimal neurodevelopment were the prior cause of psychiatric disease and early mortality. Both of these possibilities were discussed by Batty, Deary, and Gottfredson (2007).
[b]Note that system integrity is shown as antecedent to IQ and mortality. In this pathway, lower IQ is not a cause of mortality, but both IQ and mortality are influenced by this more fundamental physiological integrity.

risk factors for mortality and morbidity. For example, weight gain from adolescence to middle age (Chandola, Deary, Blane, & Batty, 2006); frequency of hangovers after drinking alcohol (Batty, Deary, & Macintyre, 2006); eating a nonvegetarian diet (Gale, Deary, Schoon, & Batty, 2007); smoking, heavy alcohol consumption, obesity, and overweight (Batty, Deary, & Macintyre, 2007); and eating fewer fresh and cooked vegetables, whole grain bread, poultry, and fish, but more French fries, non–whole-grain bread, and cakes and biscuits, and taking less exercise (Batty, Deary, Schoon, & Gale, 2007) were all associated significantly with lower childhood IQ. Another approach was to examine larger studies that were more informative about specific causes of mortality; for example, there was little relation between early adult IQ scores and risk of cancer up to middle age in 1 million Swedish men (Batty, Wennerstad, et al., 2007). One of the suggested mediators between childhood IQ and mortality in Figure 3.4 is socioeconomic position; however, there is some evidence that, by contrast, it is cognitive ability that explains the association between social position and health outcomes rather than vice versa (Batty, Der, Macintyre, & Deary, 2006).

One suggestion that continued to intrigue, but was difficult to test, was the possibility that some underlying general bodily system integrity might account for some of the overlap between cognitive ability and health differences (see Figure 3.4). One possible indicator of such integrity was the efficiency of fundamental information processing that was indexed by reaction time. Slower and more variable reaction times are associated with a greater mortality risk (Shipley, Der, Taylor, & Deary, 2006). Reaction time did account for the majority of the association between IQ and mortality (Deary & Der, 2005).

Many developments are needed before further progress can be made in the field of cognitive epidemiology. More studies are required that contain childhood IQ, potential confounders and mediators, and morbidity and mortality outcomes. More studies also are required that have candidates for the construct of *system integrity*, some fundamental biological source of variance that affects the efficiency of the brain and body throughout life, if such exists. The field is new and healthy, with IQ playing a prominent role in the thinking about individual differences in health alongside—perhaps as an alternative, perhaps a complement; it is not yet clear—more prominent suggestions, such as social status and the associated stress processes (Deary, Batty, & Gottfredson, 2005; Sapolsky, 2005). The Scottish Mental Surveys have played a part in this relatively new role for IQ scores as predictors of mortality and morbidity by introducing to a new constituency of researchers mental test scores as health-relevant variables.

4
CHILDHOOD IQ AND MENTAL ILLNESS

Ultimately, all illnesses have a physical basis. However, it is still customary to separate psychiatric from so-called physical illnesses, and we follow that tradition here. This chapter examines whether childhood IQ, from the Scottish Mental Survey of 1932 (SMS1932), is associated with later psychiatric illnesses. These illnesses are divided into dementia and other psychiatric illnesses. Within the dementias, we examine those with early and later onsets.

CHILDHOOD IQ AND DEMENTIA

Research into whether people with different levels of IQ experience different trajectories of cognitive decline has a long history. Time after time, this uncertainty has been formulated into the following question: Is age kinder to those who are initially more able (Deary, Starr, & MacLennan, 1998)? The SMS1932 data set was used to push this question beyond the confines of normal cognitive aging to the study of dementia, to ask whether people with lower childhood IQs were more likely to experience dementia later in life. There already were some suggestive results. Some studies had found that people with less education were more likely to be diagnosed with dementia later in life; education is associated with intelligence and could be acting as a proxy measure (Katzman, 1993). The Nun Study (Snowdon et al., 1996) had found that better linguistic scores, extracted from biographies handwritten at approximately age 22 and used as indicators of cognitive ability level, were associated with less cognitive decline and dementia (Snowdon et al., 1996). Whalley et al. (2000) used the SMS1932 data to examine the association between childhood IQ and early- and late-onset dementias.

The association between childhood IQ and early-onset dementia benefited from a prior epidemiological study of this disease conducted by members of our research group (McGonigal et al., 1993). All persons were identified who, between 1974 and 1988, had attended general hospitals or mental health units in Scotland and had a diagnosis of early-onset dementia. The authors reckoned that the study achieved better than 93% case ascertainment. A reading of individual case files indicated that 1,217 individuals met the criteria for early-onset dementia. Cases were excluded if they were caused by alcohol, neurotoxins, head trauma, or central nervous system diseases other than Alzheimer's and cerebrovascular disease.

This was a good start: A whole-population (almost) study of childhood IQ (SMS1932) could be linked with a whole-population (as far as could be expected) ascertainment of early-onset dementia. Of the 1,217 individuals identified by McGonigal et al. (1993), 67 were born in 1921 and were born in regions where SMS1932 ledgers were extant (Whalley et al., 2000). Only 8 of these cases could not be linked by us to the SMS1932 data. Two control persons were sought for each person diagnosed with early-onset dementia. This was done at the public repository of all Scottish births, in Register House, Edinburgh. First, the birth record of the person with dementia was identified. Next, the nearest preceding and succeeding births, matched for sex, birth district, and paternal occupation (using the UK Office for Population Censuses and Studies' classifications of occupations), were chosen as controls. Birth dates of control persons were typically about 2 months from those of the index case. Once identified in the birth register, the control persons' Moray House Test (MHT) scores in the SMS1932 were sought. A total of 118 control persons' mental test scores were found. The mean MHT score for the 59 individuals with early-onset dementia in the SMS1932 was 32.6 (95% confidence interval [CI]: 28.5, 35.4), and for the 118 control individuals it was 32.8 (95% CI: 30.2, 35.4). These are very similar and not significantly different. The whole-population ($N = 87,498$) SMS1932 mean MHT score was 34.5 (95% CI: 34.4, 34.6). The group with early-onset dementia did not differ significantly from this, either. It was concluded that there was no association between childhood IQ and early-onset dementia, but with a caveat. There might have been a Type II statistical error, caused by overmatching. By matching for birth district and paternal occupational social class, it is possible that some of the childhood factors that might be associated with risk for dementia (and related to childhood IQ) were removed. This is in part supported by the lower whole-population MHT score, although a larger sample of people with early-onset dementia would be required before one could explore whether this was a true difference and not due to chance.

The examination of childhood IQ in relation to late-onset (age 65 or over) dementia was not so straightforward (Whalley et al., 2000). There was no national register of late-onset dementia cases with which the SMS1932 mental test scores might be linked. Once again, as was done with our first study of all-cause mortality, the study was conducted in Aberdeen. The measures taken were aimed at being as thorough as possible. The Grampian Psychiatric Case Register was consulted. The register was started in 1963 and records all contacts with psychiatric services in Aberdeen. Within this register there were 75 people born in 1921, alive until at least 1986 (i.e., age 65) and with a diagnosis that was compatible with late-onset dementia. Using name and date of birth, all were successfully linked with individuals who took part in the SMS1932. Psychiatrically qualified members of the research team were allowed (a) to read the case files for each person, (b) to make sure that the onset of dementia was later than age 64, and (c) to make a diagnosis of dementia from the recorded information per the *International Classification of Diseases* (*ICD*; World Health Organization, 1994). Of the 75 patients, 38 were excluded either because the onset age was less than 65 years or because the dementia was not due to Alzheimer's disease or vascular dementia. Not every person with dementia comes into contact with services and appears in the Grampian Psychiatric Case Register; therefore, a further search was made in the community. In part, this was done among the 1921-born people who volunteered to take part in the Aberdeen Birth Cohort 1921 study. This search identified 8 people with late-onset dementia (Alzheimer's or vascular). Contacts between research team members and family doctors and the managers of nursing homes revealed another 5 people with dementia classified according to the *ICD*. This represented a total of 50 people with dementia that had an onset between 1986 and 1997. Notwithstanding the fact that this searching through multiple sources was burdensome and productive, it cannot be guaranteed that the ascertainment was complete.

Now that individuals with late-onset dementia had been identified, the problem arose of how to compare them with control individuals who did not develop dementia (Whalley et al., 2000). An obvious, but problematic, solution would have been to compare the MHT scores of the 50 people with late-onset dementia with the scores of the 2,792 children who took part in the SMS1932. Geographically, they were alike; however, there were two obvious problems. First, Whalley and Deary (2001) showed that survival to old age was associated with childhood IQ. Therefore, because one has to survive to age 65 to be diagnosed with late-onset dementia, survivor status of control participants had to be taken into account. Second, the people diagnosed with dementia were people who took part in the SMS1932 in Aberdeen city and had stayed there since. In the process of preparing the IQ/all-cause mortality report (Whalley & Deary, 2001), it became clear that people who were later traced to Aberdeen had lower mean MHT scores than people traced elsewhere: 34.2 (95% CI: 33.3, 35.0) versus 37.4 (95% CI: 36.3, 38.4, $p < .001$). Therefore, the appropriate control participants for people in Aberdeen with late-onset dementia were people who had survived to the appropriate post-65-year age and who had not emigrated from Aberdeen.

Compared with all participants who took part in the SMS1932 in Aberdeen, people with late-onset dementia had lower childhood IQ scores (see Table 4.1; see also Whalley et al., 2000). There was no significant difference between people with and without an eventual dementia diagnosis who were alive and in Aberdeen in 1986 (see Table 4.1). However, an examination of data from survivors after 1992 reveals that once they are about 72 years old, the people with a diagnosis of late-onset dementia have consistently lower MHT scores in the SMS1932. It would be easy to conclude, therefore, that late-onset, but not early-onset, dementia was associated with lower childhood IQ. However, it should be noted that the mean MHT scores for persons with early- and late-onset dementia were very similar: 32.1 and 32.6, respectively. With regard, specifically, to the group with late-onset dementia, the comparisons with people surviving in the Aberdeen area control for

TABLE 4.1
Mean Moray House Test Scores From the Scottish Mental Survey of 1932 (SMS1932) of People With Late-Onset Dementia and Local Aberdeen Residents Without Dementia Who Took Part in the SMS1932 in Aberdeen

Participants	Not dementia		Dementia		
Born in 1921	n	M (95% confidence interval)	n	M (95% confidence interval)	p value
Alive in 1932	2,792	36.2 (35.7, 36.7)	50	32.1 (27.6, 36.6)	< .03
Alive in 1986	772[a]	35.3 (34.3, 36.2)	50	32.1 (27.6, 36.6)	ns
Alive in 1992	661	35.7 (34.7, 36.8)	48	32.0 (27.3, 36.7)	ns
Alive in 1993	639	35.8 (34.7, 36.8)	45	31.0 (26.1, 36.0)	< .03
Alive in 1994	616	36.0 (35.0, 37.1)	44	30.7 (25.7, 35.7)	< .02
Alive in 1995	586	36.1 (35.1, 37.2)	41	31.2 (26.0, 36.3)	< .025
Alive in 1996	560	36.2 (35.1, 37.3)	37	30.9 (25.6, 36.2)	< .025
Alive in 1997	552	36.2 (35.1, 37.3)	34	29.6 (24.4, 34.8)	< .01

Note. People with dementia in each group include all cases alive at that point irrespective of age at dementia onset. From "Childhood Mental Ability and Dementia," by L. J. Whalley, J. M. Starr, R. Athawes, D. Hunter, A. Pattie, and I. J. Deary, 2000, Neurology, 55, p. 1457. Copyright 2000 by Lippincott Williams & Wilkins. Reprinted with permission.
[a]The numbers here and in the remainder of the column are prior to the full tracing that eventually was reported by Whalley and Deary (2001).

migration and survival, both of which are positively associated with childhood IQ. Another possible source of bias is the fact that some dementia cases were identified by a community survey. If there were a bias toward people with dementia and high childhood IQ not taking part in the survey, then the effects indicated in Table 4.1 could be overestimates of any true effect. Yet, this bias seemed unlikely, because such evidence that existed indicated that individuals who did not participate in the survey had, on average, lower childhood IQs than the participants (Whalley et al., 2000).

Two suggestions were made about the association between childhood IQ and dementia risk (Whalley et al., 2000). First, these two variables might share genetic and/or environmental influences. Second, the association between the two might be mediated by a sequence of factors, such as education and cerebrovascular disease. These findings with childhood IQ and dementia contribute to the notion that people with higher premorbid IQ have greater "cognitive reserve" capacity (Richards & Deary, 2005).

CHILDHOOD IQ AND PSYCHIATRIC ILLNESSES

The association between childhood IQ in the SMS1932 and psychiatric contact in general was examined, again in the Aberdeen area of Scotland (Walker, McConville, Hunter, Deary, & Whalley, 2002). It was known, for example, that low IQ in early life was a risk factor for schizophrenia (David, Malmberg, Brandt, Allebeck, & Lewis, 1997). One previous study had examined school grades and educational delay in relation to later, but still young adult, psychiatric contact and found that lower grades were a risk factor for only nonpsychotic disorders (Isohanni et al., 1998).

The SMS1932-based study of childhood IQ and psychiatric disorders covered Aberdeen city and other counties in the northeast of Scotland (i.e., Aberdeen, Kincardine, Banff, & Moray; Walker et al., 2002). Links were made between SMS1932 and health service records from the area. SMS1932 data were used to provide childhood IQ. Two medical databases were used to establish that people had not migrated away from the area. The Aberdeen Royal Hospital's National Health Service Trust supplied details of all patients known to them since 1955 and with a birth year of 1921. The Grampian Health Board supplied details of people registered with a general practitioner in their Community Health Index. Last, an attempt was made to identify everyone with a birth year of 1921 who had received psychiatric services in the area. This used a database called the North-East Scottish Psychiatric Case Register, which was replaced in 1996 by the Patient Centred Management System. The former system contained details of all psychiatric contacts between 1963 and 1996. Both systems contain contacts with the full range of psychiatric services in the area: child, adolescent, adult mental health, geriatric psychiatry, and treatment for learning disability. The North-East Scottish Psychiatric Case Register contained details of pre-1963 contacts if the person was still in contact with the services in 1963 or was seen again later. Individuals whose contact with mental health services was complete before 1963 were sought by searches of the area's handwritten mental health registers between 1932 and 1963. People in the psychiatric registers who were born in 1921 were linked with their data in the SMS1932. There was some underidentification of females, because birth names were not always recorded in psychiatric records. Their lifetime psychiatric diagnoses were made using the OPCRIT system (McGuffin, Farmer, & Harvey, 1991). The reliability of these diagnoses was checked. The balance of participants in the SMS1932 in this geographical area were the control participants. People diagnosed with a learning disability were excluded from the analyses.

The results of the case identification process are shown in Figure 4.1 (Walker et al., 2002). Of the 8,477 children in the SMS1932's relevant school registers, 8,073 (95.2%) had an MHT score. Just over half of these (n = 4,205) were identified as still living in the area in adulthood. Of the 1,008 people in the psychiatric case registers with a birth year of 1921, 435 had not been diagnosed with a learning disability and were linked to the SMS1932. The largest single category of diagnosis was affective disorders (N = 162), with other categories having 75 or fewer individuals. Age-corrected IQ scores were derived from the SMS1932 MHT scores in the area; they are not based on the whole of Scotland.

The mean IQ of people who had not received a psychiatric diagnosis was 99.3 (95% CI: 98.9, 99.8), and the mean IQ of people who had received a psychiatric diagnosis was 97.7 (95% CI: 96.2, 99.1), and this difference was significant (p = .026; Walker et al., 2002). There was no difference between the mean IQ of any individual diagnostic group and the control participants. An analysis was performed to quantify the risk of contact with psychiatric services and childhood IQ level. For this purpose, childhood IQ was split into three groups: below average (< 85), average (85–115), and above average (> 115). Logistic regression was used, and the reference group (with an odds ratio set at 1.0) was the average IQ group. The odds ratio of the group with above-average IQ was very similar (0.97, 95% CI: 0.71, 1.32). The odds ratio of the group with below-average IQ was significantly different (1.37, 95% CI: 1.08, 1.75), indicating that the increased chance of contact with psychiatric services was concentrated among people with IQs less than 85. Analysis by subgroups revealed that this result was significant for men, but not for women, and for urban residents, but not rural residents. Additional analyses were undertaken based on the time to first psychiatric contact. The group with below-average IQ was at greater risk of contact with psychiatric services and with earlier contact (see Figure 4.1). Multivariate Cox proportional hazards regression analysis, adjusting for sex and urban–rural status,

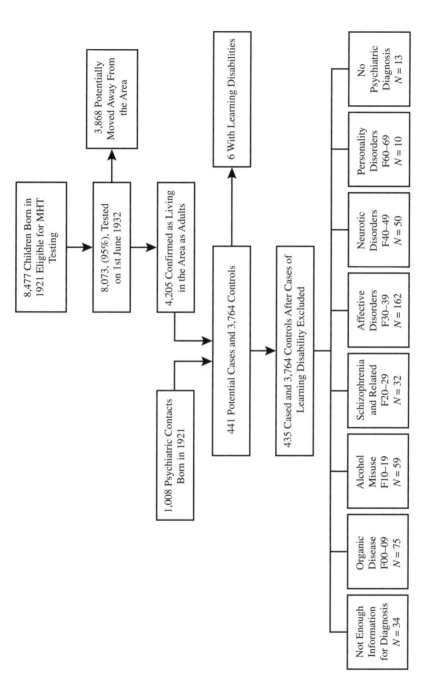

Figure 4.1. Participants and matched controls and diagnostic breakdown from a study of the association between childhood IQ and lifetime contact with psychiatric services in the northeast of Scotland. The F terms are *International Classification of Diseases* code ranges. MHT = Moray House Test. From "Childhood Mental Ability and Lifetime Psychiatric Contact: A 66-Year Follow-Up Study of the 1932 Scottish Mental Ability Survey," by N. P. Walker, P. M. McConville, D. Hunter, I. J. Deary, and L. J. Whalley, 2002, *Intelligence, 30*, p. 237. Copyright 2002 by Elsevier Limited. Reprinted with permission.

revealed that there was a 12% increased risk of psychiatric contact based on a 1 standard deviation disadvantage in childhood IQ (*p* = .018).

This study of childhood IQ as a risk factor for contact with psychiatric services was limited in that it had insufficient power within any one diagnostic category to provide more specific information about where the risks lay. However, if, in fact, lower IQ scores were a general risk for the need for psychiatric services, then the studies that examined only schizophrenia might be confounded by this (David et al., 1997). Another limitation is the lack of individual measures that were available to adjust for socioeconomic background factors. In Walker et al.'s (2002) study, only the overcrowding index in the school catchment area was available, although it did not account for the association between IQ and psychiatric contact. The study was biased toward more serious psychiatric illnesses. The survival plots in Figure 4.2 show that, by the end of the long observation period, only about 10% of the entire sample had made contact with psychiatric services. This will have

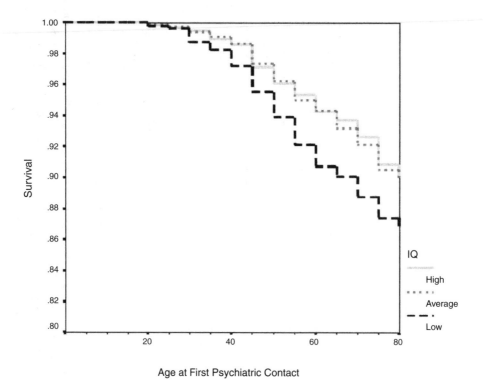

Age at First Psychiatric Contact

Figure 4.2. Survival to contact with psychiatric services, by IQ group based on Moray House Test scores from the Scottish Mental Survey of 1932. From "Childhood Mental Ability and Lifetime Psychiatric Contact: A 66-Year Follow-Up Study of the 1932 Scottish Mental Ability Survey," by N. P. Walker, P. M. McConville, D. Hunter, I. J. Deary, and L. J. Whalley, 2002, *Intelligence, 30,* p. 241. Copyright 2002 by Elsevier Limited. Reprinted with permission.

omitted the large burden of more minor mental disorders that do not result in specialist care. Advantages over the limited amount of previous research were the inclusion of both sexes, a complete range of psychiatric diagnoses, and a valid mental test applied at a time prior to the risk period for most mental illnesses. The mechanisms of the association were not known. They might include childhood IQ being an indicator of social and educational disadvantage that predispose one to mental illness. However, lower IQ might be an indicator of mild neurodevelopmental impairment that makes the person more liable to mental disorder. A third possibility is that, because the study was aimed at contact with psychiatric services, the finding reflects the fact that people with higher IQs cope more effectively with mental disorders and present less often, and later, to psychiatric services.

III

WHAT CAUSES COGNITIVE AGING?

WHAT CAUSES COGNITIVE AGING?

As mentioned previously, the major aim of the follow-up studies of the Scottish Mental Surveys (SMSs) of 1932 and 1947 (SMS1932 and SMS1947) was to study the determinants of human cognitive aging: What factors contribute to individual differences in cognitive ability in old age, after adjusting for individual differences in cognitive ability in youth? If we take a group of people who have identical IQs at age 11, what are the factors, apart from chance, that cause some individuals to do better or worse in later life than their same-childhood-IQ peers? To study how and why people age cognitively—that is, how and why intelligence changes over time—we need data about cognitive abilities both late in life and early in life. To explain this need more clearly, we offer the following example of height.

A person enters a doctor's office and tells the doctor that he is worried about growing shorter. The doctor measures the person's height. The next thing the doctor does, of course, is ask the person what height he used to be. If there is a measurable downward difference in the current height, then the person is shrinking. The case of cognition is similar: If one's mental capabilities are declining faster than would be expected for one's age, then there is a problem. Just setting a threshold that represents an acceptable score does not work. Of course, very low cognition is always a problem because it makes people dependent on others for decision making and care. However, in studying cognitive aging, it is the amount of change from a previous level of cognition that matters.

Prior to our discovery of the original SMSs, few researchers had access to any prior estimation of cognitive ability among older samples. The data from the original SMSs provided an unprecedented opportunity to conduct follow-up testing on the cohorts, assess cognitive aging of the individuals, and look for associations between cognitive aging and other factors—both biological and sociobehavioral.

Unlike the study of epidemiology, studying cognitive aging required more than merely matching names, birth dates, and other information from various sources and then crunching the numbers accordingly to see what associations existed. Instead, the cognitive aging studies involved extensive tracing, recruitment, and follow-up testing of the original SMS test-takers. We had to administer a battery of tests for cognitive aging, and then we had to test for a variety of factors that might have been associated with cognitive aging: genes, brain structure, smoking, nutrition, and so forth. Our research teams were involved in the administration of brain scans, molecular genetic testing, interviewing, and so forth. In the end, our findings reflect the analysis of extensive data.

The locations of the researchers determined where the follow-up studies took place. We worked closely together, often in daily contact, with Lawrence J. Whalley leading and overseeing the day-to-day running of the Aberdeen work, Ian J. Deary leading and overseeing the Edinburgh area (Lothian) work, and John M. Starr serving as the geriatric medical expert to both. These locations mean, of course, that we have never yet recruited from Scotland's most populous area: Glasgow and the surrounding towns in the west of Scotland. The work that is recounted in this part is based on the samples recruited and tested in the Aberdeen and Lothian (Edinburgh and its environs) areas of Scotland. Therefore, we describe the samples before we discuss the findings. The numbers reported in each study will vary within each cohort, depending on the data that are available for each variable.

In chapter 5, we describe how we recruited the cohorts for the cognitive aging studies, as well as our findings on the overall stability of intelligence among the participants from childhood to old age. In chapter 6, we describe our findings on biological factors associated with cognitive aging. In chapter 7, we describe our findings on health and nutrition-related factors associated with cognitive aging.

A NOTE ABOUT TECHNOLOGY CHANGES

Before reading the chapters that form this part, the reader should note that changes in technology over the course of 10 years—the duration of our follow-up studies—have had implications for cognitive research: The participants in the follow-up studies of the SMSs of 1932 and 1947 have found themselves in a series of fast-paced scientific worlds.

When the follow-up studies were begun, the cost of typing a single genetic single nucleotide polymorphism (SNP) was almost two orders of magnitude greater than at the time of this writing. We have moved from testing SNPs in single or a few candidate genes, to considering whole systems of genes amounting to the testing of hundreds of SNPs; the next step is genome-wide association using hundreds of thousands of SNPs spread across the human genome. The latter approach brings obvious problems of Type I statistical errors; therefore, future studies are likely to be more collaborative, with discovery and replication being part of the same reports. The Aberdeen Birth Cohort and Lothian Birth Cohort samples, then, are likely to be involved in joint efforts with other research groups' samples, although there are none as yet known that have had cognitive ability tested over such a long period. It is not yet obvious that any single gene contributes more than a small amount of variance to cognitive ability or cognitive aging. Time will tell whether there are any substantial genetic contributions to mental ability and its changes with age, but it is possible that the high heritability of differences in cognitive functioning is spread across many genes, each with very small effects.

Brain imaging techniques have also moved apace since the beginning of the SMS follow-up studies. The importance of brain white matter integrity for successful cognitive aging is strongly suggested by the studies described herein as well as those of others. The supporting results come from studies of white matter lesions and from diffusion tensor imaging. Advances in white matter imaging include the *magnetization transfer ratio*, which can give an indication of the macromolecules, such as myelin, in a given brain area. A pilot study of this technique in the Lothian Birth Cohort 1921 did not find any contribution to cognitive aging (Deary, Bastin, et al., 2006), although it remains to be tested in larger studies. An extension of diffusion tensor imaging is the better quantification of anisotropy with individual white matter tracts. Therefore, one aspect of future studies will be discovering whether intact white matter within specific tracts is important for successful cognitive aging.

The influences of smoking, physical fitness, and nutritional state and diet all have suggestive findings, with relatively small effects. However, such small effects can be large at the level of the population. Perhaps all of these factors, though, emphasize the problems of the direction of causation and of mechanistic explanation. The former is moot in some cases—made less so by the availability of childhood IQ in the SMS follow-up studies—and the latter often remains mysterious and prey to hand-waving and speculation. Another issue made clear by the results described in this part of the book is that the multivariate recipe for successful cognitive aging—which, surely, is the principal outcome of association studies—is built from studies that often focus on a single contributing variable, or a single set. In part, this has to do with scientific pragmatism: Journals like a focus on a particular exposure, and a rationale along such a basis must be made. In part, it has to do with power: With too many predictors, each of which might have its recognized potential mediators and confounders, sample sizes such as those described in the chapters of this part become quickly inadequate. Nevertheless, a future improvement in methodology must come with the simultaneous multivariate replication of the protective and harmful effects on cognitive aging in different samples. Another potential that multivariable studies possess is the examination of interaction effects, which will also be demanding in terms of power.

A NOTE ABOUT NOMENCLATURE

The abbreviations *SMS1932* and *SMS1947* have been used repeatedly in the book thus far to refer to the surveys as a whole. The area-based, follow-up cohort samples that were recruited from the surveys were given their own names. In the samples, the suffix number refers to the year in which they were born, not the year in which they took the SMS Moray House Test. Also, we refer to the samples as *birth cohorts*. This is not strictly correct. They are called birth cohorts because they were born in the years that are in the title of the sample. However, of course, they are not birth cohorts because they had to be alive at age 11 to take part in the SMS. These comments notwithstanding, the sample from the Aberdeen area that took part in the SMS1932 is called the *Aberdeen Birth Cohort 1921* (i.e., ABC1921). The sample from the Aberdeen area that took part in the SMS1947 is called the *Aberdeen Birth Cohort 1936* (i.e., ABC1936). The sample from the Edinburgh area that took part in the SMS1932 is called the *Lothian Birth Cohort 1921* (i.e., LBC1921). The sample from the Edinburgh area that took part in the SMS1947 is called the *Lothian Birth Cohort 1936* (i.e., LBC1936). Recruitment of this last cohort has only just been completed at the time of this writing, and therefore no findings can be reported on this cohort. However, findings from the other three cohorts are reported herein.

5

RECRUITING THE ABERDEEN BIRTH COHORTS 1921 AND 1936 AND THE LOTHIAN BIRTH COHORT 1921 AND ASSESSING THE STABILITY OF INTELLIGENCE ACROSS THE LIFE SPAN

Since 1997 and 1999, respectively, surviving participants in the Scottish Mental Survey (SMS) of 1932 (SMS1932) have been recruited from the Aberdeen and Edinburgh areas of Scotland. Aberdeen-centered recruitment of participants in the SMS of 1947 (SMS1947) began in 1999. Edinburgh-centered recruitment of SMS1947 participants began in 2004. General publicity and some recruitment were done using printed and broadcast media (i.e., radio, television, and newspapers) and newspaper advertising. More targeted recruitment used Scotland's community health indices that we described earlier. These are area-based lists of people's registration with a general medical practitioner. Because of the United Kingdom's free National Health Service, more than 99% of the Scottish population appears on such a list. We obtained permission from area health boards to identify people on the Aberdeen- and Edinburgh-area lists who were born in 1921 and 1936. In some

Portions of this chapter are reprinted from "Cerebral White Matter Abnormalities and Lifetime Cognitive Change: A 67-Year Follow-Up of the Scottish Mental Survey of 1932," by I. J. Deary, S. A. Leaper, A. D. Murray, R. T. Staff, and L. J. Whalley, 2003, *Psychology and Aging, 18,* pp. 140–148, and "The Impact of Childhood Intelligence on Later Life: Following up the Scottish Mental Surveys of 1932 and 1947," by I. J. Deary, M. C. Whiteman, J. M. Starr, L. J. Whalley, and H. C. Fox, 2004, *Journal of Personality and Social Psychology,* 86 pp. 130–147. Copyright 2003 and 2004 by the American Psychological Association.

instances, at our request, general medical practitioners wrote to those individuals who were living independently in the community and were relatively healthy and invited them to take part in our research program to follow up SMS1932 and SMS1947. In the Edinburgh area, some individuals born in 1921, and all of the people born in 1936, were written to, on our behalf, by the director of public health for the area. Using these procedures, we recruited and tested 235 people in the Aberdeen area (the Aberdeen Birth Cohort 1921 [ABC1921]) and 550 in the Edinburgh area (the Lothian Birth Cohort 1921 [LBC1921]; Lothian is the broader geographic area around Edinburgh) who were born in 1921. Many of the individuals in the ABC1921 have been followed up on three times since their original visit to our centers. In total, 506 people born in 1947 were recruited from the Aberdeen area (the Aberdeen Birth Cohort 1936 [ABC1936]) and have now been seen three times in old age. All participants, when they were first seen by our research teams, took part in a half-day assessment that included the collection of psychological, social, medical, and physiological data. Blood was taken for biochemical, hematological, endocrine, lipid and other analyses, and for DNA extraction. Some of the participants from ABC1921, ABC1936, and LBC1921 underwent magnetic resonance imaging of the brain. The newest cohort, the 1,091-strong Lothian Birth Cohort 1936, who were recruited from surviving participants of the SMS1947 living in the Edinburgh area, are at too early a stage of investigation to be dealt with in this book (Deary, Gow, et al., 2007).

That is a very brief account of the four follow-up samples we recruited and reported on during the 10-year period between 1997 and 2007. In the following sections, we provide some more detail. In doing this, we seek to provide the most generic material of the samples so that we do not need to repeat these details when we recount the results of individual studies. Therefore, among the principal details are the descriptions of the samples and the mental tests applied to them. After providing these, we describe our assessment of the stability of intelligence from childhood to old age among these samples.

ABERDEEN BIRTH COHORT 1921 STUDY

The following sections describe the participants of, and testing applied to, the ABC1921 study.

Participants

Potential volunteers were identified as follows. In 1997, the views of the local general practitioner committee were sought and adhered to as closely as possible. This committee required that all local family doctors should first be informed and asked to agree to support the study. All Aberdeen general practitioners, with the exception of three groups of doctors, did so. The committee stipulated that family doctors be given the names of those among their patients who had been identified as potential volunteers. The committee also requested that family doctors could decline to include any among their patients who were currently ill and requiring intervention and those who had been bereaved in the past 6 months. The Family Doctor Committee also asked whether general practitioners could be informed if the researchers identified physical abnormalities suggestive of current disease or increased disease risk. These procedures, recommended by local family doctors, became the cornerstone of our overall sampling design and was acceptable to the local Ethics of Research Committee.

The next step was to identify potential local volunteers on the nominal rolls for the SMS1932. We initially intended to include only the Aberdeen city schools as given in the nominal rolls, but because the city boundaries have extended substantially since 1932, all schools located within present-day Aberdeen city were included.

Next, the Grampian Health Board Community Health Index was used to identify all local residents born in 1921 by birth name and date of birth. Exact matches were immediately accepted; however, when the day or month of birth varied by one digit and the birth name was the same as on the SMS nominal roll, this was identified as a possible match, and when contact was made with the potential volunteer, he or she was given the opportunity confirm or deny his or her attendance at a particular school in 1932. Uncertainties arose for some children who had been known by a diminutive of their given name or by another "pet" name, and again this uncertainty was explained to a potential volunteer when first making contact. Later in the study, it became clear that a minority of children were known by another family name (usually their mother's maiden name) when at school, and these were overlooked until an individual volunteered by another route (usually personal contact with a school friend who had already volunteered). This work came to the attention of the local press, whose coverage of a reunion of the volunteers (at that time, about 77 years old) generated wide interest in the local community and prompted others who had not by that time been approached to volunteer. In this circumstance, the general practitioner was informed before recruitment.

Volunteers who attended and appeared to experience cognitive impairment to a degree that impaired their capacity to live independently (e.g., a Mini-Mental State Examination score below 24; Folstein, Folstein, & McHugh, 1975) were assessed by a psychiatrist and, if a diagnosis of dementia seemed likely, this was recorded, and the assessment continued as for other volunteers. Between November 1997 and December 1998, 295 local people had been identified as eligible for inclusion, who had taken part in the

SMS1932 when attending a school in the Aberdeen area and who were living in northeast Scotland, mostly in Aberdeen city. Of these 285, 235 (80%) agreed to a visit by a research nurse at home or attended the research center. Of these 235, 10 were excluded at initial assessment because they did not meet inclusion criteria; for example, they had been diagnosed with dementia, were currently ill, were recently bereaved, or experienced sensory impairment to a degree that made cognitive testing unreliable. Recruitment was halted when 200 participants had met all inclusion criteria, provided demographic and medical information, undergone a physical examination, provided a blood sample, and undertaken a minimum cognitive data set (i.e., the Mini-Mental State Examination and Raven's Standard Progressive Matrices).

Cognitive Tests Applied to the Aberdeen Birth Cohort 1921

The mental tests discussed in the sections that follow composed the battery administered to the ABC1921.

Moray House Test

The Moray House Test (MHT) is the general mental ability test participants took at age 11, in 1932 (Scottish Council for Research in Education [SCRE], 1933). Two items were altered slightly because of changes in usage that might have caused confusion. Instructions and the time limit were also kept the same as the original test. This test was taken by only a subsample of the ABC1921, by none of the ABC1936, but by all of the LBC1921 and LBC1936.

Mini-Mental State Examination

The Mini-Mental State Examination (Folstein et al., 1975) was used as a screening test for dementia. It was originally designed as a brief bedside screening test for cognitive impairment. The maximum score is 30; scores lower than 24 are used by some researchers and clinicians to indicate possible dementia. This threshold can be varied to adjust for the effects of age and premorbid mental ability.

Raven's Standard Progressive Matrices

Raven's Standard Progressive Matrices (Raven, Court, & Raven, 1977) were used as a measure of nonverbal reasoning. This is one of the best individual tests with respect to loadings on the General Cognitive Ability factor (Carroll, 1993). There are 60 items organized in five groups of 12. Participants were allowed 20 minutes to complete the test. The score is the number of correctly completed items.

Rey Auditory Verbal Learning Test

The Rey Auditory Verbal Learning Test (AVLT; Lezak, 1995, pp. 438–446) was used to assess short-term and longer term memory and learning. Participants were given five trials to learn a list of 15 words. They were asked to recall as many of the words as possible immediately after hearing each repetition of the list. At the conclusion of these five trials, a list of 15 new words was read to them. The participants were asked to recall as many of these new words as possible immediately after the list was read. Distraction was then provided by structured discussion with the tester for 5 minutes. After this, participants were asked to recall as many of the original list's 15 words as possible without having the list read to them again. Most correlations among these seven AVLT scores were high ($rs > .5$). Principal components analysis on the scores revealed a single component (visual examination of the scree slope was used to determine the number of components) accounting for 65.7% of the total score variance. Therefore, the standardized score from this single component (the unrotated first principal component) was used as the AVLT memory score.

Uses of Common Objects

Lezak (1995) referred to Uses of Common Objects (or Uses of Objects; p. 667) as a test of executive function or purposive action. Participants were asked to name as many uses as they could think of for a bottle, a paper clip, and a felt hat. They were allowed 90 seconds for each item. Before starting, participants were given several examples of different uses for a sheet of paper. They were allowed to use multiple occurrences of the objects in their suggested uses. The score was the total number of acceptable uses for all three objects.

Digit Symbol

The Digit Symbol subtest of the Wechsler Adult Intelligence Scale—Revised (Wechsler, 1981) was used as an indicator of speed of information processing (Salthouse, 1996). The test instructs the respondent to substitute symbols for numbers according to an explicit code. It was administered as instructed in the test manual. The score was the number of correct substitutions in 90 seconds.

National Adult Reading Test

The National Adult Reading Test (Nelson & Willison, 1991) is used as an estimate of premorbid or prior cognitive ability. The test requires the participant to pronounce 50 words that are irregular in terms of pronunciation and/or stress patterns.

Hospital Anxiety Depression Scale

The Hospital Anxiety Depression Scale (Zigmond & Snaith, 1983) contains seven items to measure anxiety and seven to measure depression. The maximum score on each scale is 21, with probable anxiety or depression assumed at scores of 11 or over.

Health Outcomes

Specific disease categories and any regular medications were recorded at interview (see Starr, Deary, Lemmon, & Whalley, 2000). The following physiological measures were taken: height, weight, blood pressure, pulse, peak expiratory flow rate from the lungs, forced expiratory volume from the lungs in 1 second, forced vital lung capacity, time to walk 6 meters at the person's usual pace, and visual acuity. Functional independence was assessed using the self-completed Barthel score (Collin, Wade, Davies, & Horne, 1988).

ABERDEEN BIRTH COHORT 1936 STUDY

The following sections describe the participants of, and testing applied to, the ABC1936 study.

Participants

We followed the same procedures to match and locate local survivors of the SMS1947 that we had established for the ABC1921. As before, the local Ethics of Research Committee considered and approved the protocol. In June 1999, there began recruitment of local survivors from the SMS1947 into the ABC1936. Invitations had been offered to 647 local people to take part, of whom 506 (75%) attended the first interview. Of these 506, 22 did not complete the protocol on their first occasion. The last participant (No. 484) was recruited in December 2003. Ages of ABC1936 participants when first seen varied between 62 years, 8 months and 67 years, 7 months. The mean age was 64 years, 7 months ($SD = 10.8$ months).

Cognitive Tests Applied to the Aberdeen Birth Cohort 1936

The ABC1936 participants took the same mental and other tests as did the ABC1921 participants.

LOTHIAN BIRTH COHORT 1921 STUDY

The following sections describe the participants of, and testing applied to, the LBC1921 study.

Participants

The LBC1921 study was approved by the Lothian Health Research Ethics Committee. The SMS1932 data were kept in area-based, handwritten ledgers in Edinburgh at the SCRE.[1] The pupils' MHT scores are recorded within schools, in order of their dates of birth. Before LBC1921 study recruitment began (in 1999), the Edinburgh and Lothian ledgers were transcribed into a computer database. To construct the LBC1921, we searched for SMS1932 survivors by identifying people in the Edinburgh area who were born in 1921 and asking them whether they had attended school in Scotland in 1932. We searched for 1921-born people in two ways: (a) through the Community Health Index for Edinburgh and its surrounding area (Lothian region) and (b) through advertisements placed in local, regional, and national newspapers. After viewing the advertisements, 423 people telephoned for further information. Of these, 368 (86.9%) fulfilled study criteria, and 321 (87.2%) of the eligible sample agreed to take part. On the basis of the Community Health Index information, local doctors sent leaflets on our behalf to 1,120 people. Of these, 728 (59.6%) replied, with 501 (68.8% of replies) fulfilling study criteria. Of the eligible 501 people, 260 (51.8%) took part in the study. In all, 550 (234 men and 316 women) ambulant, independent participants were recruited and tested, and they constitute the LBC1921.

Cognitive Tests Applied to the Lothian Birth Cohort 1921

In addition to the cognitive tests described in the following sections, LBC1921 participants also completed the MHT, the Mini-Mental State Examination, Raven's Standard Progressive Matrices, the National Adult Reading Test, and the Hospital Anxiety Depression Scale, all of which are described in the preceding paragraphs.

Logical Memory

The Logical Memory assessment is from the Wechsler Memory Scale—Revised (Wechsler, 1987). Two short stories containing 25 memory items each are read aloud. Immediately after hearing each, the participant is asked to tell the interviewer as much as he or she remembers about it. After a

---

[1]The ledgers are now in the SCRE archives at the University of Glasgow, Scotland.

minimum of 30 minutes' delay, participants are again asked to recall as much as they can about the stories. In most reported studies, the total score was used.

Verbal Fluency

The Verbal Fluency task (Lezak, 1995) is said to assess executive function. The participant is asked to name as many words as possible beginning with the letters C, F, and L, and is given 1 minute for each letter. Proper names are not allowed, and repeated words are scored only once.

Physical Tests

The purpose of the physical tests was to obtain markers of health and fitness. The test battery comprised the following assessments: height, weight and demi-span (i.e., distance from the sternal notch to the web of skin between the second and third fingers); visual acuity; time to walk 6 meters; blood for biochemical and haematological factors; blood for DNA extraction for later identification of genotypes related to cognition and cognitive aging; lung function (i.e., peak flow, forced vital capacity, forced expiratory volume, and forced expiratory rate); blood pressure; grip strength (using a Jamar hand-held dynamometer); and resting, 12-lead electrocardiogram.

The Townsend Disability Scale (Bond & Carstairs, 1982; Townsend, 1979) also was administered. Scores of 0 (*no difficulty*), 1 (*some difficulty*), or 2 (*unable to do*) were recorded for a series of nine questions, such as "Are you able to: cut your own toe-nails?; wash all over or bathe?; and shop and carry heavy bags?"

Procedure

LBC1921 participants were tested at the Wellcome Trust Clinical Research Facility at the Western General Hospital, Edinburgh. Two nurses were specially trained to carry out the physical testing of the participants. Trained researchers carried out cognitive testing and interviewing. Testing took place from September 1999 until July 2001. Each appointment lasted approximately 3 hours and contained one tea break and lunch. All testing was carried out on an individual basis.

Participants were first interviewed about their medical history, educational and employment history, and smoking and alcohol consumption. The Mini-Mental State Examination was administered next, followed by the first reading of the Logical Memory stories from the Wechsler Memory Scale—Revised. Participants then took the MHT (the whole first session lasted about 1 hour, with exactly 45 minutes allocated for the MHT). The tea break was next (20 minutes), followed by the physical testing (40–45 minutes). The final session comprised three further cognitive tests (30 minutes). The order of physical tests and final cognitive session were sometimes reversed to facilitate the simultaneous testing of a few participants.

In the next chapters in this part, we describe the findings on cognitive aging that have emerged from the ABC1921, LBC1921, and ABC1936. First, though, we investigate the lifetime stability of cognitive ability differences.

STABILITY OF INTELLIGENCE FROM CHILDHOOD TO OLD AGE

The foundation of the research on factors affecting cognitive aging was the availability of MHT scores at age 11 years in the SMS participants. The assumption was that, in studying mental function in old age, it was important to adjust for prior ability—truly prior ability, before any effects of aging had occurred. We wished to ask this question: What was the relative change—up, or down, or none—for that particular person? Therefore, the first task was to examine the stability of individual differences in mental ability across the life span. This was facilitated by obtaining a copy of MHT No. 12 (the SMS1932 test) and the instructions (see Figure 5.1). These are reprinted in the original description of the SMS1932 (SCRE, 1933). Therefore, the same test could be applied in old age that had been used in youth. Just how high the correlation might be was a moot point. The MHT was originally administered at age 11, and the plan was to administer it again when people were in their late 70s. There is still mental development toward a cognitive peak after age 11 and, no matter how optimistic one is about cognitive aging, most people have experienced deterioration in some mental skills by their late 70s. The MHT had been proven valid at age 11 because it correlated with the Stanford revision of the Binet–Simon Test (SCRE, 1933), but would it prove to be a valid mental test for older people? A low correlation between the age 11 and late-70s scores on the MHT might indicate that test scores from age 11 have little relevance as baseline scores from which to examine any lifelong cognitive change.

A narrative review of previous studies of the stability of cognitive ability differences was conducted (Deary, Whalley, Lemmon, Crawford, & Starr, 2000). There were studies across various periods of the human life span, including within-childhood studies. Some were from childhood to middle adulthood, some were from young adulthood to middle adulthood, and some were within old age. All stability coefficients were quite high, with many from about .5 to about .8. A notable study was the Concordia follow-up study of Canadian servicemen from World War II (Schwartzman, Gold, Andres, Arbuckle, & Chaikelson, 1987). The participants had taken the Revised Examination "M" at age 25 years and again at age 65. The correlation across

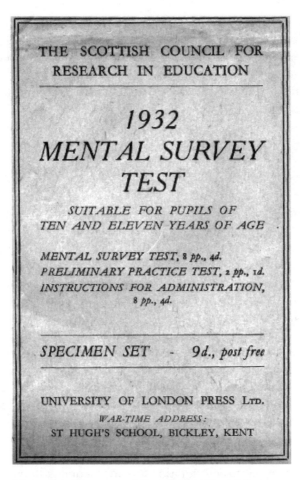

Figure 5.1. The cover of the Scottish Mental Survey
Test of 1932: Moray House Test No. 12.

this 40-year gap was .78, demonstrating high stability of individual differences
from young adulthood to the brink of old age.

The first examination of the stability of intelligence differences among
the follow-up studies of the SMSs took place with a subsample of the
ABC1921 (Deary et al., 2000). All testing of the samples takes place individually, with this one exception. On June 1, 1998, exactly 66 years to the day
after the SMS1932, a mass retesting of some of the original participants was
arranged. It took place at the Music Hall in Union Street, Aberdeen. The hall
was specially furnished with tables and chairs for the occasion (see Figure 5.2).
There were 73 members of the ABC1921. The same MHT No. 12 (the
SMS1932 test) was used, with the same instructions and the same 45-minute
time limit as the participants had taken at age 11. They were asked as a group
whether they recalled having taken the original test, and only a few hands

Figure 5.2. Individuals from the Aberdeen Birth Cohort 1921 on June 1, 1998, waiting to be retested on Moray House Test No. 12 that they had taken exactly 66 years earlier.

were raised. At periods up to 5 months later, another 28 participants retook the MHT with the same instructions and time limit, to give a total of 101 people. None was experiencing mental or significant current physical illness, or on medication that might affect cognitive function.

Two slight changes had to be made to the MHT at retesting. First, a change was made to a question about shillings and pence. Money had changed from a duodecimal to a decimal system in the United Kingdom on February 15, 1971. Therefore, this item would be more difficult and unfamiliar in 1998 than it had been in 1932. However, the principal measurements of length in the United Kingdom, especially among this age group, are still duodecimal. Therefore, the question was changed to feet and inches instead of shillings and pence. The other change was to alter a reference to the archaic *vitamine* to *vitamins*. (This is a reminder of how long ago 1932 was.) The 101 participants' MHT scores were identified from the SMS1932 records.

The 101 Aberdeen-based participants scored better on the MHT at age 77 than they had done at age 11, with respective means of 54.2 ($SD = 11.8$) versus 43.3 ($SD = 11.9$; Deary et al., 2000). The sample was not fully representative of the original Scotland-wide population, which had an age 11 mean of 34.5 ($SD = 15.5$). The sample was 0.57 standard deviation units higher, and the spread was approximately 77% that of the whole, 11-year-old population. An analysis of variance, with sex as a fixed effect and age-11 versus age-77 MHT score as a repeated measure, showed a trend toward a Sex × Time interaction: Men tended to score better at age 77 than would be expected by their scores at age 11 ($p = .1$). The correlation between MHT score at age 77 and contemporaneous Raven scores was .57 ($p < .001$).

Therefore, the MHT showed concurrent validity at age 11 and in old age. The correlation between the MHT score at age 11 and Raven scores at age 77 was .48 ($p < .001$). The comparison between the correlation of the contemporaneous MHT and Raven test scores at age 77 (.57) and the correlation of the time-lagged MHT score at age 11 with the Ravens at age 77 (.48) provides an indication of the relatively high stability of the latent trait.

The main novel result was the lifetime stability coefficient of the MHT (Deary et al., 2000). The raw correlation between the scores at age 11 and age 77 was .63 ($p < .001$; 95% confidence interval: .50, .74). If this is disattenuated for the restriction of range in the sample versus the original population, the value is .73. Whichever value is viewed as the better estimate, this result shows considerable stability of individual differences in cognitive ability across almost all of the human life span. Moreover, these correlations are not corrected for measurement error on both occasions of testing.

The results provided a good foundation for studies of cognitive aging. If the correlations are squared to obtain the variance that is stable between age 11 and age 77, then the value is approximately half. That means that there is about as much change variance as there is stability. Looking at the results from one direction, there is remarkable stability across a very long age gap, perhaps a decade or so longer than any previous study using the same test on both occasions (Deary et al., 2000). Viewed from another perspective, the instability across the life span was a large, tempting target. Finding factors that accounted for the rest of the variance in old age was the main aim of the research program from then on. Strictly speaking, some of the variance in "change" would be measurement error. First, though, a replication of the stability coefficient was attempted.

The LBC1921 sample provided people who took MHT No. 12 in the SMS1932 and were then individually examined on the same test between 1999 and 2001 at an average age of over 79[2] (Deary, Whiteman, Starr, et al., 2004). Of the 550 people in the LBC1921, 493 had identifiable MHT scores at age 11, with a mean of 46.4 and a standard deviation of 11.9. There were 542 people with MHT scores at age 79, with a mean of 59.2 and a standard deviation of 10.8. There were 541 people with age-79 scores on both the MHT and the Raven. The contemporaneous age-79 correlation between the MHT and Raven was .71 ($p < .001$), providing concurrent validity for the MHT in old age in this sample. The raw Pearson correlation coefficient between the scores at age 11 and at age 79 was .66 ($p < .001$). The values for men and women were .62 and .69, respectively. When the correlation for all participants was disattenuated for restriction of range, it was .73, the same as that found in the ABC1921 (Deary et al., 2000). The MHT raw scores from age 11 and age 79 were age corrected (although the age range at each age was

---

[2]In Deary, Whiteman, Starr, et al. (2004), the age is rounded to 80.

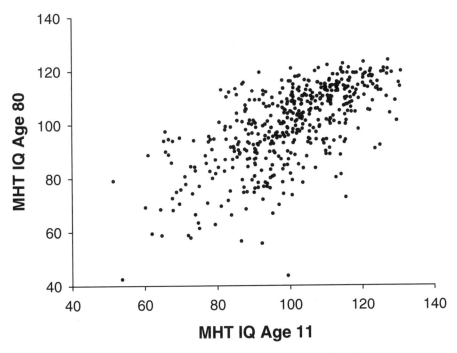

Figure 5.3. Scattergram of age-corrected Moray House Test (MHT) scores at age 11 and age 80 for participants in the Lothian Birth Cohort 1921 of the Scottish Mental Survey 1932. Reprinted from "The Impact of Childhood Intelligence on Later Life: Following up the Scottish Mental Surveys of 1932 and 1947," by I. J. Deary, M. C. Whiteman, J. M. Starr, L. J. Whalley, & H. C. Fox, 2004, *Journal of Personality and Social Psychology, 86,* p. 135. Copyright 2004 by the American Psychological Association.

small) and then converted to IQ-type scores, with means of 100 and standard deviations of 15 at both ages. The scattergram is shown in Figure 5.3. In a regression analysis, the linear effect in this association accounts for 43.4% of the variance. The quadratic effect was significant ($p < .001$), but very small, accounting for 0.3% of the variance (Deary, Whiteman, Starr, et al., 2004).

It was now clear that cognition at age 11 years was a substantial predictor of cognition even as late as almost 80 years; not only that, but it appeared to be an excellent baseline measure from which to compare individual differences in old age. The research program we describe in chapters 6 and 7 was built to achieve a simple aim: to find what accounted for the variance not accounted for by childhood cognitive ability. A strength of the project was that there was a great deal of time between age 11 and old age, so there was much time for change to have taken place and, therefore, a large variance target to hit. The weakness of this setup was that any predictor of change would have, if it were causal, acted at some unspecified time in that long period.

A wide view was taken about the possible causes of cognitive change. This was combined with pragmatic collaborations based on expertise local to Aberdeen and Edinburgh. In both cities, there were experts on brain imaging with whom we collaborated. In Aberdeen, the Rowett Research Institute provided experts in human nutrition. In Edinburgh, the Medical Research Council's Human Genetics Unit provided expertise in molecular genetics. As will become clear, other expertise was provided along the way, as individual studies took place.

6

FINDINGS ON BIOLOGICAL FACTORS

There are many sources of individual differences in aging: biological factors, health-related factors, sociobehavioral factors, and other factors, including chance. Although it is not possible to analyze chance, we did analyze biological and health and nutrition-related factors to investigate what associations with cognitive aging could be determined. In this chapter, we discuss our findings regarding biological factors, and in chapter 7 we discuss our health and nutrition-related findings.

GENES

The genetic material in humans is carried in the 22 autosomes and in the X and Y sex chromosomes. There is also some genetic material in mitochondria. The DNA of humans has more than 3 billion nucleotide bases. Areas of DNA that code for proteins, probably less than 2% of the total, are genes. Most genes have approximately 3,000 nucleotide bases, but some have as many as 2 million. Humans have approximately 20,000 to 25,000 genes; the estimated number varies. Not all humans have the same string of nucleotide bases on their DNA. In somewhere between every 100 and 300 of the bases, more than 1% of humans have a base that is different. This is the most common type of DNA difference: a *single-nucleotide polymorphism* (SNP). On the one hand, this means that more than 99% of the DNA in humans is identical. On the other hand, it means that there are between 3 million and 10 million SNPs. Most SNPs are silent, but some make a difference to the function of the relevant protein and have biological consequences. There are other types of genetic variation beyond SNPs. These include shortish sequences of DNA that are, for example, repeated by different amounts in different people, called *copy number variations*. There also are sequences of DNA that are inserted, deleted, and reversed between individuals. However, our account here deals only with genetic variation caused by SNPs.

We and our colleagues used three strategies to search for genes related to cognitive aging. First, we specifically targeted candidate genes (Deary, Wright, Harris, Whalley, & Starr, 2004); that is, there were some genes that other researchers had already found to be related to cognitive pathology, and these could be tested in the participants of the follow-up studies of the Scottish Mental Surveys (SMSs). A good example of this type of gene was the gene coding for *apolipoprotein E* (APOE). Differences in *APOE* genotype are associated with the risk of developing Alzheimer's disease. Second, we could target systems instead of a single gene with a known association with cognitive pathology. For example, the process of *oxidative stress* has deleterious effects on neurons. Individual differences in oxidative stress have been implicated strongly in neurodegeneration. Many genes code for proteins related to oxidative defenses, and so this general system of genes could be a target. In a third strategy, one can dispense with a priori hypotheses and simply examine many thousands of SNPs along the entire human genome. It is not possible yet to examine all of the millions of SNPs—but neither is it necessary to do so. SNPs that are close to each other on the genome tend to be inherited together, under the process of *linkage disequilibrium*. This redundancy is the basis of the human HapMap project (http://www.hapmap.org). Therefore, sometimes testing one SNP yields good information about whether people have another one. Therefore, if seeking a specific gene—of the 20,000+, and there might be more than one function-affecting SNP in any one gene—is like shooting with a hunting rifle, and going for a "system" of genes is like hunting with a shotgun, then genome-wide association is like trawling (with apologies for the change in metaphor).

Apolipoprotein E (APOE)

An obvious first gene to examine was the gene coding for apolipoprotein E. In humans, the abbreviation for the protein is APOE and for the gene is *APOE*. The coding region for this human chromosome 19 gene contains two polymorphic regions. As a result, people end up having three types of APOE. The genetic forms APOE e2, e3, and e4 lead to the same-named proteins. Individuals with an e4 version of the gene are more likely to develop late-onset Alzheimer's disease, and those with two of the e4 genes are even more likely to develop late-onset Alzheimer's disease (Corder et al., 1993). During the latter half of the 1990s, there was dispute about whether variation in the gene for APOE was associated with differences in nondementia cognitive aging, with no clear consensus (Anstey & Christensen, 2000).

We realized that we could do more than examine the influence of variation in APOE on cognitive change across a remarkable time gap. We could examine three things in relation APOE and other genetic variation: (a) the association with cognition at age 11, (b) the association with cognition in old age, and (c) the association with the change in cognition between the two ages.

The first study of the APOE–cognition association—although, because of different publication delays of different journals, not the article with the earliest date—was conducted on 234 members of the Aberdeen Birth Cohort 1921 (ABC1921; Deary, Whalley, St. Clair, et al., 2003). The analytical sample, which required participants to have Moray House Test (MHT) scores at age 11 and scores on Raven's Standard Progressive Matrices (Raven, Court, & Raven, 1977) at about age 77, and successful genotyping for APOE, comprised 173 participants (86 men and 87 women). Each person's DNA was typed twice for APOE. There were 42 people with the e4 allele of APOE and 131 without, which is a typical percentage in the United Kingdom. MHT and Raven's Standard Progressive Matrices scores were both converted to IQ-type scores ($M = 100$, $SD = 15$). The mean MHT IQ at age 11 for people without the APOE e4 allele was 101.0 ($SD = 14.4$), and for those with the e4 allele it was 98.0 ($SD = 16.2$). These were not significantly different. The mean Raven's Standard Progressive Matrices IQ at age 77 for people without the APOE e4 allele was 99.7 ($SD = 15.4$), and for those with the e4 allele it was 99.8 ($SD = 13.5$). These were not significantly different. There was no significant effect of APOE e4 allele on cognitive change from age 11 to age 77. This was examined as a Time × Genotype interaction in analysis of variance with APOE e4 allele status as a fixed effect and cognitive testing at the two ages as a repeated measure. In this first study, then, genetic variation in the gene for APOE appeared to have no effect on cognitive ability or change. It was relatively unusual to have studied the effect of variation in this gene on cognition in childhood, and the only other study also found no effect (Turic, Fisher, Plomin, & Owen, 2001).

A larger study of variation in the gene for APOE and lifetime cognitive change involved participants in the Lothian Birth Cohort 1921 (LBC1921; Deary et al., 2002). They had taken MHT at age 11 and the same test again at a mean age of 79. The MHT scores were adjusted for age (in days) at the time of testing and converted to IQ scores ($M = 100$, $SD = 15$) at each age.

Excluded from the LBC1921 for these analyses were 8 people with Mini-Mental State Examination (Folstein, Folstein, & McHugh, 1975) scores less than 24, and 5 with medical histories suggestive of possible dementia. There were 466 members of the LBC1921 (190 men) who had MHT scores at both ages and had successful genotyping for APOE. Of the 466, 121 (26.0%) had at least one copy of the e4 allele of APOE. At age 11, those without an e4 allele had a mean IQ of 100.8 (SD = 14.4), and those who had at least one e4 allele had a mean IQ of 99.4 (SD = 15.2). These were not significantly different (p = .36). At age 79, individuals without an e4 allele had a mean IQ of 101.1 (SD = 14.2), and those who had at least one e4 allele had a mean IQ of 97.0 (SD = 15.7). These were significantly different (p = .009).

General linear modeling was then used to examine the effect of APOE e4 allele status on cognitive change between age 11 and age 79 (Deary et al., 2002). Sex and e4 allele status were fixed effects, MHT IQ score at age 11 was a covariable, and MHT score at age 79 was the dependent variable. The effects of age 11 IQ (p < .001, η^2 = .42) and sex (p = .003, η^2 = .018) were significant. People with better scores on the MHT at age 11 did better at age 79. With age 11 IQ in the model as a covariable, men did slightly better than women at age 79. This does not necessarily mean that being male helps protect against cognitive aging. A smaller proportion of men than women are alive at age 79. It might be that, in part, being alive and male at age 79 requires advantageous cognitive aging. With sex and childhood IQ in the model, the effect of APOE e4 allele status was significant (p = .02) and accounted for 1.1% of the variance.

Checks were made that cardiovascular disease status in this relatively healthy group was not related to cognitive status (Deary et al., 2002). People with and without the APOE e4 allele did not differ in their number and type of medications. It is possible that the effects of the APOE e4 allele were reflecting incipient dementia in the Lothian Birth Cohort 1936. It is not possible entirely to exclude this possibility but, for a number of reasons, this seems unlikely to explain a substantial proportion of the effect. First, APOE e4 allele status still had a significant effect when only participants with a Mini-Mental State Examination score greater than or equal to 28 were included. Second, when those who had declined more than 2 standard deviations in MHT IQ score were excluded, the effect was still significant. Third, computation of the number of likely, eventual cases of Alzheimer's disease in the sample and the effect size of APOE e4 allele status on risk for Alzheimer's disease required unfeasibly large mental test score declines in each potential case to generate the overall effect found in the study.

The influence of APOE e4 allele status on cognitive aging is interesting. Finding out more about the mechanism of APOE will be informative about how the brain ages and might offer targets for intervention. There is another interesting aspect of this result, this time to researchers who are examining the genetic contribution to intelligence differences. The results suggest that, although intelligence differences are quite highly heritable from childhood onward (Deary, Spinath, & Bates, 2006), the individual molecular genetic contributions to this overall heritability might change with age; that is, the heritability of intelligence is not the same thing at different ages. Reflecting on the possible functions of APOE gives some clues to why this might be so (Huang, Weisgraber, Mucke, & Mahley, 2004). For example, if APOE is involved in neuronal repair, and if the different isoforms of the protein are associated with differential efficiency of repair, then it is understandable that the effect of APOE e4 allele status might appear only after organisms have had some years of brain insults that have required repair. Smith (2002) suggested that, among people without dementia, APOE e4 is a "frailty gene, predisposing one to be more susceptible to injury and less likely to recover from trauma once it occurs" (p. 356).

A further, more detailed study of the full APOE genotype in the LBC1921 sample examined a range of cognitive abilities (Deary, Whiteman, Pattie, et al., 2004). This involved 462 of the LBC1921 participants who had the appropriate cognitive test data, successful genotyping for APOE, Mini-Mental State Examination test scores greater than or equal to 24, and no history of dementia. This study, in addition to examining participants according to whether they had the e4 allele of the gene for APOE, examined the full genotype. The e3 allele is the most common, with e4 and e2 being less common. The genotypes that were present in the LBC1921 in adequate numbers for analyses were the e2/e3 ($n = 66$), e3/e3 ($n = 274$), and e3/e4 ($n = 101$). There were 2 people who were e2/e2 and 3 who were e4/e4. The three common genotypes provide groups for a quasi-experimental study. Each has an e3 allele; therefore, the cognitive consequences of the additional allele—e2, e3, or e4—can be examined.

In a multivariate model with sex as a fixed effect and age 11 IQ (from the SMS of 1932 [SMS1932]) as a covariable, there was a significant effect of APOE e4 allele status on Logical Memory ($p = .005$) but not on Raven's Standard Progressive Matrices or on Verbal Fluency (see Table 6.1; Deary, Whiteman, Pattie, et al., 2004; see also discussion about Logical Memory and Verbal Fluency in chap. 5). Individuals without the e4 allele scored better, and the allele contributed 1.7% of the variance to Logical Memory test scores. This indicated that APOE e4 allele status is associated with verbal declarative memory but not significantly in this sample with nonverbal reasoning or executive function. Sex, with an advantage for men, contributed to scores on Raven's Standard Progressive Matrices but not to Logical Memory or Verbal Fluency. The univariate model with Logical Memory test scores was run another four times, once with Mini-Mental State Examination test scores as a covariate and once each with the following disease states as fixed effects: cardiovascular disease, diabetes, or hypertension. The effect of APOE e4

TABLE 6.1
Estimated Marginal Means (95% Confidence Intervals) for the Effect of *Apolipoprotein E* (*APOE*) Genotypes on Cognitive Test Scores in the Lothian Birth Cohort 1921

Test	e4– (n = 342)	e4+ (n = 120)	e2/e3 (n = 66)	e3/e3 (n = 274)	e3/e4 (n = 101)
Logical Memory	32.9 (31.6, 34.2)	29.2 (26.9, 31.4)	36.9 (33.9, 39.9)	31.9 (30.4, 33.3)	28.8 (26.4, 31.2)
Raven's Standard Progressive Matrices	31.8 (31.0, 41.2)	30.8 (29.4, 32.2)	32.5 (30.6, 34.4)	31.5 (30.6, 32.5)	31.0 (29.5, 32.6)
Verbal Fluency	39.9 (38.7, 41.2)	40.1 (37.9, 42.2)	39.1 (36.2, 42.0)	40.0 (38.6, 41.4)	40.0 (37.4, 42.1)

Note. Marginal means are adjusted for sex and IQ at age 11 (Moray House Test No. 12). e4– and e4+ indicate individuals who have not and have, respectively, at least one copy of the epsilon 4 allele of the *APOE* gene. e2/e3, for example, is the genotype and indicates individuals who have epsilon 2 and epsilon 3 alleles of the *APOE* gene. Pairwise comparisons are based on estimated marginal means: *APOE* e4– versus *APOE* e4+, $p = .005$; e3/e3 versus e2/e3, $p = .003$; e3/e3 versus e3/e4, $p < .01$. Reprinted from "Apolipoprotein E Gene Variability and Cognitive Functions at Age 79: A Follow-Up of the Scottish Mental Survey of 1932," by I. J. Deary, M. C. Whiteman, A. Pattie, J. M. Starr, J. M. Hayward, A. F. Wright, et al., 2004, *Psychology and Aging, 19,* p. 369. Copyright 2004 by the American Psychological Association.

allele status remained significant throughout. Of the illnesses, only hypertension was associated with poorer memory scores ($p = .037$).

The next multivariate analyses with *APOE* included all three genotypes—e2/e3, e3/e3, and e3/e4—instead of just e4 allele status (Deary, Whiteman, Pattie, et al., 2004). This permitted testing of the hypothesis that the e2 allele might be protective to cognitive functions in addition to e4 being detrimental. The effect of genotype was not significant on Raven's Standard Progressive Matrices or Verbal Fluency. It was significant on Logical Memory ($p < .001$), accounting for 3.8% of the variance (see Table 6.1 and Figure 6.1). The comparisons among the three genotypes confirm the detrimental effect of the e4 allele. Additionally, it was found that e2 served a protective function, with participants who had e2/e3 genotypes scoring better on Logical Memory than those who had e3/e3 genotypes ($p = .003$).

The influence of *APOE* variation on memory was compatible with the meta-analytic review that found verbal memory to be especially associated with this gene (Small, Rosnick, Fratiglioni, & Backman, 2004). However, the same meta-analysis also found that variation in *APOE* was related to differences in executive function and global cognition, which was not found in the LBC1921. An effect on specific cognitive tests, or mental domains, would be compatible with what is known about the patterns of cognitive aging in multiple cognitive domains. Although there is some shared aging variance—to some extent, the aging of one cognitive domain follows that of others—there is also specific variance, such that domains such as memory age to some extent independently of others (Salthouse & Ferrer-Caja, 2003).

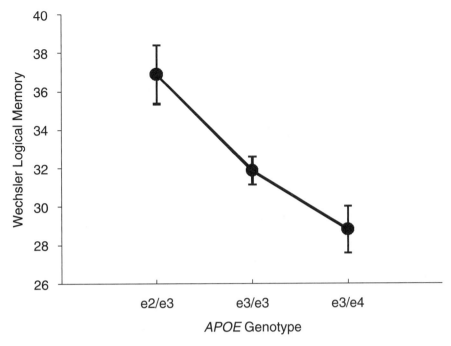

Figure 6.1. Apolipoprotein E (APOE) genotype versus Logical Memory test scores in the Lothian Birth Cohort 1921. The standard errors were computed for this figure. Data from Deary, Whiteman, Pattie, et al. (2004, Table 2).

Genes Related to Dementia, Longevity, and Oxidative Stress: *Nicastrin* and *Klotho*

Genes in these areas proved fruitful, if measured by the conventional $p < .05$ criterion. In each case, the associations found in relation to cognition and/or normal cognitive aging are quite novel, and so further studies will decide whether these are replicable genotype–phenotype associations.

The *nicastrin* gene (NCSTN) is located on chromosome 1 in humans (Deary, Hamilton, et al., 2005). *Nicastrin* (NCSTN) is a glycoprotein that sits across cell membranes. It is part of a protein complex that cleaves the Notch receptor and amyloid precursor protein. Amyloid beta protein, cleaved from the latter molecule, makes up much of the plaques found in the brains of people with Alzheimer's disease.

There was some evidence that variation in *NCSTN* was related to late-onset dementia, and it therefore was taken as a candidate gene that might influence normal cognitive aging. Variation in *NCSTN* is based on four sites in the gene that are polymorphic. A total of 535 LBC1921 participants' DNA was tested. The results of the four polymorphisms on NCSTN are expressed as groups, or *haplotypes*, and the sample was divided by these. One of the haplotypes is coded B (*Hap B*) and had been related to early-onset dementia in another study. Four hundred fifty-eight LBC1921 participants had cognitive data and met the exclusion criteria that have been described previously. There were 66 with Hap B and 392 without. People with Hap B had significantly higher age 11 ($p = .036$) and age 79 ($p = .027$) IQ scores, on the basis of MHT No. 12. There were no significant effects on Raven's Standard Progressive Matrices, Logical Memory, Verbal Fluency, or Mini-Mental State Examination scores. For example, the age 11 IQ scores for people with Hap B was 104.0 (95% confidence interval: 100.4, 107.7) versus 99.8 (95% confidence interval: 98.3, 101.3) for those without Hap B. The age 79 IQ scores were very similar to the respective age 11 IQ scores for the two groups. The effect size was typically small, with NCSTN Hap B variation accounting for about 1% of the variance in IQ scores. There were no significant effects of NCSTN Hap B on age 79 IQ after adjusting for age 11 IQ. An additional analysis was conducted with MHT IQ score as a repeated measure at age 11 and age 79, and the association between the repeated measure and NCSTN Hap B was significant ($p = .022$). These interesting and unexpected results implied that NCSTN variation was associated with the lifelong trait of cognitive ability, as measured by the MHT, and not cognitive aging, as had been hypothesized. A study that had measured cognition in old age only might well have incorrectly concluded that NCSTN Hap B status was associated with cognitive aging. Here it was possible to show that the association with cognition in old age was accounted for by the NCSTN Hap B–cognition association at age 11.

The KLOTHO gene was another candidate for cognitive aging that turned out to be associated with lifelong cognitive level rather than cognitive change (Deary, Harris, et al., 2005). Klotho was one of the three Fates in Greek mythology. She spun the thread of life; another fate (Lachesis) measured it, and the last one (Atropos) cut it. The KLOTHO protein is a beta-glucuronidase, a multifunctional protein that "regulates phosphate/calcium metabolism as well as aging" (Kuro-o, 2006, p. 437). Klotho-deficient mice have been used as a model for the human aging process. They have arteriosclerosis, osteoporosis, skin atrophy, and compared with wild-type mice, they have accelerated cognitive decline and excess damage to the hippocampus. The human KLOTHO gene is on chromosome 13, and the human KLOTHO protein shares 86% of its amino acids with the mouse protein. Variation in the KLOTHO gene has been associated with longevity and coronary heart disease in humans, but its association with cognitive aging has not been examined. Participants from the LBC1921 and the Aberdeen Birth Cohort 1936 (ABC1936) were examined. Between 461 and 464 LBC1921 participants had relevant data, depending on the analyses. In the ABC1936, the numbers in the analyses, based on the presence of appropriate data, ranged from 405 to 451. In the LBC1921, variation in KLOTHO was significantly associated with MHT IQ scores at age

11 (p = .028) and age 79 (p = .020) and with Raven's Standard Progressive Matrices at age 79 (p = .019). When age 11 IQ score was added as a covariable, the associations between *KLOTHO* and age 79 MHT IQ scores and Raven's Standard Progressive Matrices scores were no longer significant. When the MHT scores at age 11 and age 79 were treated as a repeated measure, the association with *KLOTHO* was significant at p = .011. In this analysis, *KLOTHO* variation accounted for about 2% of the variance in the lifelong stable trait of IQ.

There were some interesting developments in the *KLOTHO*–cognition association (Deary, Harris, et al., 2005). First, in the LBC1921 there was a *KLOTHO* Genotype × Sex interaction for MHT IQ scores and Raven's Standard Progressive Matrices at age 79. Women who were homozygous for the V allele of *KLOTHO* seemed especially characterized by low scores. Second, none of these significant main or interaction effects was replicated in the similarly sized ABC1936; there were no effects on the age 11 MHT IQ scores, or on Raven's Standard Progressive Matrices at age 79. The LBC1921 and ABC1936 participants took two tests in common: (a) the MHT at age 11 and (b) Raven's Standard Progressive Matrices at an older age. A joint analysis of both samples revealed a Sex × *KLOTHO* interaction on Raven's Matrices without (p = .030) and with (p = .019) age 11 IQ as a covariable. The interaction is shown in Figure 6.2. The clearest tendency is for women who are homozygous for the V allele of *KLOTHO* to score more poorly. The conclusions based on this report were cautious. First, even with both cohorts combined, there were only 12 women with the V/V genotype. Overall, these *KLOTHO* results might indicate that *KLOTHO* variation was associated with the lifelong trait of IQ, or that it was associated with cognitive aging in women, or that neither might be replicated in the future. Still, an association between *KLOTHO* and childhood IQ, if it were to be replicated, is not incompatible with KLOTHO's function as the spinner of the thread of life. As was described in Part II of this book, IQ in childhood is associated with longevity. One of the mechanisms by which KLOTHO might exert its effects on the body is via oxidative stress mechanisms, something we address in the next section.

Genes Related to Oxidative Stress: *Lactotransferrin* and *Prion Protein*

Genes related to oxidative stress were one of the systems that had been targeted as candidate contributors to cognitive aging (Deary, Wright, et al., 2004). Oxidation involved in aerobic respiration produces reactive oxygen species, free radicals that can damage macromolecules such as protein, DNA, and lipids (Hayflick, 2007). Aging is accompanied by an increase in the oxidative modification of such molecules. The brain's high rate of aerobic

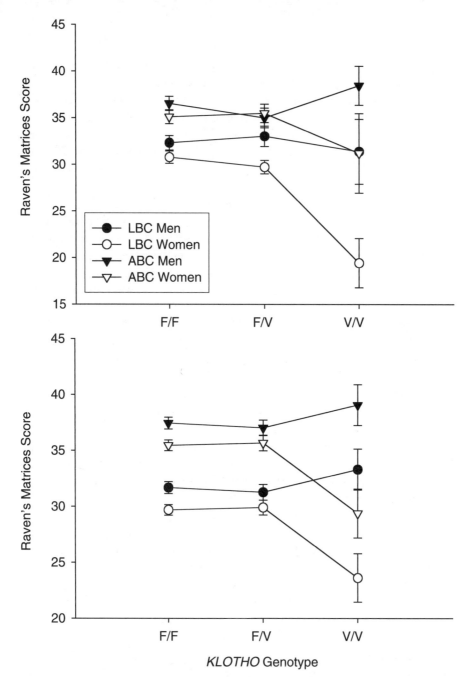

Figure 6.2. Score on Raven's Standard Progressive Matrices by *KLOTHO* genotype, sex, and cohort (age 64 for the Aberdeen Birth Cohort 1936 [ABC1936] or 79
for the Lothian Birth Cohort 1921 [LBC1921]). The top panel has raw data, and the
lower panel has estimated marginal means from a general linear model, adjusted for
Moray House Test scores at age 11. F = phenylolanine; V = valine. From "*KLOTHO*
Genotype and Cognitive Ability in Childhood and Old Age in the Same Individuals,"
by I. J. Deary, S. E. Harris, H. C. Fox, C. Hayward, A. F. Wright, J. M. Starr, and
L. J. Whalley, 2005, *Neuroscience Letters, 378,* p. 25. Copyright 2005 by Elsevier
Limited. Reprinted with permission.

respiration makes it susceptible to oxidative damage, and this has been implicated in neurodegenerative disease (Halliwell, 2006), including cognitive aging (Keller et al., 2005). At first, two genes for two oxidative stress-related proteins were examined with respect to cognition in the LBC1921: the genes coding for *lactotransferrin* (LTF) and *prion protein* (PRNP; Kachiwala et al., 2005). Thereafter, Harris et al. (2007) undertook a large, systematic study of 109 oxidative stress-related genes.

As iron accumulates in the body, so too does the catalysis of oxygen to reactive oxygen species, with an increase in oxidative stress. Such a process is thought to be involved in Parkinson's and Alzheimer's diseases. LTF, a glycoprotein, is a part of antioxidant defenses, because of its binding of iron. Two single nucleotide polymorphisms in *LTF* were examined in the LBC1921, one of which caused an amino acid change in LTF. Neither SNP was associated with cognitive ability, either at age 11 or at age 79 (Kachiwala et al., 2005).

PRNP is associated with oxidative defenses, by influencing the uptake of copper and acting as a superoxide dismutase. The gene for PRNP is on chromosome 20 in humans. A frequent SNP causes an amino acid change in the protein (valine [Val] substitutes for methionine [Met]), and this variation had been associated with cognitive function (Del Bo et al., 2006; Rujescu, Hartmann, Gonnermann, Moller, & Giegling, 2003). Variation in *PRNP* was associated significantly with MHT IQ scores at age 79 ($p = .0006$) but not with IQ scores on the same test at age 11, or on Logical Memory, Raven's Standard Progressive Matrices, or Verbal Fluency at age 79 (Kachiwala et al., 2005). People who were heterozygous (Met/Val) performed less well on the MHT at age 79 than those who were homozygous for either Met ($p = .025$) or Val ($p = .041$). As in previous genetic analyses, people with Mini-Mental State Examination scores less than 24 and those with a history of dementia were excluded. When age 11 IQ was included in the model along with sex, the *PRNP* genotype still had a significant ($p = .011$) effect on MHT scores at age 79. A further model was run that included *APOE* genotype also, and both *APOE* and *PRNP* contributed significantly to variance in MHT scores at age 79. The respective contributions were 1.7% ($p = .031$) and 1.2% ($p = .028$) of the variance. There was a suggestion of a *PRNP–KLOTHO* interaction, although cell sizes were small. Previous studies had shown that either the *PRNP* Val or Met homozygotes were associated with neural pathology. The strongest datum from this study was the cognitive advantage of being homozygous for Met ($n = 167$), although whether it is significantly better than the heterozygote and the Val homozygote ($n = 67$) probably has to do with power (see Figure 6.3). It is mechanistically possible that a Val substitution makes the protein less able to bind copper, which would allow more toxic iron to accumulate in the body. It is possible, too, that heterozygotes are protected against neurodegeneration.

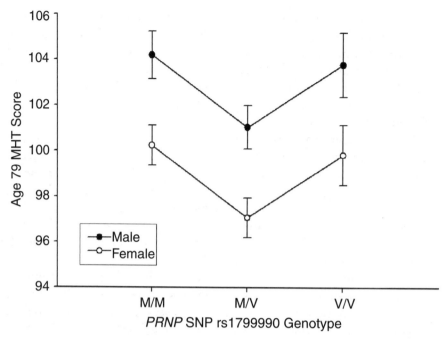

Figure 6.3. Moray House Test (MHT) IQ scores at age 79 by *prion protein* (*PRNP*) genotype and sex and cohort. These are estimated marginal means (standard errors) from a general linear model, adjusted for MHT scores at age 11. SNP = single-nucleotide polymorphism; M = methionine; V = valine. From "Genetic Influences on Oxidative Stress and Their Association With Normal Cognitive Ageing," by S. J. Kachiwala, S. E. Harris, A. F. Wright, C. Hayward, J. M. Starr, L. J. Whalley, and I. J. Deary, 2005, *Neuroscience Letters, 386,* p. 118. Copyright 2005 by Elsevier Limited. Reprinted with permission.

Genes Related to Cognition: *Disrupted in Schizophrenia 1, Catechol-O-Methyltransferase,* and *Brain-Derived Neurotrophic Factor*

The *disrupted in schizophrenia 1* gene (*DISC1*) was first identified in a family with schizophrenia, and changes in this gene are associated with the disease and with mood disorders (see Porteous, Thomson, Brandon, & Millar, 2006, for a review). The protein DISC1 interacts with other proteins involved in neural function. DISC1 is expressed in the hippocampus and other limbic brain areas. There was some suggestion that variation in *DISC1* was associated with cognitive ability in people with mental illnesses, but no study prior to the one performed with the LBC1921 had examined the gene's association with normal cognition (P. A. Thomson et al., 2005). A nonsynonymous SNP (in which cysteine replaces serine) in exon 11 was studied. There were no significant main effects of this *DISC1* variation on any of the cognitive tests (at ages 11 or 79) in the LBC1921. There was a significant ($p = .034$) Sex × Genotype interaction, whereby males and females differed considerably when they were homozygous for the cysteine allele on codon 704 (see Figure 6.4). This variant appears to be advantageous to older men ($n = 13$) but deleterious in older women ($n = 17$); however, numbers are small, and this result requires replication.

Variation in COMT, the gene coding for the protein *catechol-O-methyltransferase*(COMT), has been related to both cognitive and personality differences in humans (Harris et al., 2005; Savitz, Solms, & Ramesar, 2006). COMT is an enzyme that is involved in the breakdown of the neurotransmitter dopamine. The polymorphism found in humans that substitutes Met for Val at codon 158 results in a version of the enzyme that is less thermostable and has less activity. Therefore, those who have this change might have less power to degrade dopamine. Heterozygotes have COMT activity that lies between the two homozygotes. There was considerable interest in the cognitive effects of COMT variation in people with schizophrenia, with a focus on prefrontal cortex executive function. For example, there were indications that people homozygous for the low-activity Met allele made fewer errors of perseveration in the Wisconsin Card Sorting Test (Egan et al.,

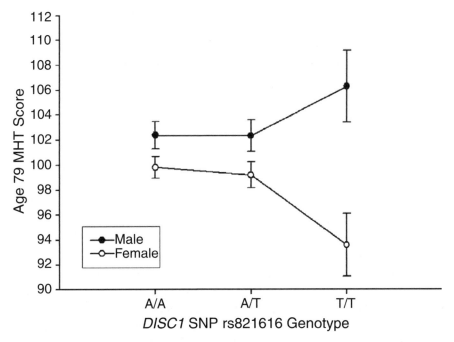

Figure 6.4. Estimated marginal means for scores on the Moray House Test (MHT) IQ at age 79 by the *disrupted in schizophrenia 1 (DISC1)* genotype and sex, adjusted for age 11 MHT scores. A = adenine nucleotide; T = thymine nucleotide; SNP = single-nucleotide polymorphism. From "Association Between Genotype at an Exonic SNP in *DISC1* and Normal Cognitive Aging," by P. A. Thomson, S. E. Harris, J. M. Starr, L. J. Whalley, D. J. Porteous, and I. J. Deary, 2005, *Neuroscience Letters, 389,* p. 43. Copyright 2005 by Elsevier Limited. Reprinted with permission.

2001). There were some studies of COMT variation and other aspects of cognition, but few consistent results. Similarly, there were some inconsistent reports of associations between COMT variation and personality traits (Harris et al., 2005). The LBC1921 was used to examine the association between the COMT Val158Met polymorphism and cognitive functions and personality traits. Cognitive functions were as described earlier. Personality traits were assessed using Goldberg's International Personality Item Pool (IPIP) 50-item questionnaire (see http://ipip.ori.org), which measures Extraversion, Agreeableness, Conscientiousness, Emotional Stability, and Intellect/Imagination (Gow, Whiteman, Pattie, & Deary, 2005a).

With the usual exclusion criteria (Mini-Mental State Examination score > 23, no history of dementia, appropriate data being available), there were 456 participants with relevant data for cognitive analyses. Numbers were smaller for the IPIP personality questionnaire but always greater than 382 (Harris et al., 2005). There was no significant effect of COMT on MHT IQ score at age 11. General linear modeling of cognitive test scores at age 79 was conducted, with sex and COMT genotype as fixed effects and age 11 IQ as a covariable. There was a significant effect of COMT genotype on Logical Memory ($p = .028$), but not on MHT, Raven's Standard Progressive Matrices, or Verbal Fluency. The Val/Met heteroygotes performed better than either of the homozygous groups: $p = .037$ versus the Val/Val group and $p = .024$ versus the Met/Met group (see Figure 6.5). There was a significant effect of COMT genotype on the personality trait of Intellect/Imagination ($p = .023$). Once more, the heterozygous group (Val/Met) scored higher on this trait than either of the homozygous groups: $p = .033$ versus the Val/Val group and $p = .021$ versus the Met/Met group (see Figure 6.5). There were trends toward an effect of COMT genotype on the personality traits of Agreeableness ($p = .094$) and Conscientiousness ($p = .070$). In all cases, there were higher scores in the heterozygous group, and the effect—though slightly less clear with Intellect/Imagination—was apparent in men and women (see Figure 6.5). Logical memory and Intellect/Imagination scores were correlated ($r = .20, p < .001$). Therefore, this was entered as a covariable, and the model with Logical Memory as an outcome variable was run again. The effect of COMT genotype remained significant. The model for Logical Memory was also rerun by entering, one at a time, genotypes for APOE, NCSTN, KLOTHO, angiotensin I converting enzyme (ACE), and 5,10-methylenetetrahydrofolate reductase (MTHFR). There were no significant interaction effects between COMT and any of these genes on Logical Memory.

There is a tenable mechanistic understanding of these results in this sample. Among the three COMT genotypic groups, members of the Met/Met group are liable to have the greatest dopamine signaling, and those in the Val/Val group are liable to have the least (Harris et al., 2005). Some other studies had indicated that the low-activity Met/Met group performed better

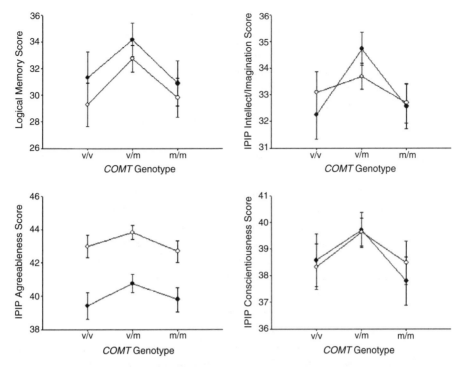

Figure 6.5. Catechol-O-methyltransferase (*COMT*) genotype versus scores (means and standard errors) on Logical Memory, International Personality Item Pool Intellect/Imagination, Agreeableness, and Conscientiousness. m = methionine; v = valine. From "The Functional *COMT* Polymorphism, Val158Met, Is Associated With Logical Memory and the Personality Trait Intellect/Imagination in a Cohort of Healthy 79-Year-Olds," by S. E. Harris, A. F. Wright, C. Hayward, J. M. Starr, L. J. Whalley, and I. J. Deary, 2005, *Neuroscience Letters, 385,* p. 4. Copyright 2005 by Elsevier Limited. Reprinted with permission.

on some cognitive tests. This was interpreted—together with evidence that there was a U-shaped function between dopamine signaling in the frontal areas and cognitive performance—as meaning that people with Met/Met were at an optimal level of dopamine signaling. The LBC1921 participants were considerably older than those in the other samples in studies of *COMT* and cognition. There is evidence that the D1 dopamine receptors—which predominate in the frontal lobes—decline with age and that, as a result, the optimal level of dopamine signaling reduces concurrently. We proposed that, in people about age 80, the Val/Met participants were now the ones who were on the optimal level of a curve in which there was a reduced level of dopamine signaling and prefrontal cortex function.

A further study on COMT variation and cognitive aging involved 473 participants of the ABC1936, of whom 125 were Val/Val, 247 were Val/Met, and 101 were Met/Met (Starr, Fox, Harris, Deary, & Whalley, 2007). Included participants had Mini-Mental State Examination scores higher than 23 and no history of dementia. In addition to MHT scores at age 11, there were cognitive data from three waves: at mean ages of (a) 64.6, (b) 66.7, and (c) 68.6 they took Raven's Standard Progressive Matrices, the Rey Auditory Verbal Learning Test, Digit Symbol, Block Design, and Uses of Common Objects. A mixed linear models approach was used to analyze the data. There were significant effects of wave of testing and a significant interaction between wave of testing and specific test type. The COMT Val158Met polymorphism had a significant overall effect on cognition ($p < .001$), with the Val/Val group being lower than the other two groups, which had similar cognitive ability levels. There was a significant interaction between COMT genotype and test type ($p = .027$), with the largest decrement in the Val/Val group being on the Digit Symbol test. This study extended upward the age at which the cognitive decrement in Val/Val participants had been identified. The difference in age between the ABC1936 and the LBC1921 might in part account for the difference in results, as discussed earlier; that is, we speculated that the shift of the inverted-U with regard to dopamine signaling might start in the 7th decade, although more human sample data were required to substantiate this.

The gene that codes for the *protein brain-derived neurotrophic factor* (BDNF) was reported as being related to memory functioning in humans (Egan et al., 2003; Savitz et al., 2006). BDNF is expressed widely throughout the brain. It is needed by some types of nerve cells for survival, differentiation, and maintenance (Harris, Fox, et al., 2006). The receptor for BDNF is *neurotrophic tyrosine kinase receptor, Type 2* (NTRK2, also known as *tyrosine kinase receptor B* [TRKB]). Both are highly expressed in the hippocampus and seem to be important in other species for learning and memory functions that are dependent on the hippocampus. Mice in whom the gene for BDNF has been rendered inactive have learning deficits, and the protein appears to be necessary for long-term potentiation, a physiological correlate of learning in the hippocampus. There has been little study of *BDNF* with respect to nonmemory cognitive functions, despite the fact that it is widely expressed in the brain. It is possible that BDNF might have a role in protecting against oxidative stress.

There is a functional polymorphism in the *BDNF* gene, a Met-to-Val substitution at codon 66. The Met allele had been associated in a few studies with poorer memory test function (the *n*-back test of working memory, and in declarative memory tests) and with poorer hippocampal function (see Harris, Fox, et al., 2006). Overall, though, the results across studies were not clear. In addition, it was uncertain whether the Val allele was associated with dementia risk, by contrast with the results in people without dementia in whom the Met allele appeared to be the "risky" allele. In addition to attempting to replicate the association between *BDNF* polymorphism and memory function, it was important to broaden the examination to other cognitive functions.

The BDNF study was performed on a combined sample of the LBC1921 and the ABC1936 (Harris, Fox, et al., 2006). The mental test that both cohorts shared was Raven's Standard Progressive Matrices, and this was the first focus of the study. In both samples, participants were included if they had MHT scores at age 11, Raven's Standard Progressive Matrices scores in old age, a Mini-Mental State Examination score of 24 or greater, and successful genotyping for the *BDNF* Val66Met polymorphism. This yielded 471 participants in the LBC1921 and 433 in the ABC1936, a total sample size of 904. First, it was established that *BDNF* variation was not associated with MHT scores at age 11. Thereafter, that childhood mental test score was used as a covariable in models of cognitive function in old age. The main results of the general linear model of Raven's Standard Progressive Matrices scores are shown in Figure 6.6. The upper panel shows the raw data. The lower panel shows the estimated marginal means from the general linear model, with age 11 MHT score as a covariable. There are three principal findings. First, men scored higher than women in both cohorts ($p < .001$), especially after adjustment for childhood IQ, suggesting, as we discussed earlier, that males in these samples show a small advantage in cognitive aging. Second, the 65-year-old ABC1936 cohort scored better than the 79-year-old LBC1921 ($p < .001$). Again, this is after adjustment for MHT score at age 11 and suggests a real effect of the age difference that accounted for about 13% of the variance in Raven's Standard Progressive Matrices scores. Third, there was a significant effect of *BDNF* genotype on Raven's Standard Progressive Matrices scores ($p = .001$), accounting for 1.5% of the variance. The Met/Met homozygotes scored better than both the Val/Val group and the Val/Met group ($p \leq .001$). Readers should bear in mind, though, that there were only 35 people out of the entire 904 who were Met/Met.

In the LBC1921 sample alone, the *BDNF* genotype was significantly associated with MHT scores ($p = .016$, $\eta^2 = .018$) at age 79, but not with Logical Memory or Verbal Fluency (Harris, Fox, et al., 2006). Again, individuals with the Met/Met homozygote scored better than both the Val/Val ($p = .004$) and Val/Met groups ($p = .012$). An examination was made specifically of the association between *BDNF* genotype and Logical Memory delay scores because a significant association had been reported in a previous study (Egan et al., 2003) but not replicated.

The study appeared to be the first report of variation in *BDNF* being associated with a domain of cognitive function outside memory. It also was the first to examine cognitive aging, by adjusting for a valid measure of cognitive ability from youth; that is, the Met/Met genotype was associated with the preservation of ability from youth to old age, irrespective of the starting level. It is possible that these results are congruent with the suggestion that the Val allele of *BDNF* is a risk factor for dementia, but that association is not certain.

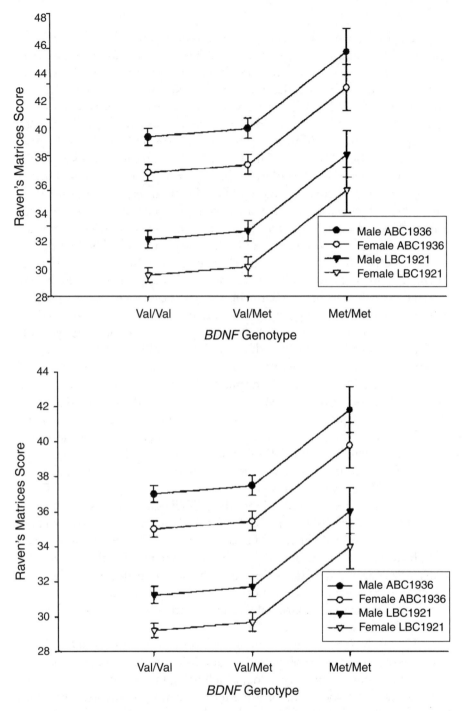

Figure 6.6. Scores on Raven's Standard Progressive Matrices by *brain-derived neurotrophic factor* (*BDNF*) genotype, sex, and cohort (the Aberdeen Birth Cohort 1936 [ABC1936] and the Lothian Birth Cohort 1921 [LBC1921]). The top panel shows raw data (means and standard errors), and the bottom panel shows estimated marginal means from a general linear model, adjusted for age 11 scores on the Moray House Test. Val = valine; Met = methionine. From "The Brain-Derived Neurotrophic Factor Val66Met Polymorphism Is Associated With Age-Related Change in Reasoning Skills," by S. E. Harris, H. Fox, A. F. Wright, C. Hayward, J. M. Starr, L. J. Whalley, and I. J. Deary, 2006, *Molecular Psychiatry, 11,* p. 509. Copyright 2006 by Nature Publishing Group. Reprinted with permission.

Candidate Genes Associated With Oxidative Stress, Longevity, Cognitive Function, Alzheimer's Genes, Stress Response, and Mitochondrial Complex 1

The genetic studies we have just described were conducted by targeting variations in individual genes for which a rationale could be made with respect to their association with cognitive ability or cognitive aging. A more general approach was taken in a study that examined 325 SNPs in 109 genes (Harris et al., 2007). Instead of following up possible cognitive associations in individual genes, we decided to target brain-expressed genes linked with more general processes. A bioinformatics search process was undertaken, and it identified 141 genes: 64 antioxidant defense genes, 14 vitagenes (longevity assurance processes-chaperones), 4 genes associated with cognitive function, 6 genes associated with Alzheimer's disease, 19 stress response genes altered in aged mouse brains, and 34 nuclear genes encoding mitochondria complex 1 proteins. Of 14,033 potential SNPs, 384 were selected for genotyping. Successful genotyping was obtained for 325 nonmonomorphic SNPs in 424 to 434 of the LBC1921 participants.

Nine SNPs were associated significantly ($p < .01$) with cognitive ability test scores in the LBC1921 (Harris et al., 2007). Three had significant associations with MHT score at age 11, and six had significant associations with cognitive test scores at age 79, adjusted for MHT score at age 11. None of these replicated (criterion: $p < .01$) with cognitive test scores in 485 participants of the ABC1936, which was used as a replication sample. Bigger samples have more power. Therefore, the LBC1921 and the ABC1936 samples were combined to examine SNPs that had shown an association with age 79 cognitive test scores in the LBC1921. The one test they had in common in old age was Raven's Standard Progressive Matrices. This yielded sample sizes of between 858 and 886, which meant that an effect size of just 2% could be detected with > 80% power and alpha set at .01. The general linear model included sex and cohort as fixed effects and MHT score at age 11 as a covariate. One SNP—rs28301202 in the gene for *amyloid beta precursor protein* (APP)—was associated significantly ($p = .003$, $\eta^2 = .014$) with Raven's Standard Progressive Matrices scores in the combined sample. G/G homozygotes scored lower than the other two genotype groups. It was emphasized that this SNP did not have a significant association in both samples on their own and that the result required replicating.

Mutations in *APP* have been associated with increased risk for Alzheimer's disease. It is possible that the normal variation in *APP* is associated with variation in oxidative stress. Among the many nonsignificant SNPs Harris et al. (2007) tested were some that had been related to cognitive functions in other studies. As such, the study made a valuable contribution toward obtaining a consensus on such phenotype–genotype associations.

Null Results 1: Genetic Variation in *ACE, MTHFR, HSD11B1, CETP, ASPM, MCPH1,* and *RIMS1*

There were good reasons, from prior research, for hypothesizing that polymorphisms in genes coding for ACE, MTHFR, *11B-hydroxysteroid dehydrogenase type 1* (HSD11B1), and *cholesteryl ester transfer protein* (CETP) would be associated with cognitive change across the life span. In studies with members of the LBC1921, none of them was (Deary, Hayward, et al., 2006; Johnson et al., 2007; Visscher et al., 2003).

There were good reasons to hypothesize that variations in the genes *abnormal spindle-like microcephaly-associated* (ASPM) and *microcephalin* (MCPH1) would be associated with human cognitive ability differences. Mutations in both are associated with primary micropcephaly, which is a developmental disorder in which the brain is abnormally small and intelligence is low. These genes also show signatures of adaptive evolution in the lineage leading to humans, and they have continued to evolve adaptively since the emergence of anatomically modern humans. Nevertheless, in an international collaborative study, which included participants in the LBC1921, the ABC1936, and Dutch and Australian samples, there was no significant association between the adaptive alleles of the *ASPM* and *MCPH1* genes and measures of intelligence (Mekel-Bobrov et al., 2007). Mutation in the gene *RIMS1* was associated with visual disturbance and cognitive enhancement in a kindred, but variation in the gene was not associated significantly with cognition in the LBC1921 (Sisodiya et al., 2007).

Null Results 2: Length of Telomeres

There were also good reasons for hypothesizing that the lengths of the *telomeres*—the nucleo-protein complexes at the ends of chromosomes—would be associated with cognitive aging. This was not the case, and in the LBC1921 telomere length was also not associated with general physical health and mortality (Harris, Deary, et al., 2006). However, among the LBC1921 participants, those with ischemic heart disease, but not those with conduction defects in the heart, had significantly shorter telomeres (Starr, McGurn, et al., 2007).

BRAIN STRUCTURE

Brains change as we grow older (Raz & Rodrique, 2006). Common parlance is to refer to the gray matter as the "thinking stuff" in the brain. It contains the nerve cell bodies, and it does shrink as people grow older. However, the brain contains white matter—the connections between the nerve cells with their insulating and supporting structures—as well. It appears more white because of the fatty myelin sheath that surrounds axons, affording faster transmission along the lengths of these "communicating-wire" nerve cell outgrowths.

White Matter Hyperintensities (or Lesions, or Abnormalities)

The examination of the brains of people of different ages with magnetic resonance imaging has revealed new information about white matter changes. Within the white matter there are, as people grew older, increasing amounts of *white matter hyperintensities*. They are called this because they appear hyperintense—very white—on T2-weighted magnetic resonance imaging. Over the years, such changes in the white matter have been noted and given a variety of other names, such as *leukoariosis, white matter abnormalities*, and *white matter lesions*. It is thought that their origin is in vascular changes and that they are scarlike presences in previously normal white matter. The functional implication is that they are interruptions in the white matter, the bundles of fibers connecting different parts of the brain. It was thought possible that the origins of the white matter changes was different in different brain regions. Whereas the origin of those hyperintensities in the subcortical and deep white matter might be vascular, the changes that surround the ventricles—*periventricular changes*—might arise from problems with the ependyma (Leaper et al., 2001).

It is well recognized that white matter hyperintensities appear in the brains of people without overt symptoms of any disease. However, there did appear to be associations between the burden of white matter lesions and cognitive test scores, especially for processing speed, memory, executive function, and global cognitive functioning (Gunning-Dixon & Raz, 2000). In vivo examination of the brains of people in the follow-up studies of the SMS had two advantages. First, it could add to the relatively limited amount of information on the association between cognitive functions and brain white matter hyperintensities. Second, it could address the issue of reverse causation. It is often assumed that the accumulation of these white matter changes causes a lowering of cognitive function, but causality might be in the opposite direction. Lower prior cognitive ability might, for example, influence lifestyle choices, including diet or disease management, and thereby cause the accumulation of white matter hyperintensities. Also, because cognitive ability differences are stable across decades, the correlation between white matter hyperintensities and cognitive ability in old age might in fact be a continuation of any association between white matter hyperintensities and cognitive ability in youth.

The first group to be examined were members of the ABC1921 (Leaper et al., 2001). From their total number, 131 were asked to take part in a magnetic resonance brain imaging study. Medical problems prevented 17 from taking part, and 21 refused, leaving 95 (58 men) who agreed to brain imaging. Images were obtained in the transverse plane on a 1.0-Tesla unit, with a T2-weighted fast spin-echo sequence. Visual inspection of these images was conducted, and the white matter hyperintensity load was rated using the scale devised by Fazekas. This scale rates the severity of the hyperintensities separately in the subcortical/deep white matter and in the periventricular areas. The scale ranges from 0 to 3 (see Figure 6.7). For subcortical/deep lesions the scale is as follows: Zero is normal; 1 records the presence of punctate lesions; 2 indicates larger, coalescing lesions; and a 3 is recorded when the lesions are in confluent areas. There is a similar scale of increasing severity for periventricular lesions. Both interrater (three raters) and intrarater (for one rater) reliability of the Fazekas scale ratings were checked. Intrarater reliability was .85, and interrater reliability was, on average, above .70.

The results were first clear in ruling out reverse causation (Leaper et al., 2001). The correlations between the white matter hyperintensity load in both the subcortical/deep white matter and in the periventricular areas and childhood mental test scores from the SMS1932 and the National Adult Reading Test (Nelson & Willison, 1991) were close to zero (see Table 6.2). Therefore, both actual and estimated prior mental ability had no significant associations with the quantity of white matter lesions. All four tests of current cognitive ability had significant correlations with deep/subcortical white matter lesions, with a relatively narrow range between −.24 and −.33 (see

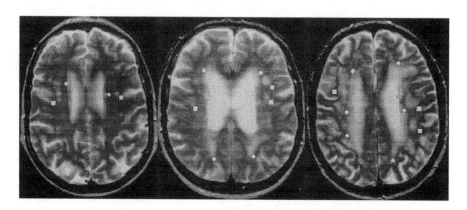

Figure 6.7. All three images are transverse T2-weighted fast spin-echo magnetic resonance images. Small squares indicate subcortical/deep white matter lesions. Small circles indicate periventricular lesions; from left to right: Grade 1 lesions, Grade 2 lesions, Grade 3 lesions. From "Neuropsychologic Correlates of Brain White Matter Lesions Depicted on MR Images: 1921 Aberdeen Birth Cohort," by S. A. Leaper, A. D. Murray, H. A. Lemmon, R. T. Staff, I. J. Deary, J. R. Crawford, and L. J. Whalley, 2001, *Radiology, 221,* p. 52. Copyright 2001 by the Radiology Society of North America. Reprinted with permission.

TABLE 6.2
Pearson Correlations Between Fazekas White Matter Lesion Ratings and Mental Test Scores

Test	Deep/subcortical white matter lesions		Periventricular white matter lesions	
	r	N	r	N
Moray House Test score from SMS1932	.08	95	.11	95
National Adult Reading Test	−.02	95	−.003	95
Raven's Standard Progressive Matrices	−.33**	95	−.26*	95
Digit Symbol	−.24*	85	−.19	85
Block Design	−.25*	80	−.16	80
Uses for Common Objects	−.28**	86	−.18	86

Note. SMS1932 = Scottish Mental Survey of 1932. From "Neuropsychologic Correlates of Brain White Matter Lesions Depicted on MR Images: 1921 Aberdeen Birth Cohort," by S. A. Leaper, A. D. Murray, H. A. Lemmon, R. T. Staff, I. J. Deary, J. R. Crawford, and L. J. Whalley, 2001, *Radiology, 221*, p. 54. Copyright 2001 by the Radiological Society of North America. Reprinted with permission.
*$p < .05$. **$p < .01$.

Table 6.2). In all cases, people with more white matter lesions in these areas had poorer scores in tests covering nonverbal reasoning, processing speed, constructional ability, and executive function. The correlations between cognitive test scores and lesion load in the periventricular areas were nonsignificant, except for that with Raven's Standard Progressive Matrices. However, in terms of effect size, the correlations were not very different and were all in the expected direction.

The principal contribution of this study was the suggestion that the accumulation of lesions in the white matter might contribute to individual differences in cognitive ability in old age that are independent of cognitive ability in youth. The same ABC1921 brain imaging data, and the same and some additional cognitive data, were analyzed further to address the extent to which white matter lesions contributed to general mental ability versus specific abilities, and the role of hypertension in this association (Deary, Leaper, et al., 2003). For these analyses there were 83 people with relevant data, and they were 78 years old. All scored 24 or better on the Mini-Mental State Examination. There was a detailed description of their medical status, the most relevant including that 40 had a diagnosis of hypertension, of whom 39 were taking antihypertensive medication. Analyses were conducted separately with the subcortical/deep white matter lesions and the periventricular lesions. Also, these two types of white matter hyperintensities were summed to give a total white matter lesions score. Similar findings were found in all three sets of analyses and, therefore, only the analyses with total white matter lesion scores are given here.

The well-fitting model is shown in Figure 6.8 (for more details and more models, see Deary, Leaper, et al., 2003, Figure 2). Total white matter lesion

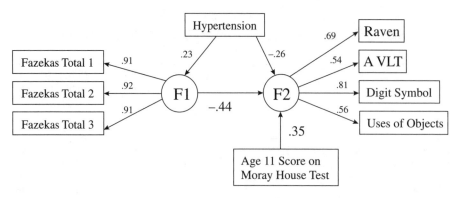

Figure 6.8. Structural equation model of the contributions to cognitive ability in old age from mental ability test scores at age 11, hypertension, and Fazekas total scores for white matter hyperintensities. The numbers on the paths between adjacent variables may be squared to find the percentage of variance contributed by these immediate associations. The fit information for this model is as follows: average of the off-diagonal standardized residuals = .067; χ^2 = 41.5, *df* = 25, *p* = .02; comparative fit index = .948. AVLT = Auditory Verbal Learning Test; F1 = Fazekas score latent trait; F2 = cognitive ability latent trait. Reprinted from "Cerebral White Matter Abnormalities and Lifetime Cognitive Change: A 67-Year Follow-Up of the Scottish Mental Survey of 1932," by I. J. Deary, S. A. Leaper, A. D. Murray, R. T. Staff, and L. J. Whalley, 2003, *Psychology and Aging, 18,* p. 146. Copyright 2003 by the American Psychological Association.

load (deep/subcortical and periventricular scores added together) was rated by three separate individuals. In the model, their scores are used as three indicators of a latent trait of white matter lesion load. All three load very highly on the latent trait. Current cognitive abilities were assessed using four mental tests: (a) Raven's Standard Progressive Matrices, (b) the Rey Auditory Verbal Learning Test, (c) Digit Symbol, and (d) Uses for Common Objects. Correlations among these mental tests' scores ranged from .277 to .538, with *p* values almost .01 or lower than .01. Therefore, the model contained a general cognitive factor on which all tests had high loadings. In the model, hypertension contributed significantly to white matter lesion load. There are three contributors to cognitive function at age 78. The first is MHT score at age 11. The second and third contributions are independent of this; that is, childhood mental ability did not influence, in this sample, either white matter lesion load or hypertension. The second contribution is from the total white matter lesion load. It is larger, in this sample and with these cognitive ability tests, than the contribution from childhood IQ. The third contribution is from hypertension, which is partly direct and partly mediated via white matter lesion load.

Further models were tested that included additional pathways from the Fazekas total white matter lesion load to the individual cognitive tests (Deary, Leaper, et al., 2003). None of these was significant, which suggests that, in this sample, the contribution of white matter lesions was to general cognitive ability in old age, adjusted for prior ability. To date, white matter lesions remain the largest single contributor to lifelong cognitive change that has been identified in the follow-up studies of the SMSs. In the models that did not include hypertension, white matter lesions contributed approximately 14% of the variance in cognition in old age, all of which was independent of prior ability and some of which was related to hypertension. This encourages more research on the etiology of white matter hyperintensities, which will be relevant to what contributes to differential cognitive aging.

White Matter Disconnection

One contribution that white matter lesions are thought to make to cognitive decline is via a *cortical disconnection syndrome*; that is, the aging of cognitive functions might in part be accounted for by deterioration in the white matter tracts in the cortex, such that areas become less well connected. Such changes in aging human brains and their possible associations have been recognized for some time, with the possibility that white matter deterioration in the anterior regions of the cortex might be especially important (O'Sullivan et al., 2001; Tang, Nyengaard, Pakkenberg, & Gundersen, 1997). White matter hyperintensities, as seen in T2-weighted magnetic resonance imaging, are likely to offer only a crude estimate of the degree of white matter disconnection. The capability of measuring white matter integrity in vivo increased enormously with the availability of diffusion tensor magnetic resonance imaging. The basic principle of this technique is that it assesses the directional flow of water in whatever tissue is being imaged (Shenkin et al., 2003). If the diffusion is unconstrained, as a drop of ink would be in a bucket of water, then the diffusion occurs equally in all directions and is called *isotropic*. However, if diffusion is constrained, as a drop of ink would be along a bundle of water-filled drinking straws, then the flow is called *anisotropic*, and it tends to be more linear. In the brain, the presence of densely packed axons and myelin constrains water flow to be more anisotropic in the white matter. Diffusion tensor magnetic resonance brain imaging offers two parameters thought to relate to the integrity of the white matter. *Mean diffusivity* denotes the magnitude of water molecule diffusion. *Fractional anisotropy* gives an index of the degree to which water diffusion deviates from isotropic diffusion. The further it deviates, the closer to 1 it is in a 0-to-1 scale, the more linear is the diffusion. Diffusivity is greater in older brains, and associated with age among older people, and fractional anisotropy is lower—flow is less linear—in older people (O'Sullivan et al., 2001). Also, given that fractional anisotropy is related to age and possible indicators of the integrity of brain connectivity—surely important for complex thinking—then perhaps these magnetic resonance indices would be related to cognitive ability. Some evidence for this was found with respect to executive function in a small sample of older people (O'Sullivan et al., 2001).

Following up on these possibilities, a small number of the LBC1921 took part in a diffusion tensor magnetic resonance imaging study (Shenkin et al., 2003). The novel aspects of the study in this context were the examination of some cognitive functions beyond executive function and the availability of childhood IQ. The latter is important because it could not, at that stage, be ruled out that diffusivity and fractional anisotropy of the white matter in old age related to cognitive functions could be a result of cognitive function differences in youth leading to brain changes in old age, that is, reverse causality.

Thirty members of the LBC1921, with a mean age of 80 years, took part (Shenkin et al., 2003). Mental tests were as described earlier for this sample. Their brains were imaged using a GE Signa LX 1.5 Tesla scanner. Each participant undertook axial T1-weighted spin-echo, T2-weighted fast spin-echo, and fast fluid-attenuated inversion recovery spin-echo imaging. They also undertook a diffusion tensor protocol. The diffusivity and fractional anisotropy values were calculated from regions of normal-appearing white matter. These were decided on the basis of T2-weighted images (see Figure 6.9 for examples of placement of regions of interest). Frontal and occipital periventricular white matter was examined, as was the centrum semiovale. The centrum semiovale is an especially useful region in which to assess white matter integrity, because it is a great mass of white matter with bundles running in parallel. The person choosing the regions of interest was unaware of the participants' cognitive test scores. Three of the 30 participants had missing data.

There were 30 correlations between diffusion tensor parameters and cognitive functions computed in this analysis (Shenkin et al., 2003). There were six diffusion tensor parameters: diffusivity and fractional anisotropy in the frontal area, the occipital area, and the centrum semiovale. There were five cognitive ability tests: the MHT at ages 11 and 80, and, at age 80, the National Adult Reading Test, the Mini-Mental State Examination, and Verbal Fluency. Five correlations (all Spearman's rho) were significant at $p < .05$. All were in a direction whereby higher mental test scores were associated with white matter of greater integrity. MHT scores at age 80 correlated .50 ($p = .01$) with fractional anisotropy in the frontal white matter. The four remaining significant correlations were in the centrum semiovale. Mini-Mental State Examination scores correlated $-.41$ ($p = .03$) with diffusivity in the centrum semiovale. MHT scores at age 80 correlated $-.41$ ($p = .03$) with diffusivity in the centrum semiovale. Therefore, there was some evidence that greater white matter integrity, especially in the centrum semiovale, was associated with better cognitive function in old age. The remaining two significant correlations provided a surprise. MHT scores at age 11 (childhood IQ) and National Adult Reading Test Scores at age 80 (estimated prior mental ability)

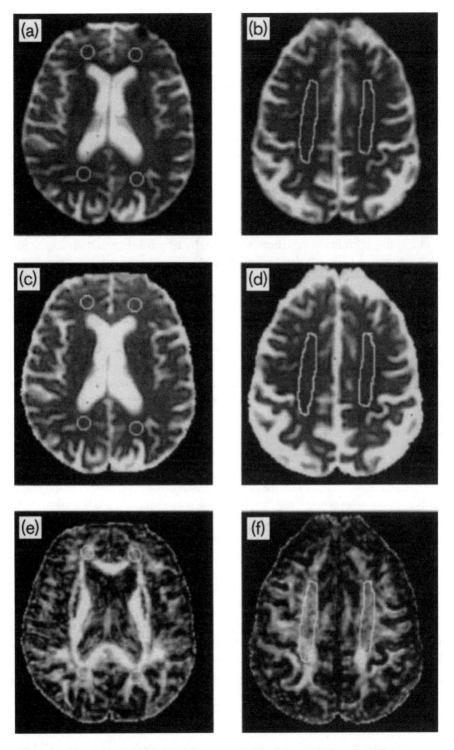

Figure 6.9. Illustration of diffusion tensor magnetic resonance imaging. These images show the typical location of regions of interest on the T2-weighted single-shot spin-echo echoplanar images and are used to measure mean diffusivity and fractional anisotropy in normal-appearing frontal and occipital periventricular white matter and centrum semiovale. (a) and (b) = maps of T2-wieghted signal intensity; (c) and (d) = maps of mean diffusivity; (e) and (f) = maps of fractional anisotropy. From "Childhood and Current Cognitive Function in Healthy 80-Year-Olds: A DT–MRI Study," by S. D. Shenkin, M. E. Bastin, T. J. MacGillivray, I. J. Deary, J. M. Starr, and J. M. Wardlaw, 2003, *NeuroReport, 14,* p. 347. Copyright 2003 by Lippincott Williams & Wilkins. Reprinted with permission.

correlated .42 ($p = .03$) and .46 ($p = .01$), respectively, with fractional anisotropy in the centrum semiovale.

Given the theoretical basis of anisotropic flow in the brain, it is likely that aging-related loss of small myelinated white matter fibers would lead to greater diffusivity and lower fractional anisotropy. These changes are likely to lower the efficiency of processing in a parallel distributed system (Mesulam, 1990). The region-of-interest approach to measurement, which was adopted in the LBC1921 study, is rather crude; it is not known how much of the white matter within the regions contains functionally important tracts. Although the study had replicated the cross-sectional association between diffusion tensor parameters (proxies, it is thought, for white matter integrity) and cognitive functioning, there was also the new finding that childhood IQ and estimated prior ability had significant associations with white matter integrity in old age (Shenkin et al., 2003). This might point to some causal process whereby cognitive differences precede lifestyle or other changes that in turn influence white matter state later in life. Therefore, the results point to a need to examine the developmental influences on brain white matter integrity. Compared with other studies, the narrow range of ages in the LBC1921 meant that any associations were not confounded with chronological age; there was variation in white matter integrity even within these people of very similar ages. The small number of participants and the large number of correlations performed mean that the interpretation of the results should be done cautiously. Nevertheless, they did point, especially, to the integrity of the white matter in centrum semiovale and its possible association with cognition, past and present.

The contribution of white matter integrity to the process of normal cognitive aging was considered further in a subsequent study involving the LBC1921 (Deary, Bastin, et al., 2006). The participants in this study, with the exception of 1, were different from those in Shenkin et al.'s (2003) study. The thesis was constructed as follows. The aging of mental domains takes place in concert, to some degree; as one mental capability declines, others tend to do so, too (Salthouse & Ferrer-Caja, 2003). This shared or general aspect of cognitive aging is perhaps substantially accounted for by the aging of some general speed of processing (Salthouse, 1996). Although such findings were strong at the psychological and statistical levels, there was a lack of a biological account of processing speed and its contribution to cognitive aging (Salthouse, 2000). This explanatory gap might be filled with the notions that efficiency of fundamental information-processing speed, underlying the efficiency of more complex thinking, is supported by intact networks of white matter in the brain (Bartzokis, 2004; Tisserand & Jolles, 2003). The new magnetic resonance imaging study of a subsample of the LBC1921 was undertaken with the addition of information-processing measures as mediating constructs between white matter integrity and cognition in old age. In summary, the hypothesis tested was that, after adjusting for cognitive ability at age 11, white matter integrity would be associated with more efficient information processing, which would in turn be associated with better cognitive function.

The study referred to here was a second wave of testing within old age for the LBC1921 (Deary, Bastin, et al., 2006). It took place during 2004, when the participants were a mean age of 83 years. Seventy-one were asked to take part in a magnetic resonance imaging examination. Eventually, 43 of these participants were imaged, and 40 had usable imaging data. The cognitive tests they took were the same as those for the LBC1921 examination that took place at age 79, with the addition of two extra tests. The Wechsler Digit Symbol (said to assess processing speed) and Letter–Number Sequencing (said to assess working memory) tests were added (Wechsler, 1997). Also added at this wave of testing were tests of simple and choice reaction time. Reaction time tests differ from standard psychometric tests. They require just a speeded response to a "go" signal. Therefore, they were viewed as possible intermediate phenotypes or *endophenotypes*—representing speed of information processing—between white matter integrity and higher level, more complex cognitive functioning. The means and the standard deviations of the simple and choice reaction time tasks were gathered. Both the central tendency (mean) and the inconsistency (standard deviation) of reaction time appear to be important in cognitive aging (Der & Deary, 2006). Diffusion tensor magnetic resonance brain imaging was performed using a region-of-interest approach to obtain measures of diffusivity and fractional anisotropy (putative indices of white matter integrity).

The results replicated some of Shenkin et al.'s (2003) key findings. Most of the significant associations between white matter integrity and cognitive test scores were again found within the centrum semiovale (Deary, Bastin, et al., 2006). Within that area there were significant associations with both diffusivity and fractional anisotropy. However, for purposes of brevity, we recount only the latter here. There were, in agreement with Shenkin et al., significant associations (Pearson's r) between fractional anisotropy in the centrum semiovale and MHT scores at age 11 ($r = .37$, $p < .05$) and contemporaneous National Adult Reading Test scores at age 83 ($r = .42$, $p < .01$). Once again, then, there was this interesting association between prior ability and white matter integrity. Significant associations between fractional anisotropy in the centrum semiovale and psychometric and information-processing test scores at age 83 were as follows (all are $p < .01$ unless indicated): Raven's Standard Progressive Matrices ($r = .38$, $p < .05$), Letter–Number Sequencing ($r = .41$), Verbal Fluency ($r = .56$), Digit Symbol ($r = .36$, $p < .05$), simple reaction time mean ($r = -.45$), simple reaction time standard deviation ($r = -.52$), and choice reaction time mean ($r = -.40$). Note the negative sign between fractional anisotropy and reaction time parameters: Greater integrity of white matter goes with faster and more consistent information processing. There were no significant associations between fractional anisotropy in the centrum semiovale and scores on Logical Memory or on simple reaction time standard deviation.

The five psychometric test scores from age 83 (Raven's Standard Progressive Matrices, Letter–Number Sequencing, Logical Memory, Verbal Fluency, and Digit Symbol) were subjected to principal components analysis (Deary, Bastin, et al., 2006). This suggested that a single component accounted for over 60% of the total test score variance. Therefore, scores on the general cognitive component (the first unrotated principal component) were saved for each participant. This general cognitive component correlated significantly ($r = .49, p < .01$) with fractional anisotropy in the centrum semiovale. Therefore, the following component parts were available to test the processing speed hypothesis of cognitive aging: childhood IQ, white matter integrity, efficiency of information processing, and general cognitive function at age 83.

The hypothesis was set out as a path analysis, which was tested for goodness of fit using the EQS structural equation modeling program (see Figure 6.10). The numbers of participants available for this analysis were very small, and so it may be considered only a pilot study. The three key constructs are (a) white matter integrity (centrum semiovale fractional anisotropy), (b) information-processing efficiency (here indexed by simple reaction time standard deviation, for the pragmatic reason that it had the highest association with white matter integrity), (c) and general mental ability in old age. The influence of white matter integrity on general cognitive ability is hypothesized to be mediated through information-processing

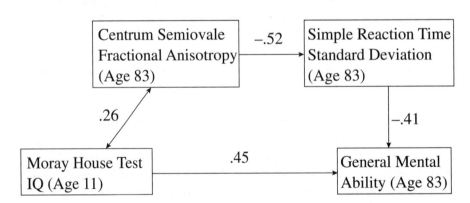

Figure 6.10. Path diagram showing possible influences among childhood and old age cognitive ability, efficiency of information processing (simple reaction time standard deviation), and integrity of white matter as assessed by fractional anisotropy in the centrum semiovale. From "White Matter Integrity and Cognition in Childhood and Old Age," by I. J. Deary, M. E. Bastin, A. Pattie, J. D. Clayden, L. J. Whalley, J. M. Starr, and J. M. Wardlaw, 2006, *Neurology, 66,* p. 509. Copyright 2006 by Lippincott Williams & Wilkins. Reprinted with permission.

efficiency. An additional important aspect of the model is that the contribution of white matter integrity, through information processing, adds information to cognitive ability in old age that is independent of cognitive ability in youth. The fit information for the model in Figure 6.10 is as follows: average of the off-diagonal standardized residuals = .037; $\chi^2 = 1.61$, $p = .45$; comparative fit index = 1.00. This well-fitting model indicates that two contributions to cognitive ability differences at age 83 in this sample are (a) childhood IQ and (b) white matter integrity, with the influence of the latter acting through efficiency of fundamental information processing. In addition, there is a significant association between childhood IQ and white matter integrity at age 83.

This study provided further evidence for the importance of intact white-matter-based networks for preserved cognitive function in old age (Deary, Bastin, et al., 2006). The data also confirm an association between white matter integrity and executive function (O'Sullivan et al., 2001) and suggest that there are also significant associations with other cognitive domains (although not verbal declarative memory): general cognitive ability and efficiency of information processing. The data warrant further investigation into why people with higher childhood intelligence have perennially more intact white matter integrity. All of these conclusions and suggestions must be accepted with the strong caution that the numbers of participants in the study are very modest. The reason for the most consistent significant associations occurring in the centrum semiovale was, perhaps, that this region had fibers oriented most homogeneously, with most of them traveling in an inferior–superior direction. Also, there tend to be more white matter lesions in the frontal lobes. Therefore, although all regions of interest were selected for their being normal-appearing white matter, this might most correctly have been accomplished in the centrum semiovale.

White Matter Effects on Mood, Balance, and Walking Speed

There have been reports of people with more white matter lesions tending to have more depressed mood, worse balance, and slower gait time (i.e., walking speed; Starr et al., 2003). It was possible that the physical problems of gait and balance might be mediated by cognitive and mood disturbances. Alternatively, it was possible that all of these brain-related functions declined because of some common cause, related to white matter deterioration. To test these ideas, the ABC1921 sample was examined; specifically, the subsample of 97 participants who took part in a brain magnetic resonance imaging examination. In addition to the cognitive and mood tests and walk time described earlier, they were tested for the ability to balance on one leg. The data on white matter hyperintensities (the Fazekas scale) in the deep/subcortical and periventricular white matter were used here. These were extended to obtain

Fazekas scores in the brainstem, an area of the brain more relevant to coordinated movements (see Figure 6.11).

People's gait time (walking speed) was associated significantly ($p = .009$) with brainstem white matter lesions but not with those in deep/subcortical or periventricular areas (Starr et al., 2003). The ability to balance was significantly associated with white matter lesions in all three regions ($ps = .003, .003,$ and $.038$, respectively). In all cases, having more white matter lesions was associated with poorer function. People with less good balance had slower gait times ($p < .001$), poorer scores on Raven's Standard Progressive Matrices ($p = .042$), and tended to have higher depression scores ($p = .051$). This interesting web of associations was modeled using a confirmatory factor analysis structure within the EQS structural equations modeling program. The variables included in the model and its structure are shown in Figure 6.12. The fit information for the model in Figure 6.12 is as follows: average of the off-diagonal standardized residuals = .04; $\chi^2 = 11.0$, $df = 10$, $p = .36$; comparative fit index = .99. The measured amounts of white matter lesions in the three different areas of the brain were conceptualized as a latent trait of brain white matter lesion load. The motor, cognitive, and mood tests were modeled as a latent trait of higher brain functions, all of which were known to be affected adversely by white matter lesions. Confirmation of these latent traits' validities was the relatively strong loadings of the measured variables on them. The deep/subcortical and periventricular white matter lesions had especially high loadings on the white matter lesions factor. Brainstem white matter lesions loaded on both latent traits, suggesting a special association with coordinated activity. Balance and walk time had a high loadings on the second factor, and the other variables' loadings were significant. The second factor does suggest a general latent trait of organizational capability in the brain. Note that the latent trait of higher level function does a reasonably good job of accounting

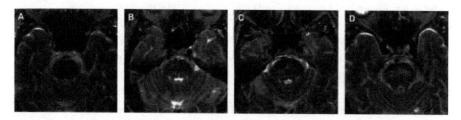

Figure 6.11. T2-weighted magnetic resonance images of the pons showing (A) normal appearance (Grade 0), (B) punctuate change (Grade 1), (C) coalescing change (Grade 2), and (D) confluent change (Grade 3) in the brainstem. From "Brain White Matter Lesions Detected by Magnetic Resonance Imaging Are Associated With Balance and Gait Speed," by J. M. Starr, S. A. Leaper, A. D. Murray, H. A. Lemmon, R. T. Staff, I. J. Deary, and L. J. Whalley, 2003, *Journal of Neurology, Neurosurgery and Psychiatry, 74,* p. 95. Copyright 2003 by BMJ Publishing Group Ltd. Reprinted with permission.

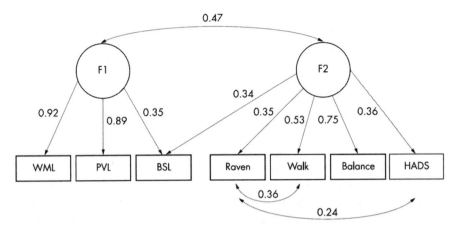

Figure 6.12. Structural equation model of the relations between magnetic resonance imaging–detected white matter lesions (WML), periventricular lesions (PVL), and brainstem lesions (BSL) with fluid intelligence (Raven's Standard Progressive Matrices [Raven]), walking time, balance, and Hospital Anxiety Depression Scale score (HADS). All variables have been constructed so that higher scores represent a worsening of outcome. F1 = latent trait of white matter lesion; F2 = latent trait of higher functions. From "Brain White Matter Lesions Detected by Magnetic Resonance Imaging Are Associated With Balance and Gait Speed," by J. M. Starr, S. A. Leaper, A. D. Murray, H. A. Lemmon, R. T. Staff, I. J. Deary, and L. J. Whalley, 2003, *Journal of Neurology, Neurosurgery and Psychiatry, 74,* p. 96. Copyright 2003 by BMJ Publishing Group Ltd. Reprinted with permission.

for the variance shared by the four measures but that additional associations were needed fully to account for the associations between Raven's Standard Progressive Matrices and walk time and depression scores. These appear as correlated residual terms. The correlation between the two latent traits was quite strong (.47), suggesting that, overall, white matter lesion load is associated with general reduction in higher level functions. This is probably the most important result, the finding of an association between higher organizational capabilities of the brain—all of which are likely to require intact neural networks—and damage to the brain's white matter.

Mechanisms of the Association Between White Matter and Cognition

After finding an association should come the search for mechanism, with a caveat, again, that the number of participants in the studies described here is too small to have offered very robust models; they require replicating. Therefore, if white matter lesions are associated with a deterioration in cognitive functions, then finding the causes of white matter lesion variability among people becomes important. One suggestion is that white matter hyperintensities might in part be vascular in origin. Murray et al. (2005) used the ABC1921 sample to examine whether known risk factors for cerebral ischemia were also risk factors for white matter changes. There were 106 participants with magnetic resonance brain imaging data in the subsample examined. This is slightly more than in the studies involving cognitive variables, because there was no requirement for this sample to have cognitive test scores. Information on vascular risk factors was gained by interview, clinical examination, physiological testing, and laboratory investigations. The measurement of white matter hyperintensities was, as described earlier, in the deep/subcortical and periventricular areas of the brain.

The most striking associations between vascular risk factors and white matter hyperintensities were with subcortical/deep lesions, where 7 out of 16 associations had p values less than .05. The associations (Pearson's r) between Fazekas white matter hyperintensity scores and vascular risk factors in these areas were as follows: hypertension = .27 ($p < .01$), lung peak expiratory flow rate = −.27 ($p < .01$), lung forced expiratory volume in 1 second = −.26 ($p < .01$), lung forced vital capacity = −.22 ($p < .05$), cholesterol = .20 ($p < .05$), low-density lipoprotein = .24 ($p < .05$), and glycated hemoglobin = .31 ($p < .01$). There were nonsignificant associations with diabetes, cerebrovascular disease, smoking, body mass index, diastolic blood pressure, systolic blood pressure, triglycerides, high-density lipoprotein, and fasting glucose. The significant associations that were replicated in the correlations with periventricular Fazekas measurements were with lung peak expiratory flow rate ($r = −.23$, $p < .05$) and glycated hemoglobin ($r = .28, p < .01$). In a multiple linear regression analysis, glycated hemoglobin level and the presence of hypertension together accounted for approximately 16% of the variance in subcortical/deep white matter lesions. Glycated hemoglobin reflects the state of the body's glucose homeostasis over the previous 3 months or so. Hypertension and lung function are known risk factors for cerebrovascular disease. All of these findings suggest possible routes to intervention to lower the burden on white matter damage in older people.

Cerebral Reserve

If white matter hyperintensities are detrimental to brain function, including cognition, then it is interesting to ask whether people with the same childhood IQ and the same amount of white matter lesions tend to experience the same cognitive aging. If not, if they can still end up with different cognitive test scores in old age, and then the persons with higher cognitive function in old age are said to have some *cerebral reserve* (Staff, Murray, Deary, & Whalley, 2004). The concept of brain reserve was articulated in detail by Satz (1993), and Stern (2002) explained that there might be passive and active aspects to cerebral reserve. The reserve concept has been developed into a broader context of a model for examining cognitive change across the life course (Richards & Deary, 2005). Passive, or structural, cerebral reserve suggests that some overt physical aspect of the nervous system—typically, brain volume—provides the buffering-against-pathology effect that manifests as the observed reserve. Active, or functional, cerebral reserve suggests, more subtly, that some people might have alternative cognitive strategies for accomplishing cognitive tasks in the face of pathology. Active reserve might be accumulated through education or intellectual engagement at work, for example.

In setting out to test the cerebral reserve hypothesis, it was argued that such tests were rare and difficult, because studies rarely had the requisite data (Staff et al., 2004). The measured variables required include a measure of prior cognitive function, a measure of current cognitive function (together, these first two afford the measurement of cognitive change), a measure of brain pathology, and measures of active and passive reserve. The magnetic resonance brain imaging subsample of the ABC1921 provided the participants for the test. They had all the data required to test the reserve hypothesis, including age 11 MHT scores and cognitive ability measured at age 78 to 80. To assess brain pathology, each participant had white matter lesions estimated from their brain scans. There were indicators of active and passive reserve: total intracranial volume (measured from the magnetic resonance brain images), for the former, and education and occupational social class, for the latter. Here was the formal statement of cerebral reserve and how it should be tested:

> If the cerebral reserve hypothesis is correct, then the measure of reserve should account for significant variance in the cognitive outcomes in old age after adjusting for variance contributed by childhood mental ability and [brain] burden. In other words, possessing some reserve means that one's cognitive score is greater than would be predicted from the person's childhood ability and the amount of overt, accumulated burden. (Staff et al., 2004, p. 1192)

Ninety-eight ABC1921 participants had imaging data available for analyses (Staff et al., 2004). The two cognitive domains studied as the outcome variables were (a) verbal declarative memory (Rey Auditory Verbal Learning Test) and (b) nonverbal reasoning (Raven's Standard Progressive Matrices). In multiple linear regression models that included childhood intelligence from the SMS1932 and white matter lesion load, there was no additional significant variance contributed to either test score from total intracranial volume (brain size; see Table 6.3). Therefore, the passive reserve hypothesis was not supported. In a similar model, with childhood IQ and white matter lesions included as covariables, occupational social class contributed significantly to Raven's Standard Progressive Matrices scores in old age ($p = .021$, $\eta^2 = .056$). When occupational social class was replaced with education as the indicator of active reserve in the same type of model,

TABLE 6.3
Influence of Putative Reserve Measures on Cognitive Test Scores in Old
Age After Adjustment for Moray House Test Score at Age 11 (Prior Ability)
and White Matter Hyperintensities Measured in Old Age (Brain Burden)

Indicator of reserve	Memory (Auditory Verbal Learning Test total score)		Nonverbal reasoning (Raven's Standard Progressive Matrices)	
	p	η^2	p	η^2
Passive				
Total intracranial volume (brain size)	.85	< .001	.37	.009
Active				
Occupational social class	.094	.032	.021	.056
Years of education	.024	.057	.828	.001

Note. From "What Provides Cerebral Reserve?" by R. T. Staff, A. D. Murray, I. J. Deary, and L. J. Whalley, 2004, *Brain, 127,* p. 1195. Copyright 2004 by Oxford University Press. Adapted with permission.

education contributed significantly to Rey Auditory Verbal Learning Test scores in old age (p = .024, η^2 = .057). Occupational social class did not contribute significantly to Rey Auditory Verbal Learning Test scores, and education did not contribute significantly to Raven's Standard Progressive Matrices scores (see Table 6.3).

These results constitute some patchy support for the active cerebral reserve hypothesis, but not for the passive reserve hypothesis (Staff et al., 2004). Occupation contributed 5.6% of the variance in nonverbal reasoning scores, above that contributed by prior ability and brain burden (white matter lesions). Education contributed 5.7% of the variance in verbal declarative memory test scores, with prior ability and brain burden in the model. Assuming that the results of this modestly sized study are replicable then, childhood IQ and white matter lesion load being equal, on average, a person with a more professional job will tend to reason better in old age, and a person with more years of education will remember verbal material better. Such specificity of occupation's and education's effects were not hypothesized a priori. There was a tendency for occupation to contribute to memory scores (see Table 6.3). The results were far from definitive, but they were an unusually informative, large, and stringent test of the active and passive forms of the cerebral reserve hypothesis. Other measures of passive reserve might prove more effective, such as the size of important brain areas, including the hippocampus, or harder-to-measure constructs such as neural number or the number of synapses. The significant associations found with education and occupation might be causal or spurious. For example, a causal explanation for occupation's contribution to reasoning skills in old age could be that white collar workers are exposed to fewer and less neurotoxins. However, if education and occupation are merely acting as proxy measures of that part of the cognitive ability variance in old age that is not picked up by childhood IQ, then the results suggest nothing more profound than that young adult mental ability adds some explanatory variance to ability in old age beyond that captured in childhood. Thus, the conclusion that "the intellectual challenges experienced during life, such as education and occupation, accumulate reserve and allow cognitive function to be maintained in old age" (Staff et al., 2004, p. 1191), begs the question of mechanisms and is only one interpretation of the nondefinitive results.

Brain Volume

In the analyses just described, total intracranial volume did not contribute to cognitive ability in old age in models that had childhood IQ and white matter lesion scores as covariables. Thus, it failed as a measure of passive reserve. Nevertheless, brains do shrink with age, and some cognitive functions decline, so it is likely that there is some relation between age-related changes in brain size and cognition (Hedden & Gabrieli, 2004). The association between brain size and cognition and cognitive aging was examined in the ABC1921, using another type of magnetic resonance imaging analysis: voxel-based morphometry (Staff, Murray, Deary, & Whalley, 2006). The evidence that contributed to the rationale for this study was as follows. As has already been described, there appear to be general and specific aspects to cognitive aging, with different cognitive domains declining partly in concert and party independently (e.g., Salthouse & Ferrer-Caja, 2003). Brain size correlates positively and modestly with cognitive test scores (McDaniel, 2005), with some studies suggesting that it is overall brain size that is important and that the correlation between brain size and intelligence is caused to a large extent by shared genetic influences (Posthuma et al., 2003). There had been relatively little study of general and specific (regional) age-related brain shrinkage and the association with general and specific cognitive abilities. Participants in the ABC1921 sample had useful data to conduct such a study. There were childhood IQ scores, as well as tests of different cognitive domains in old age. There also were brain imaging data. These provided data for two important measures. First, total intracranial volume provided a record of the space inside the head that was taken by the brain; this falls with age from a high of around 95% in youth (Staff et al., 2006); that is, there is a good estimate of the size an individual's brain was in youth. Second, the magnetic resonance imaging data record the size of the brain in old age. Therefore, the ABC1921 had measures of cognitive function and brain size in youth and old age.

Ninety-eight people from the ABC1921 had imaging and cognitive data (Staff et al., 2006). From their cognitive data—Raven's Standard Progressive Matrices, the Rey Auditory Verbal Learning Test, the National Adult Reading Test, and Digit Symbol—a general cognitive factor (g) was extracted that accounted for 56.9% of the total variance. Analyses were performed on each individual cognitive test and on the g factor score. Voxel-based morphometry analysis of the brain imaging data allow the volumes of gray matter, white matter, and cerebrospinal fluid to be measured in each person's brains. The total of all three is the *total intracranial volume*, the estimate of brain size in youth. The total of the gray and white matter volumes is the *current brain volume*.

The first set of analyses (general linear models) examined the associations, separately, between total gray matter volume and total white matter volume and the four cognitive test scores plus g (Staff et al., 2006). Gender was a fixed effect in the models. There were no significant associations; that is, neither the total gray matter volume nor the total white matter volume was associated significantly with mental test scores. Next, the same models were run, but with age 11 MHT score as a covariable. This model achieves a study of the associations between gray and white matter volumes and cognitive change from age 11 to age about 80. Out of 10 analyses, there were two significant results. White matter volume was associated, after adjustment for sex and childhood mental ability, with scores on Raven's Standard Progressive Matrices ($p = .029$) and Digit Symbol ($p = .025$). This implies that the aging of nonverbal reasoning and processing speed are related to total white matter volume.

The next set of models developed the previous set by examining the association between mental test scores and gray and white matter volumes, with sex, age 11 MHT scores, and total intracranial volume in the model (Staff et al., 2006). In effect, this is testing the hypothesis that life course volume changes in the brain are associated with cognitive changes over the life course. Out of 10 analyses, 5 were significant at $p < .05$. Total gray matter, adjusted for total intracranial volume, correlated significantly with Raven's Standard Progressive Matrices ($p = .001$), Digit Symbol ($p = .049$), and g ($p = .006$), adjusted for MHT scores at age 11. Thus, the aging of nonverbal reasoning, processing speed, and general ability were associated with the relative preservation of gray matter. The effect sizes (percentage of variance accounted for) were between 4.8% and 11.6%. Total white matter, adjusted for total intracranial volume, correlated significantly with Digit Symbol ($p = .038$) and g ($p = .019$), adjusted for MHT scores at age 11. Thus, the aging of processing speed and general ability were associated with the relative preservation of white matter. The effect sizes (percentage of variance accounted for) were 6.3% and 6.6%, respectively. To an extent, then, brain shrinkage associates with cognitive decline, and both gray and white matter changes contribute to the association.

The previous analysis was helpful in that it permitted one to associate lifetime cognitive changes with lifetime brain changes and by making the result more specific by identifying whether the associations were with white and/or gray matter changes (Staff et al., 2006). Voxel-based morphometry analysis can answer an even more specific question: Are there specific regions of gray and/or white matter that are associated with cognitive ability? This analysis can search for clusters of voxels (brain regions) that, after the application of the appropriate statistical criteria for significance given the large number of tests that are involved, have significant associations with cognitive test scores. In this set of analyses, total intracranial volume and childhood IQ from the SMS1932 were included as covariables, and gender was a fixed effect. There were no significant associations with gray matter for any test, or for the *g* factor. There were associations in two white matter regions with the *g* factor: (a) the left forceps major and (b) the left corona radiata (see Figure 6.13). These were almost identical to areas that were significantly related to Digit Symbol test scores; 72% of the voxels were common to both. When *g* was covaried from the Digit Symbol data, there were no longer any significant regions. There were no significant regions of white matter that correlated with the National Adult Reading Test, the Rey Auditory Verbal Learning Test, or Raven's Standard Progressive Matrices scores.

To examine the possibility that the study results were due to a minority of people with undiagnosed or incipient dementia, the analyses were rerun with a smaller sample, excluding individuals who had developed dementia or died at or before a 4-year follow up (Staff et al., 2006). The results largely remained as described earlier, with the exception that the regional associations described in the immediately preceding paragraph were no longer significant. This might have been due to the smaller number of participants involved.

Because of the rather technical nature of the imaging analysis, and because there are both cognitive and brain imaging covariables in the analyses, the results of these contributions to cognitive aging can be hard to grasp. One summary of the findings was as follows: "There is more white matter, relative to the [total intracranial volume], in the left corona radiata and in the left forceps major in those subjects who retain more general mental ability in late life, after adjusting for childhood intelligence" (Staff et al., 2006, p. 1437).

In other words, if one wants to retain mental ability in old age, then it is advisable to retain good white matter volume in the regions shown in Figure 6.13. There are four important aspects to these findings. First, they complement the findings using white matter lesion load and fractional anisotropy, which suggested that the integrity of the white matter is important for successful cognitive aging. Second, the fact that the white matter regions associated with *g* were also largely the same as those associated with Digit Symbol—which is often used as a measure of processing speed—gives some psychobiological support to the importance of processing speed in cognitive aging (Salthouse, 1996, 2000). Third, because the brains were assessed in a cross-sectional design, notwithstanding the adjustment for total intracranial volume, it is not possible to decide whether the specific white matter

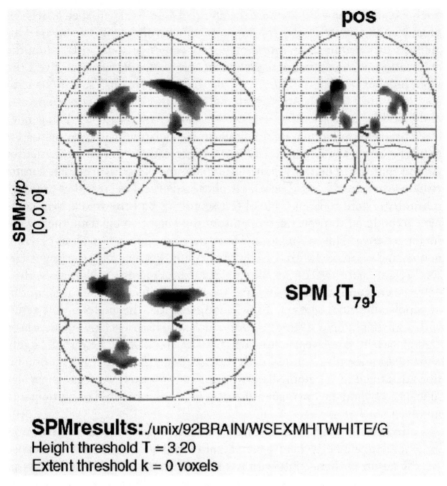

pos

SPMmip
[0,0,0]

SPM {T₇₉}

SPMresults:/unix/92BRAIN/WSEXMHTWHITE/G
Height threshold T = 3.20
Extent threshold k = 0 voxels

Figure 6.13. A "glass brain" image of the white matter regions found to correlate positively and significantly with the *g* (general cognitive ability factor) score. This image was created with an initial uncorrected probability threshold of $p < .0001$. Within two of these regions, there is a peak voxel probability of $p = .046$ (false detection rate corrected) at coordinates −19, −5, 39 and −31, −64, 19. This was done using gender, the Moray House Test score at age 11, and the total intracranial volume as covariables. SPM = statistical parametric mapping; pos = cursor position (arrowhead). From "Generality and Specificity in Cognitive Ageing: A Volumetric Brain Analysis," by R. T. Staff, A. D. Murray, I. J. Deary, and L. J. Whalley, 2006, *NeuroImage, 30,* p. 1436. Copyright 2006 by Elsevier Limited. Reprinted with permission.

regions associated with *g* and Digit Symbol were always relatively large in well-performing participants or whether these participants had less age-related deterioration in these brain regions. If the former is true, then more white matter in these areas would be an index of passive cognitive reserve. If the latter is true, then factors influencing this differential aging must be sought. Fourth, these findings open a door to the exploration of degenerative mechanisms that underlie cognitive aging. These could include problems with myelination, or the loss of connecting fibers with old age; these are possible targets for future intervention to ameliorate cognitive aging.

RETINAL VASCULAR NETWORK GEOMETRY

Cognitive function is associated with the state of the vasculature, especially the cerebral vasculature (O'Brien et al., 2003). Murray et al. (2005) showed that white matter lesions, which are associated with cognition, are worse in the presence of vascular risk factors. Therefore, it was decided to examine the state of people's blood vessels directly and examine whether this state was related to their relative amounts of cognitive change from childhood to old age. The only place in the body where blood vessels can be seen directly and photographed is on the retina at the back of the eyes, where the small vessels can easily be visualized. There was some limited evidence that abnormalities in the small vessels of the retina were associated with lower cognitive function in older people who have not been diagnosed with dementia (Wong et al., 2002). Very detailed reviews were undertaken by our team to establish the homology between the small vessels in the retina and in the brain (Patton et al., 2005) and to provide image analysis tools to obtain relevant blood vessel parameters from retinal photographs (Patton et al., 2006). From these reviews came the novel idea of suboptimality of the retinal vessels: first, that there was an optimal angle into which two daughter vessels would emerge from a parent blood vessels and, second, that there was an optimal relative diameter between the parent vessel and the daughter vessels (see Figure 6.14). Thus, the retinal small blood vessels might quantitatively be described by optimality parameters, and these parameters might be related to cognitive aging. The hypothesis—that the aging eye might be a window to the aging brain—was tested in the LBC1921 (Patton et al., 2007).

This study took place during a second wave of examination of the LBC1921 in old age (Patton et al., 2007). From the original 550 participants seen between 1999 and 2001, 321 (176 women and 145 men) were recontacted and tested between 2003 and 2005. At that time, the participants were between 83 and 84 years old. They retook the Mini-Mental State Examination, Raven's Standard Progressive Matrices, Logical Memory, and Verbal Fluency. They also underwent retinal photography. They first had their pupils dilated with 1% tropicamide drops. After the pupils were sufficiently dilated, color photographs were taken of the fundus of the eye. The photographs were then digitally scanned for image analysis. A number of retinal vessel parameters were obtained by using a custom-written software package to examine the vascular images derived from the photographs. The widths of the arteries and veins were assessed, as was their ratio (arterio:venous). In addition, for each

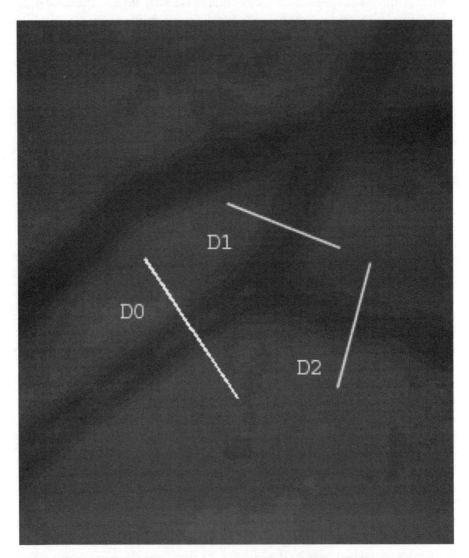

Figure 6.14. Photograph of small retinal arterioles illustrating the measure that was associated with cognitive function in the Lothian Birth Cohort 1921. This is a gray-scale image of a peripheral vascular junction; that is, a parent vessel divides into two daughter vessels. D_0 is the diameter of parent vessel, D_1 and D_2 represent diameters of the two daughter vessels. $D_0^X = D_1^X + D_2^X$, where X is the junctional exponent. From "Retinal Image Analysis: Concepts, Applications and Potential," by N. Patton, T. M. Aslam, T. MacGillivray, I. J. Deary, B. Dhillon, R. H. Eikelboom, et al., 2006, *Progress in Retinal and Eye Research, 25,* p. 116. Copyright 2006 by Elsevier Limited. Reprinted with permission.

participant there were parameters representing the deviation from optimal branching of the small arteries. One parameter described the deviation from the optimal branching angle when a parent vessel divided into two smaller vessels. The second parameter described the deviation from optimality with respect to the relative widths of the parent and daughter vessels (the *branching coefficient*). How these aspects of retinal vascular topographical geometry have a tendency to conform to principles of optimality that reduce aspects such as shear stress and work across the vascular network is explained elsewhere (Patton et al., 2006).

Of the 321 people, 289 had some usable retinal photographic data, but only 226 had data of sufficient quality to derive the branching optimality parameters (Patton et al., 2007). The widths of the small arteries and veins on the retina, and the ratio of the artery to vein widths, were not significantly related to cognitive ability scores. Deviation from the optimal branching coefficient was significantly associated with a general cognitive factor derived from Raven's Standard Progressive Matrices, Logical Memory, and Verbal Fluency ($p = .02$, $\eta^2 = .034$). Other significant contributors in this general linear model of general mental ability at age 83 were MHT score at age 11, near visual acuity, and *APOE* e4 allele status. Also in the model, but not significant, were sex, diabetes, cerebrovascular disease, smoking, blood pressure, alcohol, education, and occupational social class. Deviation from the optimal branching coefficient was also significantly associated with Verbal Fluency score ($p = .01$, $\eta^2 = .037$), and there was a trend with Raven's Standard Progressive Matrices ($p = .09$). Deviation from an optimal branching angle, at points where small arteries divided into two, was significantly associated only with Logical Memory score ($p = .03$, $\eta^2 = .026$). Of the other factors mentioned earlier with respect to branching coefficient, none except MHT score at age 11 made a significant contribution in this general linear model of verbal declarative memory at age 83.

This study provided a novel contributor to cognitive aging (Patton et al., 2007). After adjusting for MHT score at age 11, the deviation from the optimal branching coefficient of the retinal arterioles contributed 3.4% of the variance to a general cognitive ability factor at age 83. The optimality of the geometry of the retinal vessels is thought to depend on the epithelium (the lining layer of cells in the blood vessels). Deviation from optimality is thought to be associated with epithelial dysfunction and can lead to shear stresses in the blood vessels, which can further disrupt the epithelium and lead to increased inflammation and oxidative stress, both of which are associated with cognitive aging (Halliwell, 2006; Keller et al., 2005; Rafnsson et al., 2007; Zipp & Aktas, 2006). The aging eye, therefore, might provide a small window to the aging brain. These findings should be studied in association with white matter lesions and other contributors to brain aging, so that causal pathways can be better understood.

RENAL FUNCTION

If the back of the eye was an unusual place in which to look for clues to the causes of cognitive aging, then the kidney might seem even less credible. When kidney function is severely compromised—for example, in people who have renal failure and require hemodialysis—cognitive decrements are often found, and there is an increased risk of dementia (Fukunishi et al., 2002). The association between renal impairment and cognitive decrements might be caused by cardiovascular dysfunction; indeed, it might be caused by the disease in small vessels that can be seen in the retina and is associated with white matter lesions (Martinez-Vea et al., 2006). There was scant evidence as to whether there was an association between cognitive ability and renal function in the normal range, although at least one positive report existed, in menopausal women (Kurella, Yaffe, Shlipak, Wenger, & Chertow, 2005).

Kidney function and cognition were, therefore, examined in the LBC1921 (Munang, Starr, Whalley, & Deary, 2007). Serum creatinine was used to estimate glomerular filtration rate using the modification of diet in renal disease formula. Glomerular filtration rate is the standard measure of the efficiency of the kidneys. There were data on serum creatinine for 529 (225 men and 304 women) of the 550 LBC1921 participants. In men, there were significant correlations between glomerular filtration rate and Raven's Standard Progressive Matrices ($r = .14$), Verbal Fluency ($r = .15$), and MHT ($r = .16$) scores at age 79. The only correlation in women was with Verbal Fluency ($r = .13$). In men, glomerular filtration rate correlated significantly with MHT scores at age 11 ($r = .15$). After adjustment for MHT scores at age 11 there were no significant correlations between glomerular filtration rate and any cognitive test score at age 79. Therefore, the authors concluded that it appeared to be more likely that childhood IQ was associated with renal function later in life, instead of renal function later in life being associated with cognitive function (Munang et al., 2007). If this can be replicated, then, strictly speaking, this study should have been in the cognitive epidemiology part of this book instead of the cognitive aging part.

7
FINDINGS ON HEALTH
AND NUTRITION-RELATED FACTORS

In addition to analyzing genetic and brain imaging factors as well as other biological factors to see what associations with lifetime cognitive aging could be determined, we also analyzed some health and nutrition-related factors. These findings are the topic of this chapter.

SMOKING

Smoking history is a nice example of the usefulness of the data from the Scottish Mental Survey of 1932 (SMS1932) and the Scottish Mental Survey of 1947. Most people would like to know whether, in addition to the other health risks that are associated with smoking, the habit harms the brain. If a group of older people is tested for cognitive ability and, at the same time, they offer their smoking history, one might find, as Cervilla, Prince, and Mann (2000) did, that smoking is associated with poorer cognitive performance. On the basis of these data, though, it is not possible definitively to decide whether smoking is associated with a change in cognitive ability from the healthy state in youth. It is possible that people who have lower cognitive ability early in life smoked more. The SMS1932 information allowed an examination of people's childhood and old age IQ scores and their smoking status (Deary, Pattie, et al., 2003).

The study was undertaken in response to Fillit et al.'s (2002) statement that they were aware of no studies that had examined smoking in relation to normal cognitive aging. Four hundred seventy people from the Lothian Birth Cohort 1921 (LBC1921) with appropriate data, and whose Mini-Mental State Examination scores were 24 or greater (Deary, Pattie, et al., 2003), agreed to take part. Of this number, 205 had never smoked, 231 were ex-smokers, and 34 were current smokers, when seen at a mean of just over age 79. Ever-smokers had begun smoking between ages 7 and 60, and the mean age at stopping smoking was about 50, with a range from 19 to 79. The raw Moray House Test (MHT) scores for the three groups at mean ages of 11 and 79 are shown in Figure 7.1. The most obvious feature of the data is the increase in mean raw test scores from age 11 to age 79 for all three groups. Next, the groups differ very little in MHT scores at age 11. However, the current smokers have relatively low scores at age 79. A general linear model was run with age-corrected

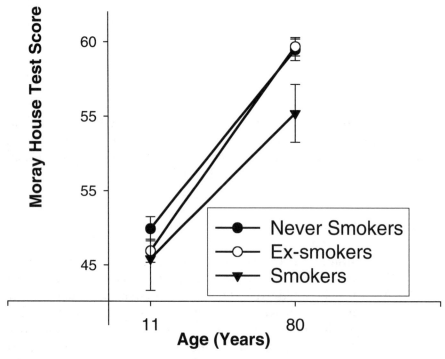

Figure 7.1. The association between smoking and Moray House Test raw scores at age 11 and age 79 in the Lothian Birth Cohort 1921. From "Smoking and Cognitive Change From Age 11 to Age 80," by I. J. Deary, A. Pattie, M. D. Taylor, M. C. Whiteman, J. M. Starr, and L. J. Whalley, 2003, *Journal of Neurology, Neurosurgery and Psychiatry, 74,* p. 1007. Copyright 2003 by BMJ Publishing Group Ltd. Adapted with permission.

MHT score at age 79 as the outcome variable, smoking status (three groups) and sex as fixed effects, and age-corrected MHT score at age 11 as a covariable. The effect of smoking was significant ($p < .039$, $\eta^2 = .014$). At age 79, the mean MHT score of smokers was lower than that of ex-smokers ($p = .016$) and never-smokers ($p = .013$). These effects remained significant after adding years of education to the model. The results are at least immune, mostly, to any confounding effects of prior smoking; only 6 of the ever-smokers started smoking before age 11. One must consider, too, the influence smoking might have had on the participants of the SMS1932 who did and did not become members of the LBC1921. It is likely that smokers in the LBC1921 would be more fit than typical smokers, of whom more would have died and be currently ill, and, therefore, any effect of smoking on cognitive ability might have been underestimated by the fact that there were especially fit smokers in the sample. The mechanisms by which smoking might lead to disadvantageous cognitive aging were speculative. They might be related to oxidative damage, poorer vascular perfusion in the brain, the thinning of the brain's gray matter, and/or more lesions in the white matter (Deary, Pattie, et al., 2003). Smoking-related disease might be the cause—indeed, it could be that smoking was, more generally, a marker variable for people who chose a less healthy lifestyle.

A more detailed examination of smoking and its association with cognitive performance was undertaken in the Aberdeen Birth Cohort 1936 at a mean age of 64 years (Whalley, Fox, Deary, & Starr, 2005). This included an examination of possible medical and social mediators of any influence of smoking on cognitive performance; more specifically, it examined the possible effect of lung function. Of the 465 Aberdeen Birth Cohort 1936 (ABC1936) participants who had been recruited at that time, there were 413 with complete cognitive data and 358 with complete cognitive and lung function data. The initial analyses of cognitive outcomes examined the effect of smoking status (never-smokers, $N = 184$; ex-smokers, $N = 139$; current smokers, $N = 90$), with age 11 MHT score as a covariate and sex as a fixed effect. Smoking status was significantly associated with Digit Symbol (Wechsler, 1981) test scores ($p < .001$, $\eta^2 = .043$). There were no significant effects on scores on the Rey Auditory Verbal Learning Test, Block Design, Uses for Common Objects, or Raven's Standard Progressive Matrices (see chap. 5 for test details). Lung function was significantly poorer in smokers.

For the main analysis, the five cognitive tests were combined using principal components analysis to yield a general cognitive ability score (Whalley et al., 2005). The first unrotated principal component accounted for 52% of the total variance. Scores on this component were saved and converted to an IQ-type score ($M = 100$, $SD = 15$). The first regression model examined the effect of childhood IQ, occupation, education, and smoking in 411 participants (see Table 7.1). All contributed significantly to general cognitive

TABLE 7.1

Summary of Three Stepwise Multiple Linear Regression Analyses
of Childhood IQ, Educational Qualifications, Occupational Category, Health
Variables, Smoking History, and Lung Functions on a Composite Score
of Cognitive Ability at Age 64

Model	Variable	Change in R^2	Standardized beta weight	p
All participants, excluding lung	Moray House Test IQ at age 11	.409	.475	< .001
function test	Occupation	.009	−.116	< .01
results ($N = 411$,	Smoking	.012	−.115	< .01
$R^2 = .477$, adjusted $R^2 = .472$)	Education	.048	.196	< .001
All participants, including lung	Moray House Test IQ at age 11	.407	.468	< .001
function test results ($N = 357$, $R^2 = .502$, adjusted $R^2 = .495$)	Lung peak expiratory flow rate	.034	.168	< .001
	Occupation	.008	−.114	< .05
	Education	.046	.172	< .001
	Smoking	.008	.092	< .02
With current and former smokers	Moray House Test IQ at age 11	.415	.545	< .001
excluded ($N = 156$,	Education	.029	.191	< .01
$R^2 = .464$, adjusted $R^2 = .454$)	Lung peak expiratory flow rate	.020	.142	< .025

Note. Participants in this study are members of the Aberdeen Birth Cohort 1936. From "Childhood IQ, Smoking, and Cognitive Change From Age 11 to 64 Years," by L. J. Whalley, H. C. Fox, I. J. Deary, and J. M. Starr, 2005, *Addictive Behaviors, 30*, p. 84. Copyright 2005 by Elsevier Limited. Adapted with permission.

ability at age 64. The largest contributor is childhood IQ, which accounted for 40.9% of the variance in ability more than 50 years later. Next, education accounted for an additional 4.8%, and occupational social class accounted for 0.9%. Smoking then contributes 1.2% independently of these other variables, a contribution similar to that found in the LBC1921 (Deary, Pattie, et al., 2003). The second regression model involved the reduced number of participants who had lung function and cognitive data (see Table 7.1). Lung peak expiratory flow rate, taken contemporaneously with the cognitive measures at age 64, accounted for 3.4% of the variance in general cognitive functioning at age 64 ($p < .001$). All of the variables from the first model were still significant. The most important result here is that the effect of smoking was still significant, and not substantially reduced, when this measure of lung function was introduced to the model in this sample. The third model included nonsmokers only ($N = 156$; see Table 7.1). The significant contributors to cognitive ability at age 64 were MHT IQ at age 11, education, and lung peak expiratory flow rate, accounting for 41.5%, 2.9%, and 2.0% of the variance, respectively. Thus, in addition to childhood IQ and education, healthy lungs contribute to more able cognition at age 64.

Therefore, smoking status contributed a minor, independent amount of variance to cognitive function (Whalley et al., 2005). Pack years of smoking was entered into models, in an attempt to measure the dose of smoking, but this did not contribute significantly. *Pack years* is the number of years of smoking multiplied by the average number of packs of 20 cigarettes smoked per day. Results from this and from Deary, Pattie, et al.'s (2003) study suggest that the effects of smoking on cognition are mostly found within current smokers; ex-smokers appear relatively cognitively healthy. A confirmatory study on the ABC1936, including an extra wave of cognitive data collected 2 years later, at age 66, found supportive evidence for the detrimental effect of smoking on Digit Symbol performance and on Rey Auditory Verbal Learning Test scores (Starr, Deary, Fox, & Whalley, 2007). This led to speculation that the cognitive decrements associated with smoking might occur relatively late in the human life course. Another finding of Whalley et al.'s (2005) study is the contribution that education and occupational social class make to cognitive aging, in agreement with the cognitive reserve study conducted on the Aberdeen Birth Cohort 1921 (ABC1921) by Staff, Murray, Deary, and Whalley (2004). Probably the most important point from the study is that smoking contributes to cognitive aging and is open to change more easily, in principle, than many other variables.

PHYSICAL FITNESS

One of the intriguing findings that were followed up from the smoking research was the fact that the health of the lungs appeared to be related to cognitive aging. It brought to mind the famous line from the Roman poet Juvenal's "Satire X": "Orandum est ut sit mens sana in corpore sano" ("It is to be prayed that the mind be sound in a sound body"). The mind is the functioning of the brain, and the brain is a part of the body and shares with other organs the endogenous and exogenous tribulations that afflict the body. The lungs, too, might not be special; their health might reflect physical fitness of the body more generally. Therefore, Deary, Whalley, Batty, and Starr (2006) examined the contribution of general physical fitness and cognitive change from childhood to old age in the LBC1921.

Previous studies had found associations between cognitive ability and measures of physical fitness, such as lung function, hand grip strength, and walking speed (e.g., Malmstrom, Wolinsky, Andresen, Miller, & Miller, 2005). One problem that researchers appreciated with such associations was that one could not take the direction of causation for granted. The first thought that came to most people's minds was that keeping the body healthy had the knock-on (causal) effect of maintaining the brain in good shape. However, the reverse might be true, too: It might be that smarter people look after their bodies better and thus stay in better shape. The work on cognitive epidemiology described in Part II certainly suggests an influence in that direction. In agreement with this line of thinking, too, the UK National Survey of Health and Development (the 1946 UK birth cohort) had found that cognitive function in adolescence was related to lung function in mature adulthood (Richards, Strachan, Hardy, Kuh, & Wadsworth, 2005). Another potential problem is that so-called physical tests might, in part, be cognitive tests. Even physical tests involve understanding and executing instructions effectively, and it is tenable, and seriously considered by researchers, that doing so is associated with cognitive status (Tabbarah, Crimmins, & Seeman, 2002). Last, to emphasize a possibility that we hinted at earlier, it might be that a healthy brain and a healthy body are the outcome of some prior, shared influences that are common to both. The LBC1921 sample and the planned analyses offered three desirable characteristics (Deary, Whalley, et al., 2006). First, because the participants were all very close in chronological age, biological and chronological age were not confounded. Second, the participants had multiple physical health markers, and thus we could examine whether they were positively associated, affording the examination of a general physical health factor. Third, reverse causality could be examined to an extent, because participants had mental test scores from childhood.

There were 460 people from the LBC1921 for the analyses involving physical fitness and cognitive aging (Deary, Whalley, et al., 2006). Scores on three fitness variables—6-meter walk time, hand grip strength, and forced expiratory volume of the lungs in 1 second—were adjusted for sex and height. They were all correlated in the expected direction—better performance always went with better performance—between .15 and .26 (all $ps < .01$). The three adjusted fitness variables were subjected to a principal components analysis. Just one component was indicated, accounting for 47.6% of the total variance. Scores on this first unrotated principal component were saved as a general fitness component, or factor. MHT IQ score from age 11 was significantly positively associated ($r = .10$, $p < .05$) with forced expiratory volume from the lungs in 1 second, but not with 6-meter walk time or hand grip strength, or with the general fitness component. MHT IQ score at age 79 correlated significantly (all $ps < .01$) with all of them: forced expiratory volume from the lungs in 1 second ($r = .13$), 6-meter walk time ($r = -.19$), hand grip strength ($r = .12$), and the general fitness component ($r = .22$). Therefore, apart from lung function, childhood IQ was not associated with fitness at age 79. There was some reverse causality, therefore, but not for the general fitness component, or for two of its indicator variables. By contrast, there were universal associations in this sample between the fitness indicators tested and MHT IQ scores at age 79.

The next step was to construct and test a multivariable model of MHT IQ score at age 79 and determine whether fitness contributed additional, independent variance (Deary, Whalley, et al., 2006). The final model is shown in Table 7.2. Smoking and education did not contribute significantly to this model and thus were omitted. Education was entered in place of occupational social class, and was significant, but the model with occupation is shown here. As readers will most likely expect by now, the first and by far the largest contributor to variance in MHT IQ score at age 79 was MHT IQ score at age 11, accounting for 41% of the variance. Adult occupational social class adds 1.0%, *apolipoprotein E* gene (*APOE*) e4 allele status a further 0.7%, and sex adds 0.6%. With all of these variables in the model, the general physical fitness component contributes 3.3%, the largest identified contributor after childhood IQ. Therefore, after adjusting for prior ability, a healthy body does help facilitate a more able mind. Also, the study largely rules out the possibility that performance on physical tests might be due to a person's lifelong mental ability, because two of the three physical tests were not related to childhood intelligence. Although there was no measure of brain burden or pathology measured in these participants, the physical fitness and occupation factors may be seen as potential cerebral reserve factors. What must not be ruled out is the possibility of some common cause that affects both fitness and cognitive function as people grow older (H. Christensen, MacKinnon, Korten, & Jorm, 2001; Li & Lindenberger, 2002). Thus, given the widening realization not only that cognitive domains tend to age in concert, as do sensory and cognitive functions, but also that cognitive sensory and physical performance tend to age in concert to some degree, we raised the possibility that there might be some general bodily processes that influence performance across the board. These processes could include oxidative stress (Lin & Beal, 2006), inflammation (Zipp & Aktas, 2006), and/or the hypothalamic–pituitary–adrenal axis and the allostatic load borne by the body (McEwen, 2006; D. B. Miller & O'Callaghan, 2005), to suggest just some

TABLE 7.2

Physical Fitness and Lifetime Cognitive Aging: Multivariable Linear
Regression of Moray House Test IQ Scores at Age 79 Years

Variable	Change in R^2	Standardized beta weight	p
Moray House Test IQ at age 11	.410	.595	< .001
Physical fitness	.033	.170	< .001
Adult occupational social class	.010	−.096	< .010
APOE e4 status	.007	.080	< .020
Sex	.006	−.080	< .021

Note. Participants in this study are members of the Lothian Birth Cohort 1921. *APOE* e4 = *Apolipoprotein E* e4 allele. From "Physical Fitness and Lifetime Cognitive Change," by I. J. Deary, L. J. Whalley, G. D. Batty, and J. M. Starr, 2006, *Neurology, 67,* p. 1198. Copyright 2006 by Lippincott Williams & Wilkins. Adapted with permission.

possibilities that will be explored by various cognitive aging research groups in the next several years.

BIOCHEMICAL MARKERS OF NUTRITION

Lifestyle choices such as smoking—and, to an extent, bodily fitness—are factors over which it is assumed that one has some control and thus there is some possibility for change. Another such factor is diet–nutrition. Popular culture promotes the idea that there are healthy diets and, more specifically, brain-healthy diets, with regard to both macronutrients and micronutrients (Bourre, 2006a, 2006b):

> Although an increasing number of genetic factors that may increase the risk of neurodegenerative disorders [that] are being identified, number [sic] of findings show that dietary factors play major roles in determining whether the brain ages successfully or experiences neurodegenerative disorders. (Bourre, 2006b, p. 386)

On the basis of the idea that eating certain foods might be associated with individual differences in cognitive aging, Duthie et al. (2002) hypothesized that folate and the B vitamins might be of particular importance. Folate and vitamins B_{12} and B_6 are essential for healthy neural functioning. With regard to mechanism, one of the consequences of folate and vitamin B_{12} deficiency is elevation in the levels of homocysteine. Plasma levels of this compound were found to be related to poorer cognition in older people (Riggs, Spiro, Tucker, & Rush, 1996); however, relatively little work had examined homocysteine and normal cognitive aging. It was important, too, to introduce prior mental ability, because there might be an element of reverse causality, whereby childhood ability might influence food intake. The participants in this study were the first-recruited members of the ABC1921 ($N = 186$) and ABC1936 ($N = 148$), who were recruited to take part in a project on brain aging, nutrition, and health. Homocysteine, folate, and vitamin B_{12} were assessed from plasma. Red blood cell folate was also assessed. It is not discussed further here; among the mental tests, it had a correlation of .19 ($p < .05$) that was no longer significant after adjustment for MHT IQ score at age 11 (Duthie et al., 2002). The plasma biomarkers were log transformed, and outliers—possibly due to participants taking vitamin supplements—were removed from the data.

Plasma homocysteine was greater in the older sample (ABC1921) than in the younger sample (ABC1936, $p < .001$; Duthie et al., 2002). In both samples there were small to modest associations between the three biomarkers: a positive association between plasma vitamin B_{12} and folate and negative associations between plasma homocysteine and vitamin B_{12} and plasma homocysteine and folate. The two samples did not differ significantly in MHT IQ at age 11, or on the National Adult Reading Test (Nelson & Willison, 1991), an estimate of prior ability. The ABC1936 sample performed significantly better than the ABC1921 sample on all the tests of current cognitive function: Mini-Mental State Examination, Raven's Standard Progressive Matrices, Rey Auditory Verbal Learning Test, Block Design, and Digit Symbol (all $ps < .001$). There were no significant associations between MHT IQ score from age 11 and any of the three plasma biomarkers (see Table 7.3). The effect sizes are .08 or lower, suggesting that childhood IQ had a negligible influence on individual differences in these nutritional factors. The ABC1936 sample showed only one significant association, between Block Design and plasma folate ($r = .24$, $p < .05$; see Table 7.3). This was in the predicted direction, with higher folate associated with better cognitive performance. There were several significant associations in the ABC1921, all of them in the predicted direction. There were significant positive associations between plasma folate and scores on the the Mini-Mental State Examination, National Adult Reading Test, Rey Auditory Verbal Learning Test, and Digit Symbol, and between vitamin B_{12} and the Mini-Mental State examination.

TABLE 7.3
Correlations Between Mental Test Scores and Homocysteine, Vitamin B_{12}, and Plasma Folate in the Aberdeen Birth Cohort 1921 (ABC1921) and the Aberdeen Birth Cohort 1936 (ABC1936)

Test	Cohort tested	Homocysteine	Vitamin B_{12}	Plasma folate
Moray House Test IQ at age 11	ABC1921 ($N = 183$)	.08	.05	.04
	ABC1936 ($N = 148$)	.05	−.04	.04
Mini-Mental State Examination	ABC1921 ($N = 165$)	−.15	.24**	.20*
	ABC1936 (N = 144)	.04	.03	.00
National Adult Reading Test	ABC1921 (N = 133)	−.10	.15	.19*
	ABC1936 ($N = 144$)	.01	.01	.16
Raven's Standard Progressive Matrices	ABC1921 ($N = 130$)	−.22*	.10	.06
	ABC1936 (N = 137)	−.03	.02	.15
Rey Auditory Verbal Learning Test	ABC1921 ($N = 121$)	−.08	.03	.19*
	ABC1936 ($N = 134$)	−.12	.00	.03
Block Design	ABC1921 ($N = 107$)	−.27**	−.06	.06
	ABC1936 ($N = 118$)	−.06	.03	.24*
Digit Symbol	ABC1921 ($N = 113$)	−.25**	−.03	.19*
	ABC1936 ($N = 120$)	.00	.10	.14

Note. From "Homocysteine, B Vitamin Status, and Cognitive Function in the Elderly," S. J. Duthie, L. J. Whalley, A. R. Collins, S. Leaper, K. Berger, and I. J. Deary, 2002, *American Journal of Clinical Nutrition, 75*, p. 910. Copyright 2002 by the American Society for Nutrition. Adapted with permission. *$p < .05$. **$p < .01$.

Correlations were typically around .2 (see Table 7.3). There were significant negative associations between plasma homocysteine and Raven's Standard Progressive Matrices ($r = -.22$), Block Design ($r = -.27$), and Digit Symbol ($r = -.25$). The correlations were almost unchanged after adjustment for MHT IQ score at age 11 (Duthie et al., 2002).

The findings in the ABC1921 suggest that in this sample, in their late 70s, plasma homocysteine might contribute about 7% of the variance to some cognitive abilities in old age, after adjustment for childhood IQ. There was little evidence that it was relevant to cognitive performance in the younger cohort. Therefore, the processes that led to the accumulation of homocysteine might be relevant to accelerated cognitive aging beyond the mid-70s. Folate and vitamin B_{12} are involved with the conversion—remethylation—of homocysteine to the amino acid methionine (Duthie et al., 2002). This in turn is converted to S-Adenosylmethionine, which acts as the principal donor of methyl groups and is important, for example, in the synthesis of the monoamine neurotransmitters dopamine and 5-HT (and serotonin). Its methylation properties also contribute to the membrane–phospholipid methylation that is required for receptor coupling and to the integrity of macromolecules such as DNA and proteins (Herrmann, 2006; A. L. Miller, 2003). In complementary medicine, S-Adenosylmethionine has been recommended as a putative enhancer of cognition and elevator of low mood (A. L. Miller, 2003; Werneke, Turner, & Priebe, 2006). Vitamin B_{12} deficiency is associated with hyperhomocysteinemia. Part of homocysteine's toxic effects may also occur via oxidative stress and excitatory neuroreceptor activation.

The possible contribution of vitamin B_{12} and/or folate deficiency in individual differences in cognitive aging was explored further in the LBC1921 (Starr, Pattie, Whiteman, Deary, & Whalley, 2005). Homocysteine was not assessed in this sample. Four hundred seventy participants had appropriate cognitive data for analysis, and all had Mini-Mental State Examination scores greater than 23 and no history of dementia. Of these, 422 had vitamin B_{12} measured from blood serum, and 391 had folate measured. MHT IQ scores at age 11 correlated significantly with serum folate ($r = .13$, $p = .010$) and nonsignificantly with serum vitamin B_{12} ($r = .04$, $p = .42$). MHT IQ scores at age 79 correlated significantly with serum folate ($r = .12$, $p = .016$) and with serum vitamin B_{12} ($r = .12$, $p = .018$). A linear regression analysis was undertaken to inquire whether either of these biomarkers contributed to cognitive function at age 79 after adjustment for MHT IQ score at age 11. This was not the case for folate. Vitamin B_{12} contributed a small amount of variance (0.8%, $p = .016$) to IQ at age 79 after IQ at age 11 was entered. Leaving out 2 people with folate concentrations below the normal range had a negligible effect on the results.

Exploration of the range of vitamin B_{12} concentrations revealed a more complex story (Starr et al., 2005). In the LBC1921 sample, for participants with appropriate data, 25 people had vitamin B_{12} concentrations below the normal range. Within this group, the correlation between MHT IQ score at age 79 and vitamin B_{12} concentration was .57 ($p < .001$), which was significantly greater than the correlation ($r = .10, p = .031$) in the group whose vitamin B_{12} concentrations were in the normal range ($p = .016$). The significant influence of vitamin B_{12} concentration on cognitive function in old age in this sample remained significant after further adjustment for sex, APOE e4 status, smoking, the use of the cholesterol-reducing statin medication, and the number of prescribed drugs. In contrast with Duthie et al.'s (2002) study, which used some more specific cognitive tests and did not repeat the MHT in old age, Starr et al.'s (2005) study found a smaller influence of vitamin B_{12} on IQ in old age. Moreover, Starr et al. found that the concentration between folate and cognitive ability in old age was accounted for by childhood IQ. The LBC1921 is the larger sample, and these latter results emphasize the usefulness of having prior ability measures to check for reverse causality with respect to putative contributors to cognition in old age.

As people grow older, and as some cognitive functions decline, the gray matter of the brain shrinks. The causes of individual differences in this change are not understood, and a study involving the ABC1921 tested some possible biochemical associations (Whalley, Staff, et al., 2003). Antioxidants might be important, so vitamin C was studied. The accumulation of homocysteine might be important, perhaps because of folate and/or vitamin B_{12} deficiency, and it was included. Advanced glycation end products might affect the aging brain, which led to the inclusion of glycated hemoglobin. High levels of cholesterol might be related to the development of cognitive problems; it was included, too. There were 82 (44 men and 38 women) participants from the ABC1921 with the relevant imaging and biochemical data. Controlling for intracranial vault size, gray matter volume derived from voxel-based analyses of magnetic resonance images was correlated with the preceding blood markers as follows: plasma homocysteine, $r = -.23, p < .05$; cholesterol, $r = -.25, p < .05$, low density lipoprotein, $r = -.29, p < .01$; red blood cell (but not plasma) folate, $r = .23, p < .05$; and vitamin C, $r = .27, p < .02$. A regression analysis was undertaken with gray matter volume as the outcome variable, sex as a fixed effect, and intracranial volume as a covariable. On entering the blood markers just listed, only vitamin C entered the model ($p < .05$), with an eta-squared value of .056. These significant results on gray matter volume were based on cross-sectional analyses, and so brain shrinkage as such—something that requires longitudinal measurement—may not be assumed. The study did not identify any significant blood marker correlates of white matter volume. In summary, some factors related to increased risk of vascular disease appeared to be related to decreased gray matter volume in the older brain.

DIETARY SUPPLEMENTS

The foregoing analyses involved blood-based biomarkers that were relevant to nutrition. Next were examinations of dietary supplements and how those were related to cognition in youth and old age (Whalley, Fox, et al., 2003; Whalley, Fox, Wahle, Starr, & Deary, 2004). These inquiries recognized that supplements are heterogeneous, coming in different combinations of various compounds. The takers of dietary supplements are potentially heterogeneous, too, with some people taking them because they think it might alleviate a disorder and some taking them as part of a healthy lifestyle package that also might include healthy diet, exercise, not smoking, and so forth. Some older people might take dietary supplements in the belief that they help cognition in old age. The findings from the cognitive epidemiology studies (see Part II, this volume) suggested another possibility: Any apparent association between healthy cognitive aging and dietary supplementation might be explained by people with higher childhood IQs taking dietary supplements in old age.

Participants in the first study were the members of ABC1921 (Whalley, Fox, et al., 2003). Part of their assessment was the completion of a self-reported (though often assisted, in this study) inventory concerning how frequently they consumed certain foodstuffs (Scottish Heart Health/MONICA questionnaire; Bolton-Smith & Milne, 1991). This had some validating data in comparisons with weighed food intake and serum measurements. There were questions about the use of supplements, including vitamin supplements (e.g., multivitamins), fish oil (e.g., cod liver oil), herbal extracts (e.g., ginko biloba, ginseng), mineral supplements (e.g., selenium), and edible oils used as supplements (e.g., primrose oil). In the study, a *supplement user* was defined a person who had taken any of these supplements for at least the past year with doses taken at least 5 days per week. This is a stringent criterion, not least in its omission of participants who took supplements on a seasonal and/or periodic basis. The sample also had blood taken for the measurement of a number of vitamins. From the ABC1921 there were 176 people with cognitive and supplement use data. Of these, there were 125 people with analyzable MONICA questionnaire returns, and 110 of these provided a fasting blood sample for the assay of micronutrients.

Dietary supplement users constitute 48 of the 176 ABC1921 participants with relevant data (Whalley, Fox, et al., 2003). Of the 48, 37 took a single supplement. The most common supplement was fish oil; 29 participants took it alone or in combination with other supplements. The supplement takers were more likely to be female and to have a lower body mass index, but they did not differ from participants who did not take supplements on education, occupational status, or deprivation of their area of residence. Neither was there any difference between the groups on the estimated intake of 15 different nutrients derived from the MONICA questionnaire. From plasma measurements, supplement users were significantly higher on vitamin C, folate α-carotene, and lower on homocysteine and γ-tocopherol. Among a number of medical and fitness variables, the only difference found was that supplement users took fewer prescribed medications. There were no significant differences between supplement users and nonusers in Raven's Standard Progressive Matrices or Mini-Mental State Examination scores in old age. The mean MHT IQ scores at age 11 were as follows: male supplement users = 114.0 (SD = 10.1, N = 16), male supplement nonusers = 101.6 (SD = 15.2, N = 66), female supplement users = 103.4 (SD = 13.8, N = 32), and female supplement nonusers = 102.0 (SD = 14.0, N = 62). There was a significant main effect of supplement use (p < .01) and a significant Supplement Use × Sex interaction in childhood IQ (p < .05). This was the most novel and provocative finding in the study: The use of supplements in old age might be an outcome of higher prior intelligence, although the effect was mostly due to the remarkably high mean IQ of the small number of supplement-taking men in the ABC1921.

Still driven by the knowledge that, although the micronutrients of antioxidant vitamins and the macronutrients of n-3 polyunsaturated fatty acids were popularly believed to be helpful for the aging brain, a further study was undertaken on the ABC1936 (Whalley, Fox, Wahle, et al., 2004). The study was completed before the ABC1936 reached its eventual size. There were 423 volunteers at this time, with 350 of them (171 women and 179 men) having full dietary, cognitive, and other data. Supplement use was asked about at interview and was categorized into four groups: (a) none (N = 229), (b) fish oil with or without antioxidant vitamins (N = 72), (c) vitamins but no fish oil (N = 29), and (d) other supplements (N = 20). Within this sample there was a nested case control study in which 60 fish oil users and nonusers were matched on sex and childhood IQ (individually and within 5 IQ points, 0.3 SD). The criterion for fish oil use was to have taken it on most days in the previous 6 months, versus not taking it.

In the ABC1936, women were more likely to take supplements (Whalley, Fox, Wahle, et al., 2004). Other than that, supplement takers and nontakers did not differ on occupation, smoking, alcohol, body mass index, or almost all other medical factors. Analysis of the intake of many dietary factors based on food frequency questionnaire analysis showed that supplement users consumed more vegetables and cereal fiber and took more vitamin C. The cognitive test differences among the four groups were interesting. There were no significant differences in MHT IQ scores at age 11, Rey Auditory Verbal Learning Test, Block Design, Uses of Common Objects, or Raven's Standard Progressive Matrices. There were significant differences in IQ age 64 (p < .01). This IQ score was computed using principal components analysis of the five cognitive tests taken at age 64; the first unrotated principal component accounted for 52% of the total variance. All three supplement-taking groups scored better than the nontakers (all $ps < .02$). There were significant differences in the Digit Symbol test scores at age 64 ($p < .001$), with all three supplement-taking groups scores better than the nontakers (all $ps < .005$). After adjustment for MHT IQ score at age 11, the Digit Symbol test scores still differed at age 64, but the age 64 IQ scores did not. Indeed, it is revealing to look at this last result in some more detail than was done in the original publication (Whalley, Fox, Wahle, et al., 2004). The MHT IQ scores from age 11 and IQ at age 64 are plotted, with standard error bars, in Figure 7.2. These data make clear that, for the three largest groups, there is very close correspondence between childhood and later life IQs. The conclusion is that it appears, if anything, that people with higher childhood IQs take supplements when they are older. There is very little evidence of supplement use improving cognition in old age over the score in youth, although the data go a little in that direction. What has happened in these data is that an only-just-nonsignificant finding for childhood IQ has become a significant difference in old age but, in fact, most of the latter effect is due to differences in the former.

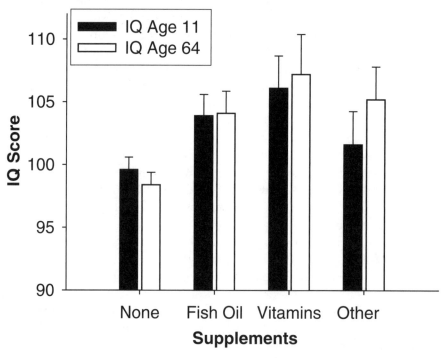

Figure 7.2. The association between dietary supplement use and Moray House Test IQ score and IQ (calculated from tests described in the text) at age 64. From "Cognitive Aging, Childhood Intelligence, and the Use of Food Supplements: Possible Involvement of n-3 Fatty Acids," by L. J. Whalley, H. C. Fox, K. W. Wahle, J. M. Starr, and I. J. Deary, 2004, American Journal of Clinical Nutrition, 80, p. 1654. Copyright 2004 by the American Society for Nutrition. Adapted with permission.

In the case control study of 60 fish oil users versus nonusers who were matched on sex and childhood IQ ($M = 100.7$, $SDs = 14.6$ vs. 100.2 and 14.2, respectively), there was a significant advantage for the users on Block Design ($p < .05$, Cohen's $d = 0.38$). There were no significant differences on IQ at age 64, Rey Auditory Verbal Learning Test, Digit Symbol, Uses of Common Objects, or Raven's Standard Progressive Matrices. Red blood cell membrane measurements revealed that the fish oil users had significantly higher n-3 polyunsaturated fatty acids and lower n-6 polyunsaturated fatty acids. Data from the 120 participants were combined for a correlational analysis. There were significant associations (all $ps < .05$) between total n-3 polyunsaturated fatty acids (positive) and n-6 fatty acids to n-3 fatty acid ratios (negative), and MHT IQ at age 11, IQ at age 64, Block Design, and Raven's Standard Progressive Matrices. All of the correlations were approximately .2 (see Table 7.4). None of the correlations with cognitive test scores at age 64 were significant after adjustment for MHT IQ at age 11. Once more, the conclusion here seems largely to be that childhood IQ has an influence on the state of the body at age 64, rather than there being some bodily contribution (viz., red cell membrane fatty acid content) to cognitive health at 63. The original publication has two exceptions to this. After adjustment for MHT IQ at age 11, the ratio of docosahexaenoic acid to arachidonic acid correlated .23 ($p < .02$) with IQ at age 64, and .25 ($p < .01$) with Block Design. Therefore, although these might be due to chance, there is a small indication of some contribution to cognitive aging.

Whalley, Fox, Wahle, et al.'s (2004) original conclusion that "use of food supplements in late adulthood is associated with cognitive performance."

TABLE 7.4

Correlations Between Cognitive Test Scores in Childhood and Old Age With Total n-3 Polyunsaturated Fatty Acids and n-6:n-3 Fatty Acid Ratios in the Red Blood Cell Membranes of 120 Members of the Aberdeen Birth Cohort 1936

Test	Total n-3 polyunsaturated fatty acids	n-6:n-3 ratio
Moray House Test IQ at age 11	.21*	−.19*
IQ at age 64	.21*	−.20*
Rey Auditory Verbal Learning Test	.15	−.13
Block Design	.21*	−.22*
Digit Symbol	.18	−.12
Uses of Common Objects	−.07	.02
Raven's Standard Progressive Matrices	.19*	−.19*

Note. The full table in the original publication also includes correlations with eicosapentaenoic acid (EPA), docosapentaenoic acid, docosahexaenoic acid (DHA), arachidonic acid (AA), EPA-to-AA ratio, and DHA-to-AA ratio. From "Cognitive Aging, Childhood Intelligence, and the Use of Food Supplements: Possible Involvement of n-3 Fatty Acids," by L. J. Whalley, H. C. Fox, K. W. Wahle, J. M. Starr, and I. J. Deary, 2004, *American Journal of Clinical Nutrition, 80,* p. 1655. Copyright 2004 by the American Society for Nutrition. Adapted with permission.
*$p < .05$.

This association does not depend on differences in cognitive ability present in childhood" (p. 1655) is only very partially correct. It applies only to the Digit Symbol test (Whalley, Fox, Wahle, et al., 2004, Table 4), and it fails fully to scrutinize the data redrawn here in Figure 7.2. Nevertheless, as was discussed, the Digit Symbol test might have particular value as a sensitive test in cognitive aging. Whalley, Fox, Wahle, et al. also concluded that "higher childhood IQ is probably associated with higher fish-oil consumption (including fish-oil supplements) in later adulthood" (p. 1655). We should note that these problems of deciding causal direction existed in a study with childhood IQ and in a sample for whom there were unusually rich dietary supplement use and biochemical data. It is a valuable reminder of the difficulty of finding clear answers for these important questions.

MEDICATIONS

Apart from dietary factors, supplements, and blood-measured variables, another set of chemicals that might potentially influence brain function is prescribed medications. A review had suggested that there was uncertainty, and possible variability, about the effects of prescribed drugs on mental function in older people and that taking multiple drugs might be especially problematic (Meador, 1998). Drugs might improve cognition (e.g., statins, which reduce cholesterol) or affect it deleteriously (e.g., some diuretics used for high blood pressure). The participants used for an investigation into drugs and cognitive change were the LBC1921 (Starr, McGurn, et al., 2004). Any diseases with which they had been diagnosed were categorized. Current medications were categorized into seven groups: (a) neuroactive drugs (e.g., major and minor tranquilizers, antidepressants, antiepileptics), (b) beta blockers, (c) angiotensin-converting enzyme inhibitors, (d) statins, (e) aspirin and nonsteroidal anti-inflammatory drugs, (f) cardiovascular medication, and (g) any other medication. There were 478 people in the LBC1921 who had not been diagnosed with dementia and who had MHT scores from childhood and old age. With childhood IQ and sex in a general linear model, the use of neuroactive drugs was associated with significantly lower MHT scores at age 79 ($p = .001$, partial $\eta^2 = .026$), and the use of statins was associated with significantly higher MHT scores at age 79 ($p = .017$, partial $\eta^2 = .013$). Also, people who, overall, took more prescribed drugs, had relatively low MHT scores at age 79 ($p = .011$, partial $\eta^2 = .014$). These effects remained significant after adjustment for education, occupational social class, smoking, living alone, and depression scores on the Hospital Anxiety Depression Scale (Zigmond & Snaith, 1983).

A further multivariable model was run that included all of the drug effects and covariables (Starr, McGurn, et al., 2004). The optimal model for predicting MHT IQ scores at age 79 included sex, total number of drugs (worsening effect on IQ in old age relative to youth), and statin use (improving effect; all $ps \leq .001$). The worsening effect of total drugs contributed about 2.2% of the variance to MHT IQ in old age, and the improving effect of statins added about 2.8%. The improving effect of statins might be related to aspects of cholesterol metabolism that can make the brain vulnerable to Alzheimer's disease. These findings were consistent with other studies that have examined statin use and cognitive problems in older people (Yaffe, Barrett-Connor, Lin, & Grady, 2002). However, it is not established that statins are helpful in the early stages of cognitive decline (Winblad, Jelic, Kershaw, & Amatniek, 2007; Xiong, Benson, & Doraiswamy, 2005). The worsening effect on old age IQ of the total number of drugs could be an effect of the underlying illnesses for which the drugs are being taken.

IV

OTHER ASSOCIATIONS
WITH CHILDHOOD IQ

OTHER ASSOCIATIONS
WITH CHILDHOOD IQ

Cognitive epidemiology and cognitive aging were the main programs of research that were set up and conducted after the rediscovery of the Scottish Mental Surveys (SMSs) of 1932 and 1947 (SMS1932 and SMS1947). However, they were not the only research output from the surveys' data. From time to time, it became clear that analysis of the data could make significant contributions outside of these important fields. This ability was due in part to having a whole population of individuals examined on the same test, something that was unique. It also was due in part to our discovering other, specific aspects of the SMSs, such as the identification of twins in the SMS1947. It was due in part to our finding other databases to which we were give permission to link the Scottish Mental Surveys, such as birth data from Edinburgh Hospitals in 1921. Last, it was due in part to there being other research questions for which we realized it would be useful to have a record of people's IQ from childhood.

In the chapters of Part IV, we relate the many factors associated with childhood IQ. In chapter 8, we discuss factors that preceded childhood IQ test scores, including sex, whether one was a twin, and birth weight. In chapter 9, we discuss factors that came after the childhood IQ test scores, including marriage, satisfaction with life, intellectual engagement and imagination, social mobility and status attainment, and quality of life.

8

FACTORS THAT PRECEDED CHILDHOOD IQ TEST SCORES

In this chapter, we discuss antecedents of scores on tests of intelligence at age 11, namely, sex, whether one is a twin, and birth weight. All of these factors are present at the moment of birth. Therefore, any strong correlations between these factors and childhood intelligence would seem to indicate that these factors influenced childhood intelligence. In the following sections, we discuss the findings of each factor in detail.

SEX

The starting point for an analysis of sex differences in the Moray House Test (MHT) scores in the Scottish Mental Survey (SMS) of 1932 (SMS1932) was a quote from the eminent British differential psychologist Alice Heim (1970):

> There is a tendency for men to be "more so" than females, whatever is being tested. Thus on intelligence tests, for instance, when groups of comparable men and women take tests, they tend to gain mean scores which are similar, but the highest and lowest scorers are liable to be male.

The finding is not confined to intelligence tests. . . . There is a tendency for women students to gain proportionately more second class degrees—and, thus, fewer firsts and thirds—in many examination subjects. . . . In the "real world" situation, the same tendency holds: men rather than women are found at the extremes. There are more male geniuses, more male criminals, more male mental defectives. (pp. 136–137)

This is a clear and general statement of the variability hypothesis that, later, mostly applied to intelligence differences (Hoddings, 1992; Shields, 1982).

The variability hypothesis notwithstanding, even the basic issue of mean differences between the sexes in general mental ability and/or more specific abilities was not settled. Although a review of previous studies had concluded that there was little, if any, difference in mean general IQ and some differences in specific mental abilities (Mackintosh, 1998a, 1998b), the study designs were problematic. Thus, the findings may be unreliable.

The largest report had been the reanalyses of six large studies that had been conducted in the United States (Hedges & Nowell, 1995). The samples included males and females from age 15 to early 20s. The samples had large numbers, and so most of the mean differences were significant, even when they were very small in effect size. Women scored better on reading comprehension, perceptual speed, and associative memory. Men scored better on mathematics and scales that involved more vocation-oriented abilities, such as mechanical reasoning. Men tended to have larger standard deviations. Even this reanalysis of very large studies was imperfect and open to bias. Many of the tests examined were work related or school related. There might be sex biases in school and college subject choices and jobs that would precede these score differences. The ages of the samples meant that some people would have left formal education and that there would be sex-biased choices of school, college, and vocational subjects. None of the samples tested comprised a complete population. For all of these reasons, it was hard to be certain that the differences reported could not be due to sample biases, something Hedges and Nowell (1995) themselves discussed.

The SMS had data that overcame these problems. It assessed an entire population, or as nearly so as is ever likely to be achieved. It was conducted at an age when there had been no loss of pupils from the educational system and when the subjects taken by boys and girls were almost identical. The mental test used was not aimed at school- or work-related achievement (Scottish Council on Research in Education [SCRE], 1933).

For the examination of sex differences in the whole population, a computerized database of the SMS1932 was used (Deary, Thorpe, Wilson, Starr, & Whalley, 2003). The data had been entered twice, and the two databases were compared for accuracy. Discrepancies were resolved by checking the original ledgers. There were 86,520 participants. These included people who had missing scores on the mental tests, mostly because they had been absent from school on the day of the test. Also, the number was short of the expected total because the original ledgers from Fife, Angus, and Wigtown were missing. In the preparation of data for this analysis, the First Picture Test, the Second Picture Test (see chap. 1, this volume), and the MHT were summed and converted to an IQ-type score, with mean of 100 and a standard deviation of 15. The reason for including the picture tests in the total score was to try to obtain more discriminating power at the lower end of the range of ability, because the picture tests involve simple, nonverbal items. The few participants who had impossible scores (i.e., greater than the maximum possible for the test), and participants with scores of zero on the picture tests were omitted. There were 79,376 children with total score information: 39,343 girls and 40,033 boys.

The mean IQ scores, based on the combination of the First Picture Test and the Second Picture Test and the MHT, were 100.64 for the girls and 100.48 for the boys ($p = .11$; Deary, Thorpe, et al., 2003). Despite the large numbers, in this almost-whole population there was no significant difference in mean IQ at age 11. The variances were significantly different ($p < .001$). To visualize the effect of this variance difference, yet no mean difference, in the population distribution of IQ scores, each person was allocated to an IQ band. The first, lowest, band was from IQ 50 to < 60, then from 60 to < 65, and so on, in 5-point increments until a top band of 130 to 140. Within each IQ band the percentages of boys and girls was computed. These percentages are plotted in Figure 8.1. In the region of the mean, from about IQ 90+ to about IQ 115, there is a small excess of girls. With a move to both extremes, the excess is male. In the IQ band from 50 to < 60, 58.6% of the population is male. If the female percentage is subtracted from the male percentage at this IQ score band, the gender gap is 17.2%. In the top band, from IQ 130 to < 140, 57.7% of the population are boys. This is a gender gap of 15.4%. The figure also contains information about the absolute numbers of boys and girls in each IQ band. These effects at the extremes are based on relatively small numbers. The excess of girls at the average IQ bands is based on large numbers. The proportion of males increases steadily as the bands move from below IQ 90 and above IQ 115.

This was the most comprehensive examination of this question ever conducted. Despite the very large numbers, there was no difference in the means. There was more variation in the boys, with approximately 1.4 boys to every girl in the highest and lowest IQ bands. There was no evidence that there had been any sex bias in the small percentage of the population born in 1921 who did not take part in the SMS1932. It is not straightforward to explain why the standard deviation, but not the mean, differs between the sexes. The apparent left–right symmetry of Figure 8.1 should not lead one to the exclusive conclusion that there has to be a single explanation that would

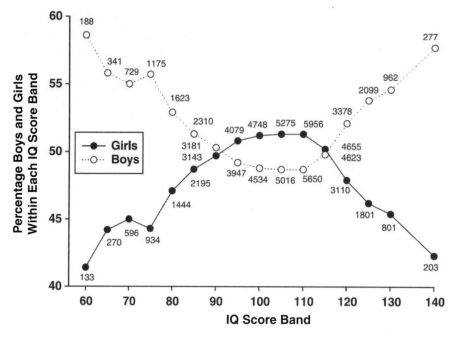

Figure 8.1. Numbers and percentages of boys and girls within each IQ score band of the Scottish population born in 1921 and tested in the Scottish Mental Survey in 1932 at age 11. The y-axis represents the percentage of each sex in each 5-point band of IQ scores. Numbers beside each point represent the absolute numbers of boys and girls in each 5-point IQ score band. From "Population Sex Differences in IQ at Age 11: The Scottish Mental Survey 1932," by I. J. Deary, G. Thorpe, V. Wilson, J. M. Starr, and L. J. Whalley, 2003, *Intelligence, 31,* p. 537. Copyright 2003 by Elsevier Limited. Reprinted with permission.

account for there being more boys at the bottom and top of the range. The causal factors at the two ends of the distribution might be different (Deary, Thorpe, et al., 2003). The excess of boys at the bottom end was known from epidemiological surveys (Rutter et al., 1990). Heim (1970) considered a range of explanations, from social to biological, for the greater variance among boys. Deary, Thorpe, et al. (2003) suggested that the greater variance among males might in part account for the different educational outcomes in males and females. They summarized data from the UK Higher Education Statistics Agency from 1994–1995 to 2000–2001. They found that, on average, 48.5% of women obtained upper-second-class degrees, but only 39.5% of men. However, more men than women graduated with pass or third-class degrees (9.5% vs. 5.1%) and with first-class degrees (8.2% vs. 7.0%). The male:female proportion of first-class degrees was steeper at the more academically elite universities. The greater male variance was replicated, at a similar age, in a far larger and more recent UK sample (Strand, Deary, & Smith, 2006), and in a U.S. sample in which brothers and sisters were compared (Deary, Irwing, Der, & Bates, 2007). Nevertheless, whatever the origins and implications of the finding, the data from the SMS1932 remain the most comprehensive demonstration of the greater variability of mental ability among males (Deary, Thorpe, et al., 2003).

TWINS

Twins were identified explicitly in the SMS of 1947 (SMS1947) but not in the SMS1932, and some analyses were performed on them (Maxwell & Pilliner, 1960). In the SMS1947, zygosity was not estimated. Both of these limitations were overcome. A way was found to identify probable twin pairs in the SMS1932. Moreover, despite the fact that zygosity is required to separate genetic and environmental contributions to a phenotype, a novel method was found to circumvent this, too. Therefore, the data from both surveys were used: first, to examine IQ's environmental and genetic origins and, second, to ask whether there is a cognitive cost to being a twin as opposed to being a singleton.

Genetic and Environmental Contributions to Twin IQ Scores

The environmental and genetic contributions to mental ability differences have been the subject of much study. Although it is generally concluded that genetic factors account for approximately 50% of the variance in mental test scores, there is still much that is not fully understood (Bouchard, 2004; Plomin & Spinath, 2004). For example, despite such a high genetic contribution, there are no replicated, individual genes that are related to intelligence differences (Deary, Spinath, & Bates, 2006). Also, the heritability of intelligence changes with the age of the individuals under study, increasing from childhood to maturity, and the profile of this change was not fully known. There is also the problem of biased estimates in the literature from selection factors in the sample under study (Bouchard & McGue, 2003). Much of the research in this area is based on volunteer samples of twins. It would be both valuable and unique to have an entire population of twins examined for mental ability. There were two barriers to achieving this in the SMS1932 and SMS1947: (a) Only the latter survey identified the twins within the population, and (b) analysis of environmental and genetic contributions requires the identification of monozygotic (identical) and dizygotic (nonidentical) twins, and that had not been done in the SMS1947.

In the SMS1947 there were 517 twin pairs, of whom 320 were same sex, and 197 opposite-sex pairs (Mehrotra & Maxwell, 1949; SCRE, 1949, 1953b). No attempt had been made to gather information about zygosity. Height and weight were measured in these twins. No attempt was made to identify twins in the SMS1932. It might be possible to do so, however. If two people in the SMS1932 had the same surname, date of birth, and school, then they were probably twins. Using these criteria, researchers found 572 presumptive pairs of twins in the SMS1932, of whom 382 were same sex and 190 were opposite sex (Benyamin, Wilson, Whalley, Visscher, & Deary, 2005). It seemed to validate, somewhat, this speculative method of identifying twins, when the percentage of twins in the population in the SMS1947 was 0.70% and in the SMS1932 was 0.64%. Therefore, a presumptive solution had been found to the problem of no twins having been identified in the SMS1932.

The more difficult problem in making any use of the surveys' data for environmental and genetic research was that there was no information gathered about zygosity. However, there was some useful information. Opposite-sex twins must be dizygotic, and the proportion of dizygotic twins assumed to be opposite sex was 0.5. In fact, this proved to be enough information for a novel application of the *finite mixture distribution method* (Neale, 2003) to separate the covariance between twin pairs into additive genetic, shared environmental contributions and unique environmental contributions. The details of this analysis are complex and can be seen in full detail in Benyamin et al. (2005). In a conceptual sense, the basis for the analysis may be seen in Figure 8.2. Among the overall distribution of same-sex twin pair differences in mental test scores it was assumed that there were two distributions: a wider distribution for dizygotic twins than for monozygotic twins, because there were genetic sources of difference for the dizygotic twins that did not apply to the monozygotic twins. These two distributions were fitted to the same-sex pair differences. There was very strong statistical support for there being two distributions instead of one. As expected, in both cohorts, the same-sex twin pair intraclass correlations were higher than those for opposite-sex pairs: .67 versus .58 in the SMS1932, and .72 versus .62 in the SMS1947. Recall that the same-sex twins include dizygotic as well as monozygotic twin pairs.

The mixture distribution model was used to estimate the variance components of the MHT score (Benyamin et al., 2005). There were no significant differences for the SMS1932 and the SMS1947, and so the combined results are considered here. The proportion of the individual differences in MHT scores due to additive genetic factors was .70 (95% confidence interval [CI]: .58, .83), due to shared environment was .21 (95% CI: .10, .32), and due to unique environment was .09 (95% CI: .06, .12). There were no significant differences between boys and girls regarding these contributions. Also, there was strong evidence that the same set of genes contributed to MHT differences in boys and girls, because the genetic correlation was not significantly different from 1.0. This study added to the literature on the etiology of individual differences in intelligence by being the first analysis of complete populations of twins. The study also provided a novel and partly validated (Benyamin, Deary, & Visscher, 2006) method for identifying twin pairs from

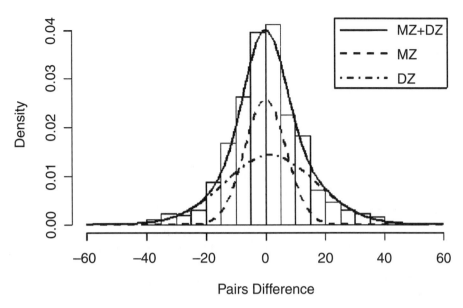

Figure 8.2. Probability density function of same-sex pair difference for the combined Moray House Test score, after adjusting for sex and cohort effects, and the fitted curves for two underlying distributions, assumed to correspond to monozygotic (MZ) and same-sex dizygotic (DZ) pairs. The histogram is the observed distribution of the same-sex pairs difference, and the solid curve is the sum of the fitted distributions from the mixture model. From "Large, Consistent Estimates of the Heritability of Cognitive Ability in Two Entire Populations of 11-Year-Old Twins From Scottish Mental Surveys of 1932 and 1947," by B. Benyamin, V. Wilson, L. J. Whalley, P. M. Visscher, and I. J. Deary, 2005, *Behavior Genetics, 35,* p. 527 Copyright 2005 by Springer. Reprinted with permission.

large population samples using minimal demographic information (Webbink, Roeleveld, & Visscher, 2006).

The Cognitive Cost of Being a Twin

It had long been debated, but never resolved, whether twins had lower mean intelligence test scores than singletons. Large studies in the United States and the United Kingdom suggested that twins might score less well than singletons on mental tests. Among the people who took the National Merit Scholarship Qualifying Test in the United States, twins had test scores that were slightly less than 0.3 standard deviation lower than singletons' scores (Breland, 1974). In the UK city of Birmingham, the age 11 verbal reasoning scores of all children born between 1950 and 1954 were examined (Record, McKeown, & Edwards, 1970). On a scale with a standard deviation of 15, singletons scored 4 to 5 points better than twins. These studies had compared twins with singletons, but not within the same families. A more up-to-date study compared twins with their singleton siblings on the Wechsler

Adult Intelligence Scale—III (Wechsler, 1997) and found no significant difference (Posthuma, De Geus, Bleichrodt, & Boomsma, 2000). Posthuma and colleagues (2000) suggested that previous studies reporting lower test scores in twins might suffer from two methodological problems. First, they were typically based on samples that might be biased. This would not have been the case with Record et al.'s (1970) study. Second, other studies at times failed to enquire whether any ability decrement among twins might be caused by differences in social background. Some information on twin–singleton differences in the SMS1947 had already been reported (Mehrotra & Maxwell, 1949; SCRE, 1953b). The data from the SMS1932 and SMS1947 were used to add more information to the dispute concerning twin–singleton mental ability differences (Deary, Pattie, Wilson, & Whalley, 2005).

For the SMS1932, the twins were identified using the procedure described earlier (Benyamin et al., 2005); that is, children with the same surname, date of birth, and in the same school were assumed to be twins. In the SMS1947 the twins were identified explicitly. In addition to MHT data from age 11, the following variables were also gathered on the twins from the 1947 survey: father's occupation (which was coded on the basis of a 5-point scale that ranged from most professional occupations to the most manual), number of people and rooms in the family house (which enabled an overcrowding index to be computed), actual and possible school attendance, and height. The SCRE (1953b) book that described the twins recorded 1,050 twins born in 1936 and on the registers of school classes in 1947. For the re-analyses, there were 1,034 sets of data located in the SCRE records (Deary, Pattie, et al., 2005). The SCRE (1953b) book had MHT scores on 974 of these twins, and there were 949 of these remaining in the SCRE records. There was at that time no computerized record of the entire SMS1947. However, the 6-Day Sample was representative of the population and had the same MHT and additional information as the twins, and therefore made a good control sample of singletons. Of the 1,208 people in the 6-Day Sample, 1,098 had MHT scores. Fourteen twins were removed from the 6-Day Sample.

The histogram (with applied normal curve) for the whole, remaining SMS1932 participants' MHT scores, and the scores for the twins, are shown in the top panels of Figure 8.3 (Deary, Pattie, et al., 2005). The shapes of the distributions are very similar, with a shoulder at the lower scores (floor effect). The peak of the twins' distribution is shifted to the left of that of the whole population. The mean MHT score for the whole population was 33.9 ($SD = 15.4$, $N = 81,140$). Note that this number is lower than that of the 87,498 who had MHT scores in the original survey (SCRE, 1933). This is because the score-containing ledgers from Fife, Angus, and Wigtown were missing. The mean MHT score for the people assumed to be twins was 28.5 ($SD = 15.1$, $N = 1,080$). The effect size of this 5.4-point difference corresponds to an effect size (Cohen's d) of 0.36. Boys and girls showed almost identical twin–singleton differences.

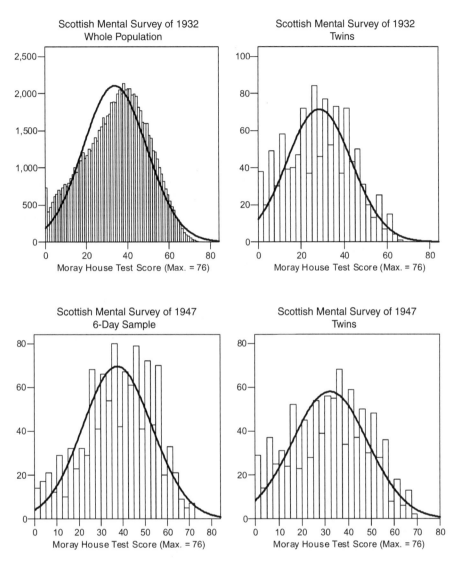

Figure 8.3. Top panels: Distributions (with normal curve added) of Moray House Test scores for the whole population (left panel) and twins (right panel) in the Scottish Mental Survey of 1932. Bottom panels: Distributions (with normal curve added) of Moray House Test scores for the 6-Day Sample (left panel) and twins (right panel) in the Scottish Mental Survey of 1947. Max. = Maximum. From "The Cognitive Cost of Being a Twin: Two Whole-Population Surveys," by I. J. Deary, A. Pattie, V. Wilson, and L. J. Whalley, 2005, *Twin Research and Human Genetics, 8,* p. 378. Copyright 2005 by Australian Academic Press. Reprinted with permission.

The histogram (with applied normal curve) for the 6-Day Sample of the SMS1947 participants' MHT scores, and the scores for the twins from the 1947 survey, are shown in the bottom panels of Figure 8.3 (Deary, Pattie, et al., 2005). In agreement with the analyses performed on the participants of the SMS1932, the shapes of the distributions are similar, with a floor effect on scores. Once again, the peak of the twins' distribution is shifted to the left of the singletons' distribution. The mean MHT score for the 6-Day Sample was 37.5 ($SD = 15.7$). The mean MHT score for twins was 32.2 ($SD = 16.3$). This 5.3-point difference corresponds to an effect size (Cohen's d) of 0.33. Further comparisons between the 6-Day Sample and the twins revealed that twins were significantly shorter and had more people in their immediate family. However, there were no significant differences between twins and singletons on father's occupational social class, overcrowding in the home, or attendance at school.

To address the possibility that the lower mental test scores in twins might especially be found in certain family backgrounds, the MHT scores for twins and singletons were separated by sex and father's social class (see Figure 8.4; see also Deary, Pattie, et al., 2005). The plots in Figure 8.4 show that there is mostly a steady decline in mean MHT scores as fathers' occupational social class goes from the most professional (Class 1) to the most manual (Class 5). The pattern is similar for the twins and the singletons, with the twins having generally parallel lower lines than the singletons. There is no evidence of a Twin × Social Class interaction, and none was found on general linear modeling (Deary, Pattie, et al., 2005). Also in the general linear model were sex, and the covariates of age at testing, overcrowding in the home, school attendance, height, and number of people in the family (see Table 8.1). All of the

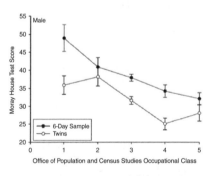
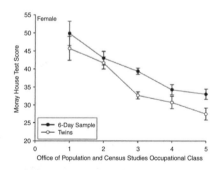

Figure 8.4. Mean Moray House Test scores (and standard errors) separated by father's occupational class of male twins and male singletons (left panel) and female twins and female singletons from the Scottish Mental Survey of 1947 (right panel). Singletons in both panels are members of the 6-Day Sample of the Scottish Mental Survey of 1947. From "The Cognitive Cost of Being a Twin: Two Whole-Population Surveys," by I. J. Deary, A. Pattie, V. Wilson, and L. J. Whalley, 2005, *Twin Research and Human Genetics, 8,* p. 380. Copyright 2005 by Australian Academic Press. Reprinted with permission.

TABLE 8.1
General Linear Modeling of Moray House Test (MHT) Scores in Twins Versus 6-Day Sample Participants From the Scottish Mental Survey of 1947

Variables in model	Effect of variable in full model			Effect of variable in reduced model with only group, sex, and social class			Group (twin vs. 6-Day) MHT difference in the reduced model[c]
	F	p	η^{2a}	F	p	η^{2b}	
Fixed effects							
Group: Twin versus singleton	26.9	< .001	.014	68.2	< .001	.033	5.7
Sex	9.9	.002	.005	6.0	.014	.003	—
Father's social class at age 11	6.6	< .001	.014	29.6	< .001	.056	—
Covariates							
Age at testing	58.4	< .001	.030	82.4	< .001	.039	5.6
Overcrowding in the home	27.3	< .001	.014	102.8	< .001	.050	5.1
School attendance (percentage)	28.6	< .001	.015	39.0	< .001	.019	5.7
Height	65.8	< .001	.033	150.2	< .001	.071	4.6
No. family members	63.8	< .001	.032	148.0	<.001	.069	3.9

Note. From "The Cognitive Cost of Being a Twin: Two Whole-Population Surveys," by I. J. Deary, A. Pattie, V. Wilson, and L. J. Whalley, 2005, *Twin Research and Human Genetics, 8,* p. 382. Copyright 2005 by Australian Academic Press. Adapted with permission.
[a]The full model contains all fixed effects and covariates in the first column. [b]The reduced model always includes the fixed effects of group (twin vs. singleton in the 6-Day Sample), sex, and father's social class, and then examines the effects of each of the covariates in isolation. [c]Differences in estimated marginal means.

covariates had significant effects on MHT score, either when they were all in the model together or when they were entered alone, along with group (twin vs. singleton in the 6-Day Sample). The effect of twin versus singleton in the estimated marginal means with only group, sex, and father's social class at age 11 in the model was 5.7 points. The only covariables that produced a non-negligible reduction of this difference were height, which reduced it to 4.6 points, and number of people in the family, which reduced it to 3.9 points.

Both of the SMSs delivered the same result: Twins had an average decrement of approximately 0.33 standard deviation in mental test scores—about 5 points on the typical IQ scale. The difference was found in whole-population groups of twins and was not due to social background as assessed by father's social class and other aspects of the home. A similar finding was obtained in an almost-comprehensive study of children who were born in Aberdeen in the 1950s (Ronalds, De Stavola, & Leon, 2005). Although these older Scottish cohorts agree that twins have a cognitive decrement, and quite closely on how much of an effect size that might be, there are possibly contradictory data. Studies on slightly older Danish twins with more recent birthdates show that there is no twin–singleton difference in educational performance (K. Christensen et al., 2006). These latter data, when combined with the findings from the SMSs and the Aberdeen children of the 1950s, raise three interesting issues (Deary, 2006).

First, it must be questioned whether there continue to be twin–singleton differences in ability among more recently born cohorts. Second, the data suggest that perhaps any twin versus singleton IQ differences disappear by young adulthood. Third, the data raise the possibility that twin–singleton IQ differences do not translate into differences in educational performance. With regard to the first question, K. Christensen et al. (2006) raised the possibility that improvements in obstetric and perinatal care might have caused the disappearance of any twin-versus-singleton IQ difference found among older cohorts. However, it is not clear how such improvements would play out. It is possible that better perinatal and obstetric care could help some premature, low birth weight twins to survive that previously would have died and who would be, on average, disadvantaged in IQ scores (Deary, 2006).

BIRTH WEIGHT

This is a story of how the luck in finding the data from the SMS1932 doubled with the finding of another database to which it was then linked. There is a hypothesis about the origins of adult chronic disease that states that some of the individual differences in predisposition originates during fetal development. It is called the *fetal origins of adult disease hypothesis*, or the *developmental origins of health and adult disease hypothesis*, or just the *fetal programming hypothesis*. The hypothesis is that periods of undernutrition during fetal development have consequences for disease susceptibility in later life (Barker, 1998, 2004). This includes the notion that brain development will be suboptimal during such periods. To date, the principal marker of the privations of maternal environment has been low birth weight—not prematurity, but being low in birth weight for gestational duration. The hypothesis does not only address very low birth weights, because it is thought that susceptibility extends across the normal range of birth weights. It has been established that low birth weight due to prematurity is associated with lower than expected cognitive ability in childhood and adolescence (Bhutta, Cleves, Casey, Cradock, & Anand, 2002). There was also some evidence that heavier birth weight in the normal range was associated with higher cognitive ability up to middle age, though that was largely accounted for by differences in cognitive ability that were present at age 8 (Richards, Hardy, Kuh, & Wadsworth, 2001). The field was relatively new, and there were unresolved issues, such as the contribution of mother's socioeconomic status, the child's gestational age, and the weight of the placenta to any manifest association between birth weight and later intelligence. An opportunity arose for a sample from the SMS1932 to address these outstanding issues.

It was discovered that, in the Lothian Health Services Archive held in the library of the University of Edinburgh, there were the original books with detailed records of all admissions to the Edinburgh Royal Maternity Hospital and Simpson's Memorial Hospital (Shenkin et al., 2001). These included the year 1921, when participants in the SMS1932 were born. The books had details of the children's birth dates and the date of the mothers' last menstrual period, meaning that gestational age could be calculated. There were also details of the children's birth weight and length, placental weight, father's occupation, the number of previous pregnancies, and the mother's age. There were 985 live, 1921-born singletons. The birth certificates of the children were traced, and these were then matched to the records in the SMS1932. There were 449 (46.5%) matches.

MHT score correlated .17 with birth weight ($p < .001$; Shenkin et al., 2001). The value for males was .15 ($p = .02$), and for females it was .21 ($p = .03$). Three hundred ninety-five participants also had data on father's occupation. Therefore, the preceding associations were repeated, partialing out paternal occupational social class. MHT score now correlated .22 with birth weight ($p < .001$). The value for males was .21 ($p = .02$), and for females it was .22 ($p = .02$). Two hundred ninety-five participants also had additional data on gestational age, maternal age, parity, and legitimacy. The preceding associations were rerun, partialing out all of these factors. MHT score now correlated .25 with birth weight ($p < .001$). The value for males was .23 ($p = .003$), and the value for females was .27 ($p = .002$). Birth length—corrected for all of the these factors except birth weight—correlated significantly with MHT scores at age 11. MHT score correlated .14 with birth length ($p < .01$) for the whole sample. The value for males was .11 ($p = .14$), and the value for females was .17 ($p = .05$). Birth weight and birth length were strongly correlated ($r = .54$, $p < .001$), and birth length no longer correlated significantly with MHT scores when corrected for birth weight.

SMS1932 MHT scores were significantly associated with father's occupational social class (Shenkin et al., 2001). The r value for the whole sample was −.26 ($p = < .001$). The value for males was −.33 ($p = < .001$), and for females it was −.18 ($p = .01$). Birth weight and father's occupational social class were not significantly correlated ($r = −.08$, $p = .12$). Multivariate analysis found that five variables (percentage of variance accounted for in the multivariable setting) contributed significantly (all $ps < .01$) to MHT scores at age 11: more professional paternal occupational social class (6.6%), heavier birth weight (3.8%), older age at testing (2.4%), lower maternal parity (2.0%), and legitimacy (1.5%).

The most contested question in the birth weight–childhood IQ association at that time was the role played by paternal socioeconomic status.

Therefore, to test this explicitly, a structural equation modeling analysis was performed (Shenkin et al., 2001). Two path models were tested. A *regression* path model hypothesized that birth weight and paternal occupational social class were independent contributors to MHT score at age 11. A *mediating* path model hypothesized that paternal occupational social class had an impact on birth weight, which in turn was associated with MHT score at age 11. The regression model provided best fit to the data. The mediating model was hindered from the outset by the lack of a significant correlation between paternal occupational social class and birth weight in this sample. The regression model had good fit statistics. The chi-square was low (8.86, $df = 6$) and nonsignificant ($p = .18$). The average of the off-diagonal absolute standardized residuals was low (.038). The Bentler–Bonett (normed and nonnormed) and comparative fit indices were .953, .973, and .984, respectively. The parameter weights for the regression model, all of which are significant, are shown in Figure 8.5. They may be squared to obtain the proportion of variance shared by adjacent variables. Note that birth weight mediated the effect of birth length on MHT score at age 11. Birth weight, paternal occupational social class, and age at the time of the SMS1932 all make significant and independent contributions to MHT score. The Lagrange Multiplier Test was applied and did not find any paths that could be added to improve the fit of the model.

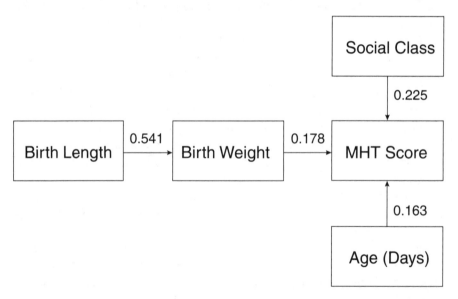

Figure 8.5. Best-fitting path model of the associations among birth weight, paternal occupational social class, age at the time of the Scottish Mental Survey of 1932, and Moray House Test (MHT) score at age 11. From "Birth Weight and Cognitive Function at Age 11 Years: The Scottish Mental Survey 1932," by S. D. Shenkin, J. M. Starr, A. Pattie, M. A. Rush, L. J. Whalley, and I. J. Deary, 2001, *Archives of Disease in Childhood, 85,* p. 193. Copyright 2001 by BMJ Publishing Group. Reprinted with permission.

Therefore, in this sample, members of which were born in hospital in Scotland in 1921, birth weight accounted for significant variance in MHT score at age 11, independently of father's occupational social class (Shenkin et al., 2001). It added to evidence from children born at other times, for example, from 1946 (Richards et al., 2001). An important aspect of the results was that the association held across the generally accepted normal range of birth weights, from 2,500 g to 4,500 g. Thus, within this range, if we divide the sample into groups that increase in weight by 500 g, the mean MHT scores increase, as follows: 2,501 g to 3,000 g = 34.4 (SD = 15.0, N = 102), 3,001 g to 3,500 g = 37.3 (SD = 14.6, N = 164), 3,501 g to 4,000 g = 37.8 (SD = 14.7, N = 115), 4,001 g to 4,500 g = 44.7 (SD = 10.6, N = 34). The mean MHT scores at age 11 for the 25 babies with birth weights below 2,500 g was 30.6 (SD = 19.4), and for the 9 babies with birth weights above 4,500 g it was 35.1 (SD = 9.4). Although there is no evidence that such factors either spuriously created or underestimated the effect sizes, a few things should be noted: The sample comprised hospital births at a time when this applied to a minority of births; there was a relatively large proportion of illegitimate births; and the tracing of births to the SMS data was less than 50%.

There are two additional notes to the story of the association between birth weight and childhood and adolescent mental ability. The team undertook a systematic review of this association, including only those studies that involved full-term births, the normal range of birth weights, and mental ability measured between age 5 and age 17 (Shenkin, Starr, & Deary, 2004). There were only six such studies, and they were too heterogeneous in their design and in the way they presented their results to conduct a meta-analysis. Nevertheless, the evidence appeared to indicate that there was a consistent and small positive association between birth weight and childhood and adolescent cognitive ability. However, in a later study, mother's IQ scores were available in addition to their children's birth weights and later mental test scores (Deary, Der, & Shenkin, 2005). After introducing this possible confounding variable, the majority of the association between birth weight and childhood IQ was accounted for by mother's IQ; that is, brighter mothers have brighter and heavier babies, and the association between birth weight and IQ in children might simply reflect this.

9

FACTORS THAT CAME AFTER
THE CHILDHOOD IQ TEST SCORES

In this chapter, we discuss lifetime consequences associated with variations in intelligence test scores at age 11, namely, marriage, satisfaction with life, intellectual engagement and imagination, social mobility and status attainment, and quality of life. All of these factors emerge much later than the childhood intelligence tests. Therefore, any strong correlations between these factors and childhood intelligence could indicate that childhood intelligence influenced these factors. In the following sections, we discuss the findings of each factor in detail.

MARRIAGE

Other studies have hinted that mental ability in childhood might be related to marriage in adult life. The U.S. National Longitudinal Survey of Youth 1979 found that people with higher mental test scores in late adolescence were more likely to be married approximately 10 years later (Herrnstein & Murray, 1994). Studies that used socioeconomic status as the predictor variable have provided some indications that men with lower status were less likely to marry than men with higher status and that this trend might be reversed in women (Emslie, Hunt, & Macintyre, 1999; Marmot et al., 1991). In both of these socioeconomic status studies, women in managerial or other professional grades were less likely to have married than men, with percentages of about 90% in men versus less than 60% in women. Given the correlation between socioeconomic status and psychometric intelligence, it is tenable that there is some association between IQ and marriage status and that it might differ between men and women.

The data set used to examine the association between childhood IQ and marriage in adulthood was the Scottish Mental Survey (SMS) of 1932 (SMS1932)–Midspan linkage study (Hart, Deary, et al., 2003). In chapter 2 of this volume, we described the Midspan Studies and the SMS1932–Midspan linkage study.

Questions about marital status were included in the questionnaire completed by the Midspan Studies' participants at approximately age 50. The questions asked people whether they had ever married and remained so, had stayed single, or were now widowed. There was an "other" category, endorsed by only 9 participants, who were excluded from further analysis. SMS1932–Midspan participants were classified according to whether, by the time of the Midspan questionnaire in midlife, they had ever been married, regardless of their actual marital status at the time of the study. There were 883 people (547 men and 336 women) with relevant data (Taylor, Hart, Davey Smith, Whalley, et al., 2005). At the time of the Midspan Studies questionnaire, when the participants were approximately age 50, 93.1% of the men and 90.2% of the women had been married. A comparison on all participants revealed no significant difference in the IQs of those who were ever married ($M = 100.1$, $SD = 14.9$) versus those who were never married ($M = 102.2$, $SD = 16.5$). However, when an analysis of variance was run with ever-versus never-married and sex as fixed effects, and childhood IQ as the dependent variable, there was a significant interaction ($p < .001$); that is, there was a different relationship between childhood IQ and marriage in the two sexes. This was most significant in the women. The mean IQ score of women who were ever married was 97.5 ($SD = 13.9$) versus 108.4 ($SD = 15.2$) for those who had never married ($p < .001$). In men, the mean IQ of those who had ever married was 101.6 ($SD = 15.2$) and the mean IQ of those who had never married was 96.8 ($SD = 15.8$), which only tended toward significance ($p = .066$). Incidentally, the same report found that there was a similar, highly significant interaction between height and marriage, with never-married women being significantly taller and never-married men being significantly shorter. There was an association between childhood IQ and height in both men ($r = .26$, $p < .001$) and women ($r = .18$, $p = .001$).

The association between childhood IQ and marriage was also expressed as odds ratios, derived from logistic regression analyses (Taylor, Hart, Davey Smith, Whalley, et al., 2005). In women, expressed per standard deviation advantage of IQ at age 11, the odds ratio of being married by midlife was 0.42 (95% confidence interval [CI]: 0.27, 0.64). After adjustment for occupational social class at midlife, the odds ratio was attenuated by only 14% and was still 0.50 (95% CI: 0.32, 0.78). For men, again based on a 1 standard deviation advantage in IQ at age 11, the odds ratio for being married by midlife was 1.35 (95% CI: 0.98, 1.86). It may be seen that the 95% confidence interval for men just crosses 1.0, confirming that there is a trend toward, instead of a statistically significant association between, men with lower IQs being unmarried. Adjustment for adult social class attenuated the association in men by 36%, to an odds ratio of 1.21 (95% CI: 0.85, 1.73). Adjusting the IQ–marriage association for height had little attenuating effect, especially for women.

Before considering possible mechanisms for this interesting association between IQ and marriage, it is advisable to consider some factors of the sample. Although the sample is more representative than some previous, comparable studies (e.g., Marmot et al., 1991), it has limitations. Migrants—both those who emigrated from the areas after the SMS1932 and those who immigrated from outside Scotland—are not included. The sample is underrepresented, for example, by people who were unemployed and mentally unwell, and these factors might be related to marriage and IQ scores. The intervening of World War II, which started when members of the sample were approximately age 18 and ended when they were 24, will have altered marriage patterns in a cohort-specific manner. The IQ–marriage association is most clear and significant among the women and perhaps affords the most obvious explanation. It is likely that these women spent more time in education and, thereafter, pursuing a career. In Scotland at that time it was less usual for married women, especially those with children, to remain in the workplace, and the pursuit of a career is likely to have delayed marriage and, in some, to have resulted in women never marrying.

We should strongly emphasize that the IQ–marriage association among men was not significant (Taylor, Hart, Davey Smith, Whalley, et al., 2005); however, it is interesting to speculate on why men with lower IQs tend to have been less likely to marry. G. Miller (2000) suggested that IQ might act as a fitness marker in men and that behaviors linked with IQ are used by women, through sexual selection, as indicators of a man's probability of being a good provider. In this sense, a high IQ, or the behaviors and achievements associated with it, are used as indicators of good genes and good health. Women, more than men, value factors in prospective marriage partners that are known to be related to IQ, such as education and social status (Buss, 2000). In self-report studies, women are fussier than men about the intelligence level of opposite-sex partners (Kenrick, Sadala, Groth, & Trost, 1990). Finally, coming back to health, it had been reported that marriage, especially among men, is associated with better health (Gove, 1973). It might be that part of this association is accounted for by IQ (Taylor, Hart, Davey Smith, Whalley, et al., 2005).

Satisfaction with one's life is indisputably important as an outcome. It is a part of a successful old age. It is interesting to ask, therefore, whether it has any relationship with childhood IQ or with the amount of cognitive change between childhood and old age.

Satisfaction with life is a concept that comes within the remit of a group of psychologists who focus on the positive psychological aspects of human living. One of the leaders of this movement, Diener (1984), wrote that philosophers have described *happiness* as "the highest good and ultimate motivation for human action" (p. 542). Data from members of the Lothian Birth Cohort 1921 (LBC1921) were used to examine the hypothesis that people with higher childhood IQs and less lifetime cognitive decline would report being more satisfied with their lives (Gow et al., 2005). They were each mailed a copy of Diener, Emmons, Larsen, and Griffin's (1985) Satisfaction With Life Scale. This has five statements, and the respondents answer each one on a 7-point scale that ranges from *strongly disagree* to *strongly agree*.

A clear finding from the research was that people in the LBC1921 were very satisfied with their lives (Gow et al., 2005). As an illustration of this, Figure 9.1 shows the descriptive data from one of the questions in the Satisfaction With Life Scale. Note that the large majority of the almost-80-year-old men and women agree quite strongly with the statement "I am satisfied with my life." Of course, the LBC1921, a group of people who, at approximately age 80, are relatively healthy and taking part in an extensive research project, are probably not representative. They are fitter than most of their peers, and they are still willing to engage in a project that can help people who come after them. The key aspect of the project was the association between total scores on the Satisfaction With Life Scale and cognitive ability. There were 409 people with mental ability and Satisfaction With Life Scale data, and who had Mini-Mental State Examination (Folstein, Folstein, & McHugh, 1975) scores of 24 or greater. The correlations with Satisfaction With Life Scale total scores were as follows: Moray House Test (MHT) IQ score at age 11 = .00, MHT IQ score at age 79 = .04, and cognitive change between 11 and 79 = .05.

Here, then, was an important life outcome—self-reported satisfaction with life at almost age 80—that appeared to have no association whatsoever with IQ test score in childhood or late adulthood, or the change between one and the other.

It was speculated that whereas higher cognitive ability might contribute to satisfaction in some ways by providing access to more resources, it might also open up an awareness of how things could be even better (Gow et al., 2005). It was also speculated that, within a relatively healthy older group such as the LBC1921, whose cognitive abilities do not descend to pathological

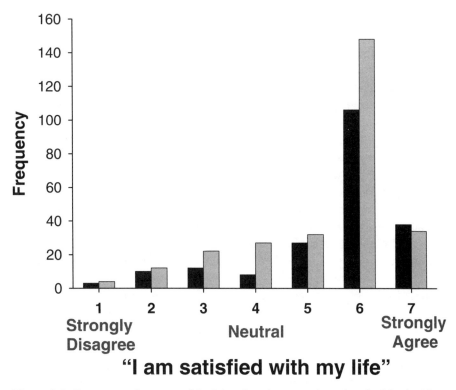

Figure 9.1. Responses from men (black bars) and women (grey bars) of the Lothian Birth Cohort 1921 to a question from the Satisfaction With Life Scale. Data from Gow et al. (2005).

levels, and who are able to lead independent lives, individual differences are irrelevant to life satisfaction. A similar idea had been rendered moot by Thomas Hobbes (1651/1885) in the *Leviathan*, over 350 years previously:

> For such is the nature of men, that howsoever they may acknowledge many others to be more witty, or more eloquent, or more learned: Yet they will hardly believe there be many so wise as themselves: For they see their own wit at hand, and other mens' at a distance. But this proveth than men are in that point equall, than unequall. For there is not ordinarily a greater signe of the equall distribution of any thing, than that every man is contented with his share. (p. 63)

The follow-up studies of the SMS1932 and the SMS of 1947 have expended much effort in researching the determinants of cognitive ability in old age. The determinants of satisfaction with life represent another important outcome, uncorrelated with cognition in this sample. They were, though, correlated with self-reported loneliness in old age (Gow, Pattie, Whiteman, Whalley, & Deary, 2007).

INTELLECTUAL ENGAGEMENT AND IMAGINATION

The SMS follow-up samples provided an unusual opportunity to examine the associations between personality traits and measured intelligence at both ends of the life course. It had been suggested that a framework was needed for the increasingly popular joint study of personality traits and cognitive test scores (Chamorro-Premuzic & Furnham, 2004). Among these suggestions was that personality traits might play a part at two stages. First, personality traits might influence people's performance on mental tests and, therefore, their measured intelligence might not be the same as their true intelligence, their latent capability. A second idea was that personality might influence intelligence over a longer time frame, by predisposing people to engage in intellectual activities, seeking knowledge and finding opportunities to learn; that is, there might be individual differences in how much people invest their cognitive apparatus in cognitively stimulating activities. This investment metaphor accords with the fluid-crystallized model of intelligence differences (Horn & Cattell, 1966). *Fluid intelligence*, the capability of the central nervous system to do cognitive work, becomes applied over time and accumulates knowledge as *crystallized stores*. Also relevant to the issue of people's differences in how much they invest their intellectual powers is the concept of *typical intellectual engagement* (TIE; Ackerman, 1996). This is a concept—arguably at the interface of personality and intelligence—that is concerned with the extent to which people, typically when using intelligence in challenging cognitive situations, tend to apply themselves to cognitive matters, such as by reading newspapers and thinking about issues and ideas. People high in TIE are thoughtful, enquiring, and tend to be seen by themselves and others as thinkers (Goff & Ackerman, 1992). In the light of these considerations it was suggested that "personality traits (notably TIE and Openness) may influence actual intelligence" (Chamorro-Premuzic & Furnham, 2004, p. 257). At the same time, it was emphasized that the proper study of these associations required longitudinal data, something that was missing from the literature.

There were data on all of these concepts in the LBC1921 (Gow, Whiteman, Pattie, & Deary, 2005b). The participants had taken the same mental ability test in childhood and at age 79. There were data on TIE and the personality factor Intellect/Imagination, a close correlate of Openness (Gow, Whiteman, Pattie, & Deary, 2005a), both reported by themselves in old age. It was hypothesized that TIE and the personality trait Intellect/Imagination would be correlated significantly, that both would be correlated with intelligence in childhood and old age. Most important—and this is where the LBC1921 provided uniquely useful data—it was hypothesized that childhood IQ would account for some of the association between intelligence in old age and TIE and Intellect/Imagination; that is, the associations within old age would in part be caused by a common source of variance that could be tracked back to childhood.

The study participants were members of the LBC1921. The personality trait of Intellect/Imagination was measured using Goldberg's 50-item International Personality Item Pool (see http://ipip.ori.org) scales. There are 10 items for each of five factors. It was shown previously that the Intellect/Imagination scale from the IPIP correlated .59 with the Openness factor from the NEO Five-Factor Inventory (Costa & McCrae, 1992) and had a Cronbach's alpha internal consistency coefficient of .73 (Gow et al., 2005a). TIE was measured using an adapted (with the permission of the scale's authors) version of Goff and Ackerman's (1992) scale. Among the 59 questions on this scale were "I think deeply about things," and, in reverse, "I rarely read widely on any one subject." The TIE questionnaire was sent out to LBC1921 participants in late 2001, some months after all had attended sessions for mental testing and medical examination. There were 469 complete questionnaires. The IPIP personality traits questionnaire was mailed to LBC1921 participants in late 2002. Four hundred sixty complete questionnaires were returned.

There was a large positive correlation between the personality trait of Intellect/Imagination from the IPIP scales and TIE ($r = .53, p < .01$; Gow et al., 2005b). There were significant positive correlations between TIE and both childhood ($r = .21, p < .01$) and age 79 ($r = .13, p < .01$) MHT score IQ. When the partial correlation between TIE and age 79 MHT IQ was computed, controlling for age 11 IQ, the association was eliminated ($r = -.01, p < .01$). There was a significant positive correlation between the IPIP personality trait Intellect/Imagination and both childhood ($r = .32, p < .01$) and age 79 ($r = .22$, $p < .01$) MHT score IQ. When the partial correlation between Intellect/ Imagination and age 79 MHT IQ was computed, controlling for age 11 IQ, the association was eliminated ($r = .02, p < .01$).

To understand more fully the associations between childhood and old age IQ and Intellect/Imagination and TIE, a path analysis was conducted using the EQS structural equation modeling program (Gow et al., 2005b). The most economical model possible was stipulated, which posited that the shared variance among the measures in old age were all traceable to MHT IQ scores at age 11. It was hypothesized that the trait of Intellect/Imagination led to greater TIE. The model is shown in Figure 9.2. It had good fit statistics. The chi-square was low (1.30, $df = 3$) and nonsignificant ($p = .73$). The average of the off-diagonal absolute standardized residuals was low (.014). The Bentler–Bonett (normed and nonnormed) and comparative fit indices were 0.996, 1.010, and 1.000, respectively. The model shows that MHT IQ at age 11 has a large effect on MHT IQ at age 79 and a moderate effect on the personality trait Intellect/Imagination, which has, in turn, a large effect on TIE.

The unusual contribution in the study of intelligence and personality traits was in showing that their association in old age was accounted for,

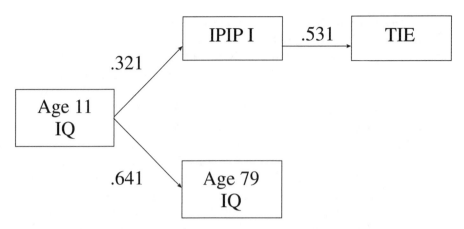

Figure 9.2. Path analysis of the associations between age 11 and age 79 Moray House Test IQ (IQ), the personality trait Intellect/Imagination (IPIP I), and typical intellectual engagement (TIE). From "The Personality–Intelligence Interface: Insights From an Ageing Cohort," by A. J. Gow, M. C. Whiteman, A. Pattie, and I. J. Deary, 2005b, *Personality and Individual Differences, 39,* p. 758. Copyright 2005 by Elsevier Limited. Reprinted with permission.

entirely, by MHT IQ score at age 11 (Gow et al., 2005b). Specifically, the results showed that the significant associations between intelligence and the personality trait of Intellect/Imagination and TIE in old age were completely accounted for by MHT IQ score at age 11. The investment theory of intelligence that was outlined earlier hypothesized that traits such as Intellect/Imagination and TIE would contribute additional, independent variance to mental ability in old age, after ability at age 11 was controlled. This was not found. It appeared that all of the associations in old age were traceable to variance in mental ability in childhood; that is, people with higher intelligence in youth grow up to be more intellectually engaged and to have higher scores on Intellect/Imagination. This was an unusual opportunity to test an important hypothesis about contributions to differences in mental ability in old age, in terms of personality trait and personal style, and the result was the opposite. It seemed, from the results in this sample, that people who performed better on the MHT as children report, by old age, more TIE and higher scores on Intellect/Imagination. Childhood intelligence contributes to personal style in old age; personal style in old age did not contribute anything to intelligence in old age beyond that accounted for by intelligence at age 11.

SOCIAL MOBILITY AND STATUS ATTAINMENT

From the preceding analyses we have seen that differences in childhood intelligence influence how we engage with the world of ideas later in life. They affect cognitive styles, part of the broad range of psychological phenomena that we call personality. To people with different scores on a mental test in childhood the world affords different possibilities for thought. More broadly, one may ask whether there are social in addition to personal psychological outcomes of childhood intelligence. Adult social status is important. It is an indicator of access to material things and environments that can make living better or worse. Its importance is underscored by the range of scientists who conduct research on its determinants: Psychologists, sociologists, geographers, demographers, epidemiologists, and experts in social medicine all contribute. One of the difficulties of the field is that there are three quite closely related variables that are associated with adult social status: (a) intelligence, (b) education, and (c) parental social class (Breen & Goldthorpe, 2001; Saunders, 1997). A survey of several studies found that childhood intelligence was predictive of early adult occupational status and that this was heavily attenuated after controlling for education (Jencks, 1979). Adolescent mental ability often remained associated with adult occupational status after education was controlled. Also, there was an intriguing suggestion that intelligence at an early age might be associated with occupational status later in adulthood rather than occupational status in the early stages of adulthood. Analyses of the 1946 British Birth Cohort (Richards & Sacker, 2003) and the U.S. National Longitudinal Survey of Youth 1979 (Herrnstein & Murray, 1994) both found that childhood mental ability was associated with adult occupational status, and they emphasized that there was some contribution from parental social class and the person's educational attainments. The issue of how much education explains the association between childhood IQ and occupational status was the subject of a lively disagreement based on analyses of the UK National Child Development Study (the British 1958 Birth Cohort; Breen & Goldthorpe, 1999; Saunders, 2002).

Participants in the SMS1932 were able to make a contribution to this debate about the childhood origins of adult occupational and social position (Deary, Taylor, et al., 2005). Specifically, the sample that was used was the one in which the SMS1932 had been linked with the Midspan Studies in the west of Scotland (Hart, Deary, et al., 2003). Within the Midspan Studies, men who had taken part in the Collaborative Study were used. This took place in 27 workplaces in the west and central belt of Scotland. In the study of social status attainment at midlife these data provided an unusually useful combination of variables: the participant's childhood IQ and the parental occupation; the participant's education; and the participant's first job and his or her occupation and other social status variables, such as car driving and deprivation of the area in which they resided, at midlife. Participants' height was also measured, and this was used partly to indicate childhood privations. Education was based on years of education, although some analyses used age at leaving full-time education. In the linked data set between the SMS1932 and the Collaborative Study within the Midspan Studies there were 243 men with full data.

The first analyses examined social mobility, asking about the change in occupational status from parent's to own (Deary, Taylor, et al., 2005). This was based on the standard six-level UK system, from unskilled manual to professional occupations (see chap. 2, this volume, for a more detailed description of the six-level system). Of the 243 participants, there was social stability in 41%; this percentage of men had the same occupational status at midlife as did their fathers. In agreement with the secular trend in the United Kingdom, which saw many people move from industry to service occupations, there was more overall upward (45%) than downward (14%) social mobility. There were clear graded relationships between MHT IQ scores at age 11 and father's and own social class among the participants (see Table 9.1). The childhood IQ of the participants in the most professional occupations (I and II) by midlife were high, irrespective of their father's occupation.

Logistic regression analysis was used to examine the chances of upward social mobility as predicted by childhood IQ (Deary, Taylor, et al., 2005). On the basis of a 1 standard deviation advantage in IQ from the SMS1932, there was, on average, a 69% increased chance (95% CI: 30%, 120%, $p = .0001$) of upward social mobility. Height and education were also associated significantly with upward social mobility. Both of these remained significant when other variables were controlled. Childhood IQ fell to nonsignificance ($p = .06$) after adjustment for height, education, and number of siblings, and the effect was attenuated by approximately 50%. Separate analyses were conducted for downward social mobility. One standard deviation of advantage in childhood IQ meant a 42% reduced chance (95% CI: 58%, 20%, $p = .001$) of downward social mobility. This was still significant and attenuated only a little after adjustment for education height and number of siblings. In these logistic regression analyses more education was the most robust predictor of upward social mobility, and low IQ was the most robust predictor of downward social mobility.

The linkage between the SMS1932 and the Midspan Studies was a collaboration intended to combine epidemiological and individual-differences approaches. The previous paragraph contained the results obtained with standard epidemiological analyses of social mobility. More informative analyses were conducted using structural equation modeling (Deary, Taylor, et al., 2005). This had two advantages. First, it can explicitly represent mediating pathways. Second, it can be used to model latent traits and manifest variables in the same model. The associations on which the structural equation model was constructed and fitted are shown in Table 9.2. All correlations were in the expected directions; higher IQ scores, more education, and more advantageous social position tended positively to covary. MHT IQ score at age 11 was significantly, and moderately to strongly, associated with all of the other variables. The association between childhood IQ and midlife occupational social class (.52) was stronger than that between childhood IQ

TABLE 9.1

Mean Childhood IQ (Number of Cases) and Standard Deviation by Father's and Own Occupational Social Class for Men in the Collaborative Midspan Study and the Scottish Mental Survey of 1932

Father's social class	Own social class														
	I and II			IIINM			IIIM			IV and V			All		
	M	n	SD	M	n	SD	M	n	SD	M	n	SD	M	n	SD
I and II	120.6	21	7.8	105.2	3	12.3	82.9	1	—	115.7	1	—	117.2	26	11.6
IIINM	113.5	17	10.7	107.2	7	12.5	87.8	2	5.0	105.3	2	7.3	109.5	28	12.4
IIIM	112.8	27	9.4	101.4	19	14.5	97.6	49	18.4	89.4	24	13.4	100.0	119	16.9
IV and V	109.8	14	12.7	98.4	7	18.4	98.4	25	14.4	94.1	24	11.1	99.4	70	14.3
All	114.5	79	10.5	102.2	36	14.5	97.5	77	16.9	92.7	51	12.8	102.7	243	16.3

Note. I = professional; II = intermediate; IIINM = skilled nonmanual; IIIM = skilled manual; IV = semiskilled; V = unskilled. From "Intergenerational Social Mobility and Mid-Life Status Attainments: Influences of Childhood Intelligence, Childhood Social Factors, and Education," by I. J. Deary, M. D. Taylor, C. L. Hart, V. Wilson, G. Davey Smith, D. Blane, and J. M. Starr, 2005, *Intelligence, 33.* p. 462. Copyright 2005 by Elsevier Limited. Reprinted with permission.

TABLE 9.2

Correlations Among Variables Used in the Analysis of Midlife Social Status Attainment in the Study That Linked Data From the Scottish Mental Survey of 1932 and the Midspan Collaborative Study

Variable	1	2	3	4	5	6	7	M (SD)
1. Father's occupational social class	—							4.0 (1.1)
2. Moray House Test IQ at age 11	.330	—						102.8 (16.2)
3. Age at leaving full time education	.399	.314	—					15.4 (3.1)
4. Social class of participant's first occupation	.488	.344	.549	—				3.7 (1.2)
5. Social class of participant's occupation at midlife	.452	.523	.476	.520	—			3.3 (1.4)
6. Car driving	.095	.215	.227	.215	.285	—		0.51 (0.50)
7. Deprivation of the area lived in at midlife	.374	.378	.306	.276	.415	.151	—	4.3 (1.8)

Note. For the correlations, all signs have been ordered so that a higher number represents more professional occupations, higher IQ, later age at leaving education, car driving, and a less deprived area of residence. $N = 240$. From "Intergenerational Social Mobility and Mid-Life Status Attainments: Influences of Childhood Intelligence, Childhood Social Factors, and Education," I. J. Deary, M. D. Taylor, C. L. Hart, V. Wilson, G. Davey Smith, D. Blane, and J. M. Starr, 2005, *Intelligence, 33*, p. 464. Copyright 2005 by Elsevier Limited. Reprinted with permission.

and the social class of the first occupation (.34; p for comparison of the two correlations = .001).

A path model was fitted to the data using the EQS structural equation modeling program (see Figure 9.3; see also Deary, Taylor, et al., 2005). The design of the model followed simple principles. First, earlier life course variables were stipulated as influencing later variables. Second, all direct and mediating paths were included. Third, no assumption was made about the reasons for any correlation between father's social class and IQ at age 11, so these two exogenous variables had a double-headed arrow (correlation) between them. Fourth, midlife social position was a latent trait with the manifest variables being the participant's occupational social class at midlife, the (non)deprivation of the area of residence at midlife, and car driving (in the 1970s, when the midlife data were collected, driving a car was a better indicator of affluence than it was some years later, when most people drove cars). The model fitted well. The average of the off-diagonal absolute standardized residuals was .019 (root-mean-square error of approximation = .039). The chi-square was 10.9 ($df = 8$) and nonsignificant ($p = .21$). The Bentler–Bonett normed, nonnormed, and comparative fit indices were .975, .982, and .993, respectively. All of the paths in the model in Figure 9.3 were significant.

The model of midlife social position shows a strong influence from MHT IQ at age 11 (see Figure 9.3; see also Deary, Taylor, et al., 2005). This is mediated in part by education and the social class of the first occupation.

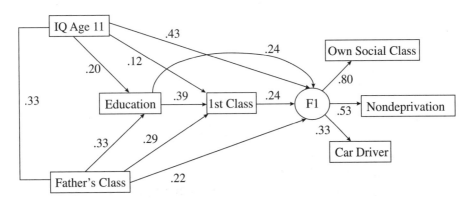

Figure 9.3. Fitted path (structural equation) model of the direct and indirect influences of childhood social position and IQ on social status attainment at midlife. Numbers beside the paths may be squared to obtain the variance shared by adjacent variables. All parameters are significant ($p < .05$). The circle (F1) represents a latent trait; rectangles represent measured variables. All variables have been coded so that higher scores refer to more professional social class, higher IQ, higher likelihood of being a car driver, and less deprivation. From "Intergenerational Social Mobility and Mid-Life Status Attainments: Influences of Childhood Intelligence, Childhood Social Factors, and Education," by I. J. Deary, M. D. Taylor, C. L. Hart, V. Wilson, G. Davey Smith, D. Blane, and J. M. Starr 2005, *Intelligence, 33,* p. 464. Copyright 2005 by Elsevier Limited. Reprinted with permission.

However, there is still a moderately strong direct association between childhood IQ and midlife social position when these potentially mediating paths are included. There is a similar set of associations for father's social class, although the direct effect on midlife social position is less strong than that of childhood IQ. Education also has a direct effect on midlife social position after the mediating effect of the social class of the first job is taken into account. The general story from the model is that father's occupational class has a stronger influence in early life course variables (education and the social class of the first occupation), but childhood IQ has a stronger influence on later outcomes. Father's social class, MHT IQ at age 11, and education all make significant and independent contributions to social position at midlife. There is, in this specific group of Scottish men who entered the labor market in the mid- to late 1930s, some evidence of meritocracy as well as some evidence of the long-enduring influence of social background.

QUALITY OF LIFE

The Aberdeen Birth Cohort 1921 was used to examine the contributions to differences in quality of life in old age. The study inquired whether there was any association between childhood IQ and quality of life in old age, whether quality of life was associated with concurrent cognitive ability, and which other factors contributed to quality of life (Bain et al., 2003). The study took place at the third follow-up wave of the Aberdeen Birth Cohort 1921, in which 155 participants were tested, and there were 88 who were able and agreed to take part in additional assessments. All participants were living independently, were ambulatory, had no serious illness, and had Mini-Mental State Examination scores greater than 24.

The instrument used to measure quality of life was the Schedule for the Evaluation of Individual Quality of Life—Direct Weighting (SEIQoL–DW; O'Boyle, Brown, Hickey, McGhee, & Joyce, 1995). By contrast with the more commonly used self-report questionnaires, the SEIQoL–DW uses a three-step procedure in the setting of a semistructured interview. First, the respondents identify the five areas of their lives that contribute to their quality of life. Next, using a scale from 0 (*worst possible*) to 100 (*best possible*), they rate their functioning and satisfaction with each of the areas. Last, using a pie chart type device, they indicate the relative importance to them of the five areas they identified. In the top panel of Figure 9.4, the horizontal axis shows the five areas of living that one individual identified as his or her main contributors to quality of life. It also shows the level of satisfaction with each area. Note the maximal satisfaction from gardening, but less satisfaction from the family. This becomes more interesting when viewed in the light of the bottom panel of Figure 9.4. There, the loving family appears to be the most important

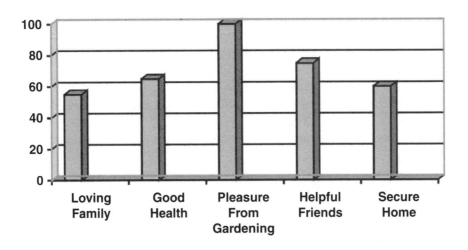

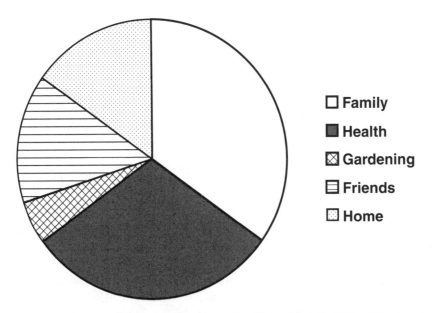

Figure 9.4. Illustrations of the Schedule for the Evaluation of Individual Quality of Life—Direct Weighting in a single participant. In the top panel of the figure, the participant has chosen five areas of living that contribute most to his or her quality of life and has also rated his or her satisfaction with them, from 0 (*worst possible*) to 100 (*best possible*). In the bottom panel of the figure, the participant has used the pie chart to indicate the relative importance of the five areas to his or her overall quality of living. From "Quality of Life in Healthy Old Age: Relationships With Childhood IQ, Minor Psychological Symptoms and Optimism," by G. H. Bain, H. Lemmon, S. Teunisse, J. M. Starr, H. C. Fox, I. J. Deary, and L. J. Whalley, 2003, *Social Psychiatry and Psychiatric Epidemiology, 38,* p. 633. Copyright 2003 by Springer Science + Business Media. Reprinted with permission

aspect of quality of life, gardening the least, with health, friends, and home also significantly more important than gardening. The eventual score for overall quality of life takes account of the relative importance and level of satisfaction of each of the nominated areas.

A number of other measures were collected that were hypothesized to be related to quality of life (Bain et al., 2003). From the fitness variables, the time to walk 6 meters and balance were selected. For childhood IQ, the MHT score (corrected for age at testing) from age 11 was used. For mental ability in old age, the score on Raven's Standard Progressive Matrices was used. The Life Orientation Test (Scheier, Carver, & Bridges, 1994) was used as a measure of trait optimism. Demographic information included the deprivation of the area of residence, years of education, whether the person lived alone, and hours per week of activity outside the home. Depression and anxiety were measured using the Hospital Anxiety and Depression Scale.

The quality of life (SEIQoL–DW) total score had significant (all $ps <$ .001) associations with Hospital Anxiety and Depression Scale depression ($r = -.45$), Life Orientation Test (optimism; $r = .36$), and MHT IQ at age 11 ($r = .37$; Bain et al., 2003). The correlations between quality of life and depression and optimism changed very little when adjusted for MHT IQ score at age 11. Correlations between quality of life and Hospital Anxiety and Depression Scale anxiety, deprivation of the area of residence, years of education, Mini-Mental State Examination, and Raven's Standard Progressive Matrices were nonsignificant. In a multiple regression model the three significantly correlated variables all contributed independent proportions of variance to quality of life, as follows: depression = .19, childhood IQ = .07, and Life Orientation Test optimism = .03.

The contemporaneous associations between quality of life and depression and optimism were thought to be unsurprising (Bain et al., 2003). Indeed, they might, to an extent, be capturing some overlapping construct variance: Life appears worse to more depressed persons, who are also liable to be less optimistic. The association between childhood IQ and quality of life in old age is more novel, especially because there was no significant association with cognition measured contemporaneously in old age. However, recall that the sample was modest in size ($N = 88$) and that the difference in the size of the correlations between quality of life and mental ability in youth and old age were not significant. Therefore, replication of this result is needed, not least because it is provocative, and possibly contradictory to the lack of association between childhood IQ and satisfaction with life in old age in the LBC1921 (Gow et al., 2005). As Bain et al. (2003) suggested, "Those with higher childhood mental ability have probably enjoyed more opportunities to master life problems more successfully and acquired a substantial body of knowledge with which to age more successfully" (p. 636).

V

CAN LIFETIME COGNITIVE CHANGES BE ESTIMATED WITHOUT PREMORBID TEST SCORES?

CAN LIFETIME COGNITIVE CHANGES BE ESTIMATED WITHOUT PREMORBID TEST SCORES?

Up until now, evaluating cognitive aging has been difficult because of the missing baseline data from early life. Clinicians presented with a person in whom there might be cognitive decline had little information about how well that person used to perform on cognitive tests. Education and occupation might give some clues. Nevertheless, any current mental test performance data that are gathered might be of limited use. A good score on tests of current mental functioning can still represent a decline from a previous very high state. A poor score might be perfectly compatible with how well that person has always performed.

For decades, tests have been devised to estimate premorbid intelligence. They involve testing the person on material that is reckoned to be associated strongly with intellectual level and that is preserved with age and neural pathology. The problem with these tests is a limited ability to assess retrospective validity for them, because such validation requires baseline data from early life. Because the Scottish Mental Surveys supplied ample baseline data from early life, the follow-up studies were able to make one more important contribution to the field of intelligence: the validation of a premorbid intelligence test. In Part V, we discuss this validation.

10

VALIDATING THE NATIONAL ADULT READING TEST

One test that is widely used in the United Kingdom to estimate premorbid intelligence is the National Adult Reading Test (NART; Nelson & Willison, 1991). The NART is simple to administer and to perform. The person taking the test is asked to look at and pronounce, aloud, 50 words. None of the words fully follows the usual rules of English grapheme–phoneme correspondence or stress (e.g., *ache, thyme, topiary*). Therefore, if a person has not encountered the NART's words previously, applying normal rules of pronunciation will not lead to the correct answer. The NART, though, lacked retrospective validity.

In comparing the NART estimates of premorbid IQ with the estimates from the Scottish Mental Surveys (SMSs), we were able to validate the NART. This important validation will allow researchers and practitioners to estimate premorbid IQ and thereby estimate lifetime cognitive change. In this chapter, we discuss how the NART was validated for older people both without and with dementia. We then discuss the use of the NART to estimate lifetime cognitive change in people without premorbid intelligence test scores.

VALIDATING THE NATIONAL ADULT READING TEST
IN OLDER PEOPLE WITHOUT DEMENTIA

The validity of the NART as a correlate of mental ability had often been studied on the basis of research in which NART and other mental test data were collected at the same time (Crawford, Stewart, Parker, Besson, & De Lacey, 1989). This is far from ideal. A study was needed in which the NART was associated with mental tests taken long before it was administered to check—retrospectively, so to speak—its validity. The samples of people who had taken part in the SMS of 1932 (SMS1932) provided an unusually helpful group in designing such a study. The first hypothesis to be tested was that the NART, if it were an estimate of prior ability, should correlate more highly with mental function tested long ago than with concurrently administered mental tests (Crawford, Deary, Starr, & Whalley, 2001). The second hypothesis to be tested concerned the known correlation between the NART and scores on tests of mental decline, such as the Mini-Mental State Examination (MMSE; Folstein, Folstein, & McHugh, 1975; Starr, Whalley, Inch, & Schering, 1992). This correlation might occur for two reasons: (a) because the NART is sensitive to current mental state or (b) because tests of current mental function are related to prior ability. If the first were true, then adjusting for true prior mental function would have little impact on the NART–MMSE association. If the latter were true, then adjusting for true prior mental ability would abolish the NART–MMSE association.

The participants in the NART validation study were from the Aberdeen Birth Cohort 1921 (ABC1921; Crawford et al., 2001). Of these, 196 took the NART and MMSE, and 97 retook the Moray House Test (MHT), all in 1998 at age 77. For the 97 participants who took all three tests, the correlations were as follows: MHT at age 11 versus MHT at age 77, $r = .64$ ($p < .001$); NART at age 77 versus MHT at age 11, $r = .69$ ($p < .001$); and MHT at age 77 versus NART at age 77, $r = .63$ ($p < .001$). The scatterplot showing the association between MHT scores at age 11 and NART scores at age 77 is shown in Figure 10.1. The association is entirely linear (Crawford et al., 2001). In summary, the NART at age 77 correlates marginally more strongly with MHT at age 11 than with the contemporaneously administered MHT and more strongly than the MHT correlates with itself from age 11 to age 77. Of course, being so similar in effect size, none of the correlations is significantly different from the others. Even though it was high, the correlation between the NART and the MHT score from age 11 was probably an underestimate because of restriction of range in the sample tested at age 77. The disattenuated correlation, without any correction for unreliability in either of the tests, was estimated to be .78. Therefore, concerning the first hypothesis, the NART does have

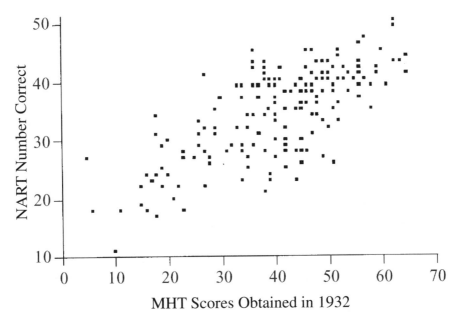

Figure 10.1. Scatterplot of the relationship between Moray House Test (MHT) scores obtained in 1932 and National Adult Reading Test (NART) scores obtained in 1998. The data in this figure are from members of the Aberdeen Birth Cohort 1921. From "The NART as an Index of Prior Intellectual Functioning: A Retrospective Validity Study Covering a 66-Year Interval," by J. R. Crawford, I. J. Deary, J. M. Starr, and L. J. Whalley, 2001, *Psychological Medicine, 31,* p. 455. Copyright 2001 by Cambridge University Press. Reprinted with permission.

strong retrospective validity in healthy older people. The NART can look back over 6 decades and account for over 50% of the variance, despite the fact that the 11-year-olds who took the MHT would not have been exposed to many of the words in the NART; despite all of the influences on the brain in the time between the two tests; and despite the fact that the NART is a narrowly focused test of word pronunciation, whereas the MHT samples a wider range of mental capabilities. The variance accounted for is greater than 60% if the disattenuated correlation is accepted.

The second hypothesis addressed the association between the NART and tests of putative mental decline. NART and MMSE scores correlated .25 ($p < .001$; Crawford et al., 2001). The partial correlation, controlling for MHT scores from age 11 in 1932, was .02 ($p = .80$). The partial correlation was significantly lower than the NART–MMSE correlation; therefore, the acceptable explanation appeared to be that NART and MMSE scores correlate significantly because the latter is sensitive to prior mental ability.

VALIDATING THE NATIONAL ADULT READING TEST IN OLDER PEOPLE WITH DEMENTIA

The NART had good retrospective validity in older people without dementia (Crawford et al., 2001) but, for the most part, it would be used in clinical situations. Most important, the NART is used to provide an estimate of prior ability in people with dementia; therefore, a case control study was conducted with people who took part in the SMS1932, some of whom did and some of whom did not have dementia at age 79 (McGurn et al., 2004). The control participants (i.e., those without dementia) were from the Lothian Birth Cohort 1921. There were 464 of these individuals with no history of dementia, an MMSE score of 24 or greater, and with scores on the NART at age 79 and the MHT at age 11. The participants with dementia came from two sources. At both sites, they were diagnosed on the basis of the criteria for dementia from the *International Classification of Diseases* (World Health Organization, 1994) and with neuropsychological test information taken into account. The first source was the Lothian Memory Treatment Centre in Edinburgh. There were 97 patients born in 1921, of whom 29 had a NART score and who could be matched to an MHT score at age 11 in the SMS1932. The second source was the ABC1921, the members of which had been followed up by that time. There were 16 ABC1921 participants with dementia.

The test scores of the participants with dementia and the control participants are shown in Table 10.1 (McGurn et al., 2004). The participants with dementia and the control participants were very similar in age. As expected, people with dementia had significantly lower MMSE test scores. This difference persisted when statistical adjustment was made for the difference in MHT score at age 11. The people with dementia had significantly lower NART scores than the control participants, with an effect size

TABLE 10.1
Mean Age and Mini-Mental State Examination (MMSE), National Adult Reading Test (NART), and Moray House Test (MHT) Scores in People With and Without Dementia

Variable	No dementia (*N* = 464)		Dementia (*N* = 45)		
	M	*SD*	*M*	*SD*	*p*
Age at NART(years)	79.1	0.6	79.0	1.5	.51
MMSE	28.4	1.3	22.3	4.2	< .001
MHT at age 11	47.0	11.5	38.0	14.2	< .001
NART	34.5	8.0	28.2	9.8	< .001

Note. Higher scores indicate better performance. From "Pronunciation of Irregular Words Is Preserved in Dementia, Validating Premorbid IQ Estimation," by B. McGurn, J. M. Starr, J. A. Topfer, A. Pattie, M. C. Whiteman, H. A. Lemmon, et al., 2004, *Neurology, 62,* p. 1185. Copyright 2004 by Lippincott Williams & Wilkins. Reprinted with permission.

(Cohen's *d*) of 0.67. After adjustment for MHT score at age 11, this difference was no longer significant, and the effect size was reduced to 0.27. Therefore, after statistically controlling for childhood IQ, and despite a large difference in MMSE scores, people with and without dementia do not differ significantly in NART scores. This was strong evidence that the ability to perform the NART holds in mild to moderate dementia. It was strong validity data for the NART as an estimate of premorbid mental ability in people with the earlier stages of dementia.

Next, the correlation between NART at age 79 and MHT score at age 11 was examined in people with dementia and in the control participants (McGurn et al., 2004). The correlations were .63 (*p* < .001) in the former group and .60 (*p* < .001) in the latter. These are not significantly different. The scatterplots for the group with dementia and group without dementia and their regression lines are plotted in Figure 10.2. The regression slopes of the two groups did not differ significantly. The NART in old age had a near-identical association with childhood IQ in people with and without dementia.

In regard to moderate dementia, then, the NART did not differ in people with and without dementia, after adjusting for childhood IQ, despite large

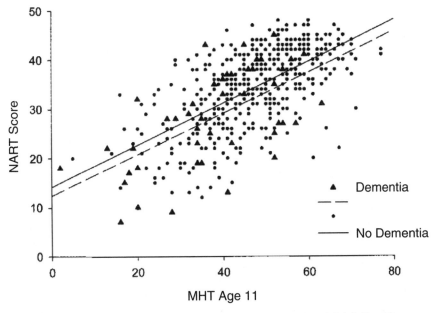

Figure 10.2. Scatterplot with fitted regression lines of National Adult Reading Test (NART) scores at age 79 and Moray House Test (MHT) scores at age 11 in people with and without dementia. From "Pronunciation of Irregular Words Is Preserved in Dementia, Validating Premorbid IQ Estimation," by B. McGurn, J. M. Starr, J. A. Topfer, A. Pattie, M. C. Whiteman, H. A. Lemmon, et al., 2004, *Neurology, 62,* p. 1185 Copyright 2004 by Lippincott Williams & Wilkins. Reprinted with permission.

differences in MMSE scores. NART scores also showed the same relationship with premorbid mental ability in the face of very different states of current mental function (McGurn et al., 2004). The NART had passed two very strict tests of validity. The people with dementia in this study would normally be classified as having mild to moderately severe disease. It is possible that the NART might not hold up so well in more severe cases of dementia.

ESTIMATING LIFETIME COGNITIVE CHANGE IN PEOPLE WITHOUT PREMORBID INTELLIGENCE TEST SCORES

The use of the NART, given its apparent validity as an estimator of prior mental ability in people with and without dementia, was taken a step further in the next study based on samples from the SMS1932 (Deary, Whalley, & Crawford, 2004). If the NART was a valid indicator of prior ability, then, if a valid measure of current ability could also be obtained, the difference between the two might be used as an estimate of cognitive change. Such individual estimates of change are increasingly seen as important in the clinical setting (Sawrie, Marson, Boothe, & Harrell, 1999). Moreover, such an estimate of cognitive change—which was called "instantaneous" because it could be taken at a single sitting—could be compared with a real measure of change in the follow-up studies of the individuals who took part in the SMS1932. The measure of current cognitive functioning chosen was Raven's Standard Progressive Matrices (Raven, Court, & Raven, 1977). Unlike the NART, performance on Raven's Standard Progressive Matrices declines with age, involves abstract reasoning, and is reckoned to be a good measure of general fluid intelligence (Carroll, 1993). The idea of using the NART–Raven comparison as an estimate of cognitive change was not new (Davis, Ho, Bradshaw, & Szaba, 2000; Freeman & Godfrey, 2000). What was novel was the possibility of correlating this estimate with an actual measure of a lifetime's cognitive change to establish its criterion validity.

The participants who provided data for this analysis were 87 people from the ABC1921 who did not have dementia (Deary, Whalley, & Crawford, 2004). These individuals had cognitive data from age 11, in the SMS1932, and from age 77 and again at age 78. The last two occasions were the first and second follow-up waves of the ABC1921. At ages 77 and 78, the participants took the NART, Raven's Standard Progressive Matrices, and the Digit Symbol and Object Assembly tests from the Wechsler Adult Intelligence Scale—Revised (WAIS–R; Wechsler, 1981). The last two tests were combined to give a brief measure of fluid-type intelligence. With these data at hand, measures of actual lifetime cognitive change were made. Raven score at age 77 was adjusted, using linear regression, for MHT score at age 11. The standardized residuals were saved as a measure of lifetime (age 11–age 77) cognitive change. The same was done for the Raven test scores from age 78 and for the WAIS–R fluid-type intelligence measure (a combination of Digit Symbol and Object Assembly) at age 77. Therefore, there were three measures of actual lifetime cognitive change, which took 66 years or more to gather.

The next stage was to compute estimated lifetime cognitive change (Deary, Whalley, & Crawford, 2004). This was done using linear regression. Raven scores from age 77 were adjusted for NART scores at age 77, and the standardized residuals were saved as estimates of lifetime cognitive change. The same was done using NART and Raven scores from age 78. Therefore, there were two measures of estimated lifetime cognitive change: from (a) age 77 and (b) age 78. With a 20-minute Raven administration, and the NART taking only a short time to complete, such estimated cognitive change measures took about half an hour to gather, compared with about two thirds of a century for actual cognitive change in the same participants.

The analyses asked how well the actual and estimated cognitive change measures agreed (Deary, Whalley, & Crawford, 2004). First, the estimated cognitive change measure—contemporaneously collected Raven scores versus NART scores—had a 1-year stability coefficient of .643 between age 77 and age 78 (see Figure 10.3). Coefficients are given to three decimal places in

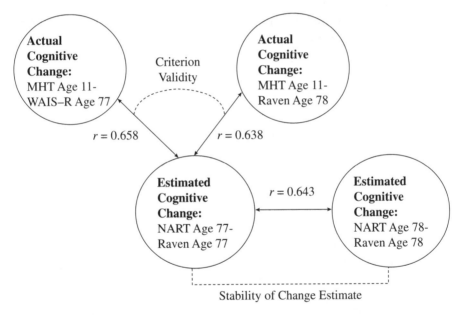

Figure 10.3. Stability and criterion validity coefficients for the cognitive change estimate based on a comparison of the contemporaneously administered National Adult Reading Test (NART) and Raven's Standard Progressive Matrices (Raven). MHT = Moray House Test; WAIS–R = Wechsler Adult Intelligence Scale—Revised. From "An 'Instantaneous' Estimate of a Lifetime's Cognitive Change," by I. J. Deary, L. J. Whalley, and J. R. Crawford, 2004, *Intelligence, 32,* p. 116. Copyright 2004 by Elsevier Limited. Reprinted with permission.

this study because they were very similar. The NART–Raven estimate of cognitive change from age 77 was compared with the actual measure of cognitive change that used the MHT score from age 11 and the Raven score from age 78. The correlation coefficient was .638 (see Figure 10.3). The reason for not using the same Raven score in the estimated and the actual cognitive change measures was that such a procedure would result in a spurious source of positive correlation between the two. As a further precaution, the NART–Raven estimate of cognitive change from age 77 was correlated with an actual measure of cognitive change that used neither of these tests, namely, the MHT age 11 and the WAIS–R measure of fluid-type ability at age 77. The estimated versus actual cognitive change correlation coefficient was .658 (see Figure 10.3). This is a stringent test of the criterion validity of the instantaneous estimate of lifetime cognitive change, because the actual lifetime cognitive change with which it was compared had entirely different mental tests.

This study discovered that an estimate of cognitive change in old age, that takes about 30 minutes to gather, was stable across a 1-year gap and correlated highly with actual cognitive change measured across more than 66 years and using different cognitive tests (Deary, Whalley, & Crawford, 2004). Therefore, the NART–Raven index of lifetime cognitive change has good stability and criterion validity. With appropriate norms, such a simple measure would have considerable clinical utility.

POSTSCRIPT: LOOKING AHEAD

In the preceding chapters, we described the 10 years of follow-up work devoted to the Scottish Mental Surveys (SMSs) of 1932 and 1947 (SMS1932 and SMS1947). At the 10-year mark precisely, we passed another milestone. In the Edinburgh area of Scotland, we were recruiting and retesting people who took part in the SMS1947. Therefore, in addition to the now-familiar Aberdeen Birth Cohort 1921, Aberdeen Birth Cohort 1936 (ABC1936), and the Lothian Birth Cohort 1921 (LBC1921), there is now a Lothian Birth Cohort 1936 (LBC1936; Deary, Gow, et al., 2007). The milestone we passed late in May 2007 was the recruiting and retesting of the last participant—the 1,091st—to take part in the first wave of the LBC1936. Therefore, it is our largest follow-up sample to date. The story of the LBC1936 will be told in the coming years. This story will comprise a combination of attempted replications of some of the results presented in this volume, and of novel empirical studies.

Data collection on the LBC1936 includes the demographic, medical, biological (including DNA), and cognitive data collected on the LBC1921 (Deary, Gow, et al., 2007). There are also some extensions. The cognitive test battery used is more extensive than that used with the LBC1921. There are additional tests aimed at a more thorough examination of the domains of memory, including working memory and some aspects of nonverbal memory. There are additional tests of processing speed, including experimental as well as psychometric tests.

There are many newly collected data on the ABC1936 that have yet to be written for publication. More than 200 of the participants have undertaken magnetic resonance imaging, including structural and functional imaging. These data, alongside the cognitive, genetic, and other data, will be published in due course in tests of hypotheses about cognitive aging. A new wave of testing is about to begin on the LBC1921, the members of which are now in their late 80s.

Thus, the cohorts based on surviving participants of the SMS1932 and SMS1947 continue to keep us busy, with the interleaved work of analyzing already-collected data and planning new data collections.

Ian J. Deary's comment to Lawrence J. Whalley at the start of this book was correct. Coming across the data from the SMS1932 and SMS1947 did change our lives—at least our lives qua researchers—and the effects are continuing. New research teams are still being managed, participants within cohorts are still being tested, data are still being collated and analyzed, and peer-reviewed articles are still being written; all of these efforts are based on a resource about which we had no knowledge on June 1, 1997. The cohorts have also had effects beyond the academic sphere. The participants and the findings related to them have appeared many times on television, on radio, and in newspapers and magazines. The temporarily forgotten—by almost everyone except the Scottish Council for Research in Education—SMSs are once again relatively famous.

But what for? What have the testees of a hoary old IQ-type test contributed in 10 years of retesting and reanalysis? We hope that the preceding pages have made this obvious and have organized the contribution to a degree. Perhaps it takes a bit of distance to discern properly the shape of the oeuvre. One reader of a draft of this book wrote to us the following:

> My main general comment would be on the cogency of what might be taken to be your main point, that IQ (or versions of it) are a far more fundamental part of personal and social behaviour than sociological fashions of the past 40 years have allowed us to suppose.

That seemed to get at the nub of things. Along with many others' investigations in the past several years, the SMS follow-up studies were easing the once-contentious topic of intelligence differences into its multifaceted role in the human life story. At many points in the human life course intelligence may be viewed as an important outcome of prior influences and a portent. An important development in intelligence research has been its well-discussed but less heated integration as an important aspect of research in epidemiology, in aging, in broader medical fields, and beyond. Discussions about the place and validity of intelligence differences now focus more on scientific matters than on political prejudices. There are other important human qualities—whether we are speaking of predictors of future well-being or outcomes of life's influences—but intelligence is a principal player.

In closing, we remember with gratitude Godfrey Thomson's devising the Moray House Test and his providing it for the SMSs. For someone whose bent was toward the technicalities of intelligence (Sharp, 1997), he could on occasion be quite starry-eyed about his subject. Going beyond the modest contributions we have suggested for intelligence in this book, he brought intelligence into the fight against the rise of totalitarianism in the world of the 1930s:

> The only hope for unity, permanent unity, among mankind is through the rule of intelligence, through the cultivation, by an education proper to each, of the intelligence of all. The schoolmaster is right who considers

that his sole business is to lead his pupils to see the truth clearly, and who holds that that in itself is character-training, and the only character-training the school may lend itself to, if it is to refrain from serving party or class, colour or race, or prejudice of whatever kind, but is to serve civilisation and all mankind. (G. Thomson, 1936, p. 32)

We should understand and value intelligence, therefore, and use it for the commonweal.

APPENDIX: SCOTLAND AT THE TIME OF THE SCOTTISH MENTAL SURVEYS OF 1932 AND 1947

The book is about people who were born in 1921 or 1936 and who were, thereafter, at school in Scotland in 1932 or 1947, respectively. The older group took part in the Scottish Mental Survey (SMS) of 1932 (SMS1932), and the younger group took part in the SMS of 1947 (SMS1947). What happened in these surveys and the rationale for the surveys are described in detail in Parts I through V of this volume. For those who require it, this appendix provides some scene setting and describes the world, the country, and the nation into which these people were born and in which they grew up.

The people in the SMS1932 were born just after World War I ended, and those in the SMS1947 were born a few years before the start of World War II. The National Health Service (NHS), which provides free medical care to all UK residents, began in 1948, 1 year after the later survey. Scotland is a nation within the United Kingdom, which comprises England, Scotland, Wales, and Northern Ireland. Scotland, to the north of England, has a population today, in the 1st decade of the 21st century, of approximately 5,100,000, very similar to the 4,900,000 population in 1921, when the participants in the SMS2932 were born. Almost three quarters of the population live in the central lowlands between Glasgow in the west and Edinburgh (the capital, although it is less populous than Glasgow) in the east. The language spoken is English, with a very small percentage of people speaking Scottish Gaelic. Most Gaelic speakers are concentrated in the islands of the Outer Hebrides and the northwest of the Scottish mainland. Important for the work on the SMSs is the fact that Scotland, for hundreds of years, has had its own educational (and legal and religious) system(s), separate from the rest of the United Kingdom. Therefore, school education, university education, and educational research are uniquely Scottish, with their own administration, infrastructure, and practices (Devine, 2006; Paterson, 2003). Scottish teachers, during all of the period dealt with in this book, were characterized by being well educated, even compared with those in other UK nations.

This appendix was written by Lawrence J. Whalley.

SCOTLAND IN 1900

Scotland is a small country. Occupying most of the northern third of the land mass the British Isles, its natural resources and population were never sufficient to make a noticeable impact on the central dramas of European history being played out to the south. For most of the time since the ancient occupation, approximately 20% of the population of the British Isles lived in Scotland. Here, about 70% of the agricultural land was fit for only grazing and some subsistence farming. Thus, it is not surprising that living standards remained low in Scotland by comparison with England and most of Europe. Laborers received approximately 10% lower pay by English standards, infant mortality and premature death were frequent, and annual migration out of Scotland remained persistently high.

From such unpromising beginnings, it is remarkable that, by 1900, Scotland had produced so many intellectual geniuses. Many were great scientists, such as James Clerk Maxwell, described by Einstein as the most important physicist after Newton. John Napier invented logarithms; Lord Kelvin proposed the second law of thermodynamics; and James Hadden, Roderick Murchison, and Charles Lyell systematized modern geology. Technological innovators, such as James Watt, who developed the steam engine, and John MacAdam, who made the first metaled roads, are noteworthy single instances, but Scottish industrial achievements were more pervasive than this. For example, when Archibald Coats of the town of Paisley joined with the company Patons in 1896 to make the world's biggest thread-making manufacturer, Coats became known as the "Napoleon of the thread trade." In the eastern city of Dundee, traditional expertise in making coarse linens was applied to the problem of jute manufacture so that, by 1890, the largest single jute complex in the world was in Dundee. Their products were exported across the world with rapidly expanding markets in North America and the British Empire. By 1914, Templeton's was the largest carpet manufacturer in Britain, reflecting the importance of textile manufacture to the Scottish economy. James "Paraffin" Young had pioneered the exploitation of shale oil deposits in West Lothian (west of the capital city of Edinburgh), producing 2 million tons per annum of shale by the early 20th century. Precision engineering in sewing machine manufacture and automobile and aircraft construction also were well represented in Scotland. For some historians of the modern world, the Scots invented capitalism; for others, they invented the modern world itself.

Employment in rapidly expanding trades and heavy industries accompanied major increases in the Scottish population. Between the census years of 1831 and 1911, the population doubled to 4.8 million. This reflected not only substantial immigration from Ireland after the Great Famine but also the demand for labor from the heartland of heavy industry in and around Glasgow. The overall picture was of steady expansion in the west, a static position in the Eastern Lowlands, and continuing depletion of the Highlands, where population had peaked by 1841 and never recovered. Work patterns shifted from farm to factory so that by the early 20th century fewer than 10% of the Scottish population worked the land. Such rapid progress in industrialization on such a massive scale had huge consequences for the Scottish economy. Not only did many individuals become conspicuously wealthy, but also substantial parts of the income from Scottish industries were reinvested in America, Australia, and Asia, rising from approximately 60 million pounds in 1870 to 500 million pounds in 1914. These investments encouraged demand for the output of Scotland's industries. Developments in world trade encouraged and stimulated the Scottish economy in an almost reciprocal fashion. Grain for export from Canada might be packaged in sacks made from jute manufactured in Dundee, taken to an eastern seaport on a Glasgow-built locomotive, then carried on a Clyde-built steamer bound for Europe.

The enormous wealth generated transformed Scotland from a country of poor subsistence farmers to one of the world's foremost manufacturing nations. In the half century before 1900, migration from the Scottish countryside and immigrants from Ireland, Italy, Lithuania, and Poland created a highly urbanized society that excelled in the production of ships, locomotives, pig iron, coal, coarse linens, and fine textiles. Agricultural improvements much needed to feed the now-numerous townspeople created small surpluses of cereals for export and rapid development of whisky production. By the early 20th century, Scotland was second only to England as the most urbanized country in the world.

The four major cities of Scotland are Glasgow, Edinburgh, Dundee, and Aberdeen and, by the census of 1911, more than 30% of all Scottish people lived in one of them. Although none of these cities became predominant, Glasgow represented the urban heartland of a country where almost 50% of the population lived in either the greater conurbation of Glasgow or its satellite towns. When Scotland acquired the title "Workshop of the World," it was to Glasgow and its associated towns, each preeminent in manufacturing, that the term was best applied. Elsewhere, the cities served the needs of both manufacturers and local agriculture. Specialist manufactures were associated with many of these smaller towns: Specific textiles flourished in medium-sized border towns such as Selkirk and Galashiels, jute was made in Dundee, and fishing was important in Aberdeen. As these major cities and smaller towns enjoyed unprecedented prosperity, so the face of Scotland changed.

That the city centers continue to show this transformation to this day is enduring evidence of the great impact of the Victorian modernizers. Sometimes the "Grecianization" of urban development produced cityscapes of unique beauty, as seen, for example, in Edinburgh's New Town. Originally developed in the 1780s, by 1840 it contained more than 40,000 residents (i.e., about 1 in 5 of Edinburgh's population), many of whom were employed either in the professions, such as law or medicine, or among the newly emerging business class of prosperous self-employed traders.

The Victorians had also made huge strides in Glasgow, where vast, newly acquired wealth was made conspicuous in the magnificent stone buildings, iron railings, gas lights, and wide streets. Modest public buildings were replaced by substantial courthouses, schools, and museums, modeled on the artistic traditions imported from Italy, Greece, and France. The Victorians were also enthusiastic church builders; by 1900, the skyscapes of all four major Scottish cities were characterized by the inspiring drama of the many churches built at a time when Scottish Presbyterianism brought religious observance to improve the new urban poor. Great railway stations (dubbed the "cathedrals of the Victorian Age") and palatial railway hotels completed the transformation of Scotland's major cities from collections of meager slum dwellings, scattered around more substantial but dilapidated stone structures, into town centers that were universally admired by visitors from overseas. Understandably, the Scots took great pride in their achievements, which were seen as consolidated by the expansion and newfound gracefulness of their new metropolises. With no little imagination, the architecture of these cities came to reflect a confident Scottishness that could trace its traditions to the immensely popular novels of Sir Walter Scott and became in time to be symbolic of a revived Scottish nation.

SOCIAL INEQUALITIES

By 1900, the principal cities of Scotland contained many beautiful buildings and much else for the visitor to admire. Yet the same casual visitors and some of the privileged residents felt, at times, much threatened by the rapidity of change. Dynamic growth came, it seemed, at the price of innercity poverty, squalor, disease, and crime. Slum dwellings were notoriously overcrowded, with minimal standards of sanitation, poor light, and negligible public services. The end of the 19th century saw epidemics of contagious disease (notably, cholera, measles, and whooping cough) sweep through the poor districts, to the alarm of the middle classes. Medical responses to these conditions were often muddled and confused and, although enlightened medical officers of health revealed the social disparities that explained the great class divides in health and mortality, the majority of doctors shared the dominant belief that the inhabitants of the slums were lazy, drunken, and personally responsible for their own squalor because of enduring defects of character. Fear of contagious disease sweeping out of the slums and devastating the wealthier areas of the city did much to promote universally available clean water and the construction of efficient sewers. Driven by fear, the middle classes gradually and reluctantly contributed to the cost of cleansing the extremes of filth from the slums, but health problems persisted. In part, these seemed attributable to the dense overcrowding that characterized Scottish cities with a marked gradient between Glasgow and Edinburgh to the extent that, in 1911, the population density of Glasgow was twice that of Edinburgh. All Scottish cities were more overcrowded than their English counterparts. These densities of population were achieved by the building of tenement blocks of apartments, rarely seen in England and often blamed for the overcrowding and poverty of the residents. Wealthier families typically occupied five rooms in well-furnished blocks with indoor sanitation, bay windows, and efficient heating. The poor lived often two or more to a room, sometimes with just one room and outdoor sanitation serving the needs of the whole family. Tenement dwellings of the poor were wretched places that seemed always to emit a foul stench and were so crowded together that little natural sunlight fell on the streets in between. Here, most of the residents spent as much time outdoors as possible, partly to escape the appalling conditions indoors and often to allow night workers who lodged with them to sleep. Poverty on this scale sustained the manufacturing industries of Scotland; low wages and low expectations went hand in hand as families struggled to survive, to maintain a semblance of respectability in the absence of secure work and the constant threat of illness or accident devastating their household economy. These appalling social conditions continued, with scarce improvement, well into the 20th century.

Charitable organizations sought to help those most afflicted by poverty to pay their rent, keep warm, and eat. Poor law relief was provided on a scale 50% lower than that of England and failed to dispel the ever-present fear of disaster waiting to happen, even to families of skilled artisans. The cost of living for Scottish families in the period leading up to World War I was always greater in Scotland than in England. Evictions, even of respectable families, were commonplace—always in excess of 3,000 per year in Glasgow and sometimes exceeding 20,000 per year when trade conditions declined. The obvious solution to many of the problems of slum families was the construction of municipal or public housing. This was not undertaken with any sense of urgency by Scottish cities, largely because the middle classes believed that the awful conditions experienced by slum dwellers were brought on by themselves and that there was no obligation for the better-off to seek to improve matters. Eventually, however, and very slowly, public housing provision was increased in Scotland, culminating in the post–World War II housing developments that were provided as part of wide-scale social reform by the enlightened politicians of the socialist Labour movement.

THE PEOPLE OF SCOTLAND

The population of Scotland has always been heterogeneous, probably more so than any other part of the British Isles. By 1900, Scotland was peopled by a mixed group who could trace their lineage to the Gaeldom of the

Irish, the Pictish (proto-British) people of the northeast, the Scandinavian descendants of Norsemen, and the true Britons and Angles. Immigration to Scotland gathered pace with the rapid industrialization of the 19th century so that large numbers of Irish and Italians settled in the west of Scotland. Later, especially during times of internal local oppression (i.e., pogroms), displaced Lithuanians, Jews, and Poles also came to and settled in Scotland. The Irish influence was most marked in areas where heavy industry was established. Even so, only a small proportion (approximately 8%) of the total migration from Ireland after the Great Famine settled in Scotland. By 1900, Irish-born residents of Scotland numbered more than 200,000. These Irish immigrants were predominantly Roman Catholic (approximately 80%), but a substantial minority were Protestants from Ulster, descendants of Scots who had accepted land grants in the 17th century and, as such, were more readily assimilated into Scottish society than the Roman Catholic Irish. For some immigrants, especially Irish Roman Catholics, working in Scotland was seen as a temporary stepping stone to their eventual settlement in North America. As such, the migrants were ready to accept menial work, often as strike breakers, just to secure money for their passage to New York or Boston. The transitory nature of the Irish-laboring navvy and the tribal prejudices ingrained in the migrant Ulster Protestants was a highly combustible mix that provoked sectarian conflict, occasionally with extremes of violence. By 1900, many Irish communities were established, mostly in the west of Scotland, with some finding work in the coalfields of Lanarkshire and the Lothians or the jute industry in Dundee. Relatively few settled in the Aberdeen area, where the local population traditionally harbored great suspicions of Irish-speaking (i.e., Gaelic) people from the Highlands and Islands of Scotland and for whom another wave of unwelcome Irish migrants was to be resisted if at all possible.

Assimilation between Irish Catholics and local Scots was made difficult by a 1908 Vatican decree prohibiting intermarriage between faiths. In turn, this was associated with sectarian divides at school, in recreation, and in housing. The desire for separate schools, it could reasonably be argued, is not sectarian but based on a desire to protect the integrity of the faith in the face of what was feared to be a de facto Protestant domination of the public schools. Enclaves of the descendants of Irish migrants paradoxically became more "Irish" as the 20th century progressed. This was in an important sense in keeping with their wish to adhere devoutly to Roman Catholic beliefs and practices but was also affected by a rising tide of Irish nationalism and anti-Englishness that sat comfortably on many Scottish shoulders. With the establishment of the Irish Free State and conclusion of the subsequent civil war, interest in Irish politics waned among the Scottish Irish, who instead transferred their allegiance to the new socialist Labour party.

EMIGRATION FROM SCOTLAND, 1900–1950

European migrants to North America and Australia have exceeded 50 million, and the present strengths of the United States would have been impossible without their contribution. Among the most numerous were the Irish and Scots (and possibly the Norwegians), who had the highest rates of emigration per head of population. These migrations took place in four great surges in the 1850s, 1870s, 1900s, and in the interwar period. Scots who stayed behind were alarmed by such loss of talent and energy and felt that the future of Scotland was threatened by the export of its most enterprising young men and women. As the Scottish labor force was industrialized, the skills of the laboring classes became exportable, and movement from one urban center to another seemed feasible and was often encouraged by earlier successful migrants. For some, migration was the only option to escape the appalling squalor of Scottish cities. For many, the relative benefits of the Scottish educational system, with high rates of literacy and numeracy, made them attractive employees. This may have contributed to the widely recognized dominance by emigrant Scots of Canadian business by 1900. The Scots migrant carried a sense of lasting ethnic identity worn with special pride among the local elite. These comprised the Masons, former elders of Scottish presbyteries, and those active in St. Andrew's Societies, which all served as networks to promote business success and future job prospects. Migration from Scotland continued throughout the first half of the 20th century, whereas migration from other countries had fallen, perhaps in step with rising local standards of living. However, although the Scottish educational system made Scots migrants attractive employees, this cannot explain why Scottish migration continued so vigorously in the years between the wars, when economic depression was widespread. It seems likely that the industrial skills acquired in the factories and shipyards of Scotland were highly prized by future employers who acquired, very cheaply, a well-disciplined, highly skilled, and ambitious immigrant workforce.

EDUCATION

The Scots take great pride in their system of education established after the Protestant Reformation in the 16th century. English politicians early in the 19th century would exhort their countrymen to adopt a system of national education, comparable with that already available for all children in Scotland. Every parish had to have a school, whether urban or rural. In practice, most of the urban parishes accepted the burgh school (managed by the burgh council) as the parish school. Public money was available to ensure that even the poorest child went to school and that lack of means would not prevent the most able continuing their education to a higher level. A local minister and churchgoing laity oversaw the work of teachers whose salaries were paid with public funds and who were encouraged to maintain high standards of teaching and achievement. Fixed parts of the school curriculum were enlightened and outward looking, with rhetoric, logic, and languages. Scottish history has, so far as can be detected, always been taught in Scottish primary schools. Although universally available, education did not become compulsory by law until the latter part of the 19th century, yet the proportion of children in primary school in Scotland exceeded that in European countries (e.g., Prussia) where education was compulsory. The great strengths of the primary Scottish education when compared with England were that it was inexpensive, supported by public funds, and that there was a legally enforceable obligation for all parishes to appoint a schoolmaster. The Scottish school could point to higher rates of literacy (almost double that in England) during the 18th century. Numeracy was also widely taught, with some schools offering more than just simple arithmetic. Some provided bookkeeping; land surveying techniques; and occasionally, geometry and algebra. By contrast, in the face of the overarching role of ministers and church elders, religion was taught (and examined) as the basic tenets of Christian moral values. Sunday schools focused entirely on such matters and, although the populous appreciated this emphasis, they more often attached greater importance to penmanship and composition. As soon as they were able, as affluence increased in the 19th century, all working class children were encouraged to go to school, where they came under the guidance of a local teacher who would often emphasize that education provided the only pathway to riches for the sons of the laboring agricultural classes. By the early 19th century, it had become clear to many commentators on Scottish education that the parish schools had given Scottish children an opportunity not shared with the English, at least to go on to higher education.

Higher education was provided in the Scottish universities founded before the Reformation (St. Andrews, King's College in Aberdeen, and Glasgow), and later in Marischal College in Aberdeen and in the University of Edinburgh. Entrance for the majority of undergraduates was at about age 14 or 15. Many were the sons of ministers or teachers; few were the sons of artisans, but the proportion of university students who were working class or peasants was high by European standards. By the end of the 19th century, the situation in terms of access to the university seemed hardly any better. The son of a minister was many times more likely to enter a university than any other paternal occupation. There were compulsory classes for all students in philosophy and the classics, and by 1892 all universities had introduced compulsory entrance examinations. This delayed entrance for most students to age about 17 or 18 and was linked to the introduction of a school Leaving Certificate. In 1900, mature students, usually from the families of the middle classes, began to enter Scottish universities in increasing numbers. In Edinburgh, around the turn of the 19th century, medical undergraduates made up almost 50% of the student body. Also at about this time women began to enter University, in small numbers at first, but by the outbreak of World War I they made up about 25% of all Scottish undergraduates. By this time, the academic structures of Scottish universities had been radically reformed and remained largely unchanged thereafter until the end of the 20th century. It is difficult to gauge the contributions of the Scottish universities to the Scottish economy in the beginning of the 20th century. Certainly, most of the successful industrialists who figured so prominently among their prospective employers had not attended University and preferred to engage (and train, if necessary) new recruits with aptitudes for practical procedures and organizational skills. In contrast, among leaders of opinion in Scottish universities such practical training was dismissed as irrelevant and not the responsibility of the university where, they argued, all emphasis should be on gaining a firm grasp of theoretical principles and the structure of argument and measurement in a way that could be examined and certified. It is not surprising that such divisions of opinion and purpose encouraged the growth of alternative facilities for higher education. This occurred in technical colleges (or institutes) that were well regarded and seen as driving forward further economic expansion and the creation of greater national wealth. The colleges provided both day and evening classes, and their students were drawn mostly from skilled or administrative occupations. The Royal College in Glasgow and Heriot Watt College in Edinburgh contributed significantly to research.

Scottish secondary school education (i.e., for those about 12 years and older) developed in quite complex ways during the 19th century, filling an acknowledged gap between the standards achieved in primary school and the needs of increasingly demanding industrialized workplaces. Secondary schooling proper barely existed in Scotland until the late 19th century. Secondary-level education was, however, provided in parish schools for the most able, and—especially—in the universities' junior classes. By the latter part of the 19th century the primary school system remained widely praised, and the high rates of literacy and numeracy achieved were envied by most of Scotland's European neighbors. Many Scots, however, had begun to appreciate the need for reform of primary schools, and as incomes of both laboring and middle classes improved the need for more and better secondary schools was widely accepted. From the end of the 18th century onward most of the public record concerns the widespread contemporary conviction that Scottish education was excellent, and it is difficult to find verifiable records of scholastic achievements to support or counter these opinions. Educational reformers of the 19th century pronounced on the self-evident deficiencies in their educational system by emphasizing failure to meet the needs of disadvantaged children (i.e., mostly street children), of girls, and of those obliged because of poverty to work from an early age. A coherent pattern of secondary school provision did not exist until the end of the 19th century in Scotland, and what was available seems to have been in considerable flux. For example, even in the same town, a single child could attend several schools, taking different subjects, in the course of a single day. This type of provision, although seemingly haphazard, may have provided an optimal educational experience that best suited the needs of individual children. It certainly produced results. During this period, the Scottish economy, already highly industrialized and urbanized, continued to grow with great dynamism to rise up the world ranking in terms of expertise, productivity, and international standing. This could not have been achieved without the introduction and improvements to the educational systems giving children an extra 3 years from ages 12 to 14 before going to work.

By 1850, Scotland had established formal teacher training, which included specialist institutions and the encouragement of older pupils to work as teachers' assistants and who might, through this type of apprenticeship, progress to train as teachers. Emigration from Scotland continued apace throughout the century and created opportunities to improve schools for the smaller number of children who remained. After 1872, efforts were made to enforce compulsory education, and this was applied with particular vigor to the children of slum dwellers who had never (traditionally) gone to school. In addition to increased economic investment in teachers and schools, the late Victorians realized quite clearly that education provided a unique opportunity to introduce many children to the instructions of the Christian church and its central moral values. Although it might seem, with the benefit of hindsight, that the social pressures that were most influential on the development of the Scottish secondary school education were driven by political factors intended to create a state educational system, this never happened in Scotland. Separate strands of educational provision were evident: The Roman Catholic Irish sought and developed separate schools. Private schools thrived in and around large towns, but their status was never higher than the best of the local board schools. These public schools, as before, were managed by local ministers and townspeople who were frequent church attenders. From 1872, the new school boards designated some town schools as "higher class public schools," which did not require government inspection and could meet their costs through fees levied on pupils.

A centralized state subsidy of secondary education was introduced in 1892. The Scottish Education Department had intended these moneys should be applied to a small proportion (about 5%) of pupils who might benefit most. Instead, the local burghs distributed the support evenly amongst schools in keeping, they argued, with the democratic ideals of the Protestant Reformers of the 16th century. These principles were widely shared among teachers and their professional organization: the Educational Institute of

Scotland, the body that would, from a part of its members' subscriptions, provide the funds that set up and ran the Scottish Council for Research in Education, which in turn conducted the SMS1932 and SMS1947. State support of education was extended by the 1918 Act of Parliament, which consolidated secondary schooling and allowed for the transfer to education authorities of schools not managed by an education authority. The overall aims were to better prepare the children of Scotland for the more demanding occupations of a complex industrialized society, but secondary aims were also widely debated. These included the importance of a well-educated employable class from whom the professional classes could also be drawn (not just the well connected or well born) and from whom Scotland might develop and maintain its competitive military strengths. Unfortunately, what is less clear is the extent to which these educational reforms benefited the Scottish people. Some commentators have since argued that they did little to encourage the expected increase in upward social mobility. The school attendance figures, however, suggest that at the least these reforms increased the proportion of Scottish children entering secondary education, although fewer did so in England. In the 1920s, approximately 12% of people who entered secondary courses gained the Leaving Certificate, but only approximately 40% of people did enter a secondary course. The proportion of the whole age group gaining the Leaving Certificate was approximately 4% or 5%.

In the early 1920s, the Educational Institute of Scotland continued its argument of universally available secondary education. Its aims were thwarted by the Scottish Education Department, which remained steadfast in supporting the principle that secondary education should be provided only for that small minority of children who might benefit. By 1925, the structure of Scottish secondary education had become firmly set, changing little until 1965 and the introduction of comprehensive education. Large towns had small numbers of private schools, often with charitable status attended as day pupils by about 5% to 10% of local children. Even fewer private schools founded on the prestigious English public school model were developed in rural locations. The mainly free public secondary schools provided many more places than the private schools. By the eve of World War I, free secondary schooling was available everywhere, and that did not change over the following decades. The best pupils were selected at this age for secondary education, and all others completed their education at Advanced Division schools with less investment, less well trained teachers, and much lower expectations. By 1950, only about 5% of all school-leavers entered higher education, and 90% had left by age 15. Compulsory education from ages 5 to 13 had begun in Scotland with an act of parliament in 1872. The school leaving age for compulsory education was raised to 14 in 1883, from 14 to 15 in 1947, and from 15 to 16 (at which it remains today) in 1972. During the remaining interwar years, powerful voices were raised against the ideological strictures of the Scottish

Education Department. The whole establishment, consolidation and inspection of the secondary schools was planned by the Scottish Education Department. The controversies over the restrictions after 1921 were intense and were centered on an interpretation of educability.

ILLNESS AND HEALTH

Attitudes toward sickness, understanding health advice, and behavior when consulting doctors changed enormously in 20th-century Scotland. Ingrained among the poor was the firm belief that medical help was an expensive commodity to be sought only in dire need and never to be frittered away. By the latter part of the century, criticisms of doctors were more frequent and more vocal, much as criticism of older generations were more frequently heard from younger generations than hitherto. These critical demands, especially of doctors from younger women, progressed in some circumstances to a rejection of medical authoritarianism to a search for alternative forms of medical treatment in ways that were alien to Scottish people in the early 20th century. At the outset, doctor–patient relationships were idealized as harmonious, with the patient playing a passive foil to the doctor's active search for understanding (i.e., diagnosis) and treatment. With better education and more available information about medical practices and the principles of treatment, patients came to realize that there could be pluralities in the doctor–patient relationship and often identified easily the attempts of doctors to retain control of that relationship through strict adherence to routines of clinical practice. The processes of consultation were measured against standards set by the doctor. For example, the patient was expected to consult a doctor promptly, as soon as the need for a medical opinion was recognized. Early in the century, although the doctor might feel a patient should have come earlier, there was wide recognition that for many early attendance was impossible: Wages could be needlessly lost; the cost of the consultation and possibly medicines of dubious efficacy must be set against the staple needs of a family; and there was often some unspoken terror at the prospect of an often-witnessed disease, such as pulmonary tuberculosis. The doctor, in the circumstances of the early 20th century, needed to be the disciplined guardian of the patient's well-being and at the same time an educator with no self-interest in the patient's compliance with advice. It is not surprising, then, that doctors who succeeded in balancing these roles displayed fine judgment and were often highly regarded among the communities they served.

Socialist thinking influenced—some say jaundiced—the views of many Scots who came to see doctors as another self-interested group, willing tools of the capitalist classes who feigned interest in self-determination and self-knowledge and wished primarily to "own" patients and their illnesses as though they were commodities in which doctors could trade. The public image of the doctor, possessed of overbearing personal qualities intended to impress and influence, exercising power over the poor and inarticulate, was both ridiculed and accepted. It was better, thought many, to tolerate this behavior than the alternative nonscientific old "wifee's" advice of a hot stocking around the neck to soothe a sore throat, raw meat on a cancer so that "the cancer ate the meat," or a porridge poultice for pleurisy. As the century progressed, free alternatives to orthodox medicine were less often sought, partly, it was felt, because material standards of living were improving and doctor's fees became affordable, but also because scientific medicines became spectacularly effective, especially in the treatment of infections.

Consultation behavior changed substantially. For example, the idea of preventive medicine is comparatively recent. The predominance among repeated prescribing of medications is the widespread use of drugs to prevent a complication arising from an asymptomatic preclinical state. For instance, in contemporary medicine, drugs to lower blood fats or lower blood pressure are among the most widely prescribed; they are taken regularly to control a physiological state of which a patient was often unaware but one that is confidently linked with increased risk of disease, such as a stroke or a heart attack. This type of prescribing was unknown in the early 20th century; raised blood pressure was understood as a response to the presence of a diseased organ, such that the diseased kidney needed raised blood pressure to function as an excretory organ. In these terms, raised blood pressure was seen as essential to the maintenance of life.

Within the family, before the introduction of the NHS, traditions were often established whereby a call for the doctor was a last resort. There were strong beliefs in getting better through force of will alone. Sometimes, these strategies were viewed not as strengths but as foibles that were ostensibly left unchallenged but circumvented through trickery so that a doctor might arrive without knowing that the patient was publicly unaware of the request for a visit but privately alerted by the notion that the doctor just happened to be passing by. These actions were tempered by the knowledge that if the doctor concluded that the call had been made too easily when nothing amiss could be detected, then the patient and perhaps the whole family might be unfairly stigmatized as attention seeking or hypochondriacal.

With the election of a socialist Labour government in 1945, the principle of free and fair access to a comprehensive health service on the basis of need and not the ability to pay became embedded in British public life. For the people of Scotland, this NHS became the primary means of access to medical care. It did not, however, produce immediate gains in the dire health statistics of the nation. Maternal and neonatal care witnessed the first improvements, with considerable reductions in puerperal sepsis afforded by prompt diagnosis and the use of antibiotics. The treatment of tuberculosis was also much improved, thanks in part to better medicines and in part to improved living conditions. The question of compliance with medical advice was answered by the introduction of free medicines for all and was widely commented on. In this regard, the laboring classes were seen as better patients (i.e., more compliant) than the administrative or professional classes, who were thought to be less likely to follow instructions. These higher class patients were thought soon after the introduction of the NHS to seek to retain something of their earlier relationships with doctors when they had been fee paying. This type of special relationship was best seen in the request for the services of a particular doctor with whom they had some sort of family or social connection.

The concept of health is subject to cultural variation so that, for some, health is all to do with the retention of physical abilities such as strength, speed, and stamina. For others, it is the absence of illness or refers to the inner reserves available to withstand such illnesses. Last, the idea of good health is being able to meet one's commitments and obligations without unnecessary worries. In the Scottish setting, it is unclear which of these several ideas about what constitutes good health have prevailed in the first part of the 20th century and how these might have varied with time. The extent to which psychological or physical explanations of common symptoms have been accepted in the popular imagination seems subject to the same variations, but these are not well quantified and remain poorly understood. In one study of older residents in Aberdeen, health was seen as primarily the strength to resist illness, to recover from observable—and, therefore, verifiable—disease. It follows that just as concepts of illness might vary, so too might ideas about the origins of good health. In the popular Scottish culture, good health is the product of good living, and often good living means simply hard working. Seen in these terms, it seems that modern Scots understand good health as having essentially moral determinants and/or practical, physical origins born out of the origins of disease.

Within these historical viewpoints, ideas about health and illness in Scotland are traceable to the folk beliefs of the peoples who settled there over the centuries; the strength of adherence to particular religious principles; and the acceptance of rational, empirical explanations of the nature of disease, coping, and the inevitability of decline and death. To understand the numerous contradictions generated in surveys of health and disease, of personal success and failure, of mental strengths and frailties, requires fresh insights in understanding the origins of individual differences identified in studies of Scots drawn from different generations. Some associations seem likely to be influenced by important temporal variations, for example, shared wartime experiences and privations, and others to remain constant from one birth epoch to another. Understanding the Scottish psyche may entail both digging up its roots in the past in which it is buried and collecting the low-hanging fruits that are the scientific legacy of our industrious forebears.

This has been an impressionistic sketch of the Scottish background against which the SMS1932 and SMS1947 took place. The reader who wants to learn more will benefit from Devine's (2006) *The Scottish Nation 1700–2007*; Royle's (1997) *Modern Britain: A Social History, 1750–1997*; Lynch's (1992) *Scotland: A New History*; and Smout's (1997) *A Century of the Scottish People, 1830–1950*. For those who want the specific background of the educational history of Scotland, including the time of the SMSs, we recommend Paterson's (2003) *Scottish Education in the Twentieth Century* and Anderson's (1997) *Scottish Education Since the Reformation*.

REFERENCES

Ackerman, P. L. (1996). A theory of adult intellectual development: Process, personality, interests, and knowledge. *Intelligence, 22,* 227–257.

Altman, D. G. (1991). *Practical statistics for medical research.* London: Chapman and Hall.

Anderson, R. D. (1997). *Scottish education since the Reformation.* Edinburgh: Scottish Economic and Social History Society.

Anstey, K., & Christensen, H. (2000). Education, activity, health, blood pressure and apolipoprotein E as predictors of cognitive change in old age: A review. *Gerontology, 46,* 163–177.

*Bain, G. H., Lemmon, H., Teunisse, S., Starr, J. M., Fox, H. C., Deary, I. J., & Whalley, L. J. (2003). Quality of life in healthy old age: Relationships with childhood IQ, minor psychological symptoms and optimism. *Social Psychiatry and Psychiatric Epidemiology, 38,* 632–636.

Barker, D. J. P. (1998). *Mothers, babies and health in later life* (2nd ed.). London: Churchill Livingstone.

Barker, D. J. P. (2004). The developmental origins of wellbeing. *Philosophical Transactions of the Royal Society of London: Series B. Biological Sciences, 59,* 1359–1366.

Bartzokis, G. (2004). Age-related myelin breakdown: A developmental model of cognitive decline and Alzheimer's disease. *Neurobiology of Aging, 25,* 49–62.

Batty, G. D., Deary, I. J., & Gottfredson, L. S. (2007). Premorbid (early life) IQ and later mortality risk: Systematic review. *Annals of Epidemiology, 17,* 278–288.

Batty, G. D., Deary, I. J., & Macintyre, S. (2006). Childhood IQ and lifecourse socioeconomic position in relations to alcohol induced hangovers in adulthood: The Aberdeen children of the 1950s study. *Journal of Epidemiology and Community Health, 60,* 872–874.

Batty, G. D., Deary, I. J., & Macintyre, S. (2007). Childhood IQ in relation to risk factors for premature mortality in middle-aged persons: The Aberdeen Children of the 1950s study. *Journal of Epidemiology and Community Health, 61,* 241–247.

Batty, G. D., Deary, I. J., Schoon, I., & Gale, C. R. (2007). Childhood mental ability in relation to food intake and physical activity in adulthood: The 1970 British Cohort Study. *Pediatrics, 119,* e38–e45.

---

* References marked with an asterisk include analyses of data from the Scottish Mental Survey of 1932 and/or 1947.

Batty, G. D., Der, G., Macintyre, S., & Deary, I. J. (2006, February 1). Does IQ explain socioeconomic inequalities in health? Evidence from a population based cohort study in the west of Scotland. *BMJ, 332,* 580–584.

Batty, G. D., Wennerstad, K. M., Smith, G. D., Gunnell, D., Deary, I. J., Tynelius, P., & Rasmussen, F. (2007). IQ in early adulthood and later cancer risk: Cohort study of one million Swedish men. *Annals of Oncology, 18,* 21–28.

Benyamin, B., Deary, I. J., & Visscher, P. M. (2006). Precision and bias of a normal finite mixture distribution model to analyze twin data when zygosity is unknown. *Behavior Genetics, 36,* 935–946.

*Benyamin, B., Wilson, V., Whalley, L. J., Visscher, P. M., & Deary, I. J. (2005). Large, consistent estimates of the heritability of cognitive ability in two entire populations of 11-year-old twins from Scottish Mental Surveys of 1932 and 1947. *Behavior Genetics, 35,* 525–534.

Bhutta, A. T., Cleves, M. A., Casey, P. H., Cradock, M. M., & Anand, K. J. S. (2002). Cognitive and behavioural outcomes of school-aged children who were born preterm: A meta-analysis. *Journal of the American Medical Association, 288,* 728–737.

Bolton-Smith, C., & Milne, A. C. (1991). Food frequency versus weighed intake data in Scottish men. *Proceedings of the Nutrition Society, 50,* 35A.

Bond, J., & Carstairs, V. (1982). *Services for the elderly: A survey of the characteristics and needs of a population of 5,000,000 old people* (Scottish Home and Health Studies No. 42). Edinburgh, Scotland: Scottish Home and Health Department.

Bouchard, T. J. (2004). Genetic and environmental influences on human psychological differences. *Current Directions in Psychological Science, 13,* 140–144.

Bouchard, T. J., & McGue, M. (2003). Genetic and environmental influences on human psychological differences. *Journal of Neurobiology, 54,* 4–45.

Bourre, J. M. (2006a). Effects of nutrients (in food) on the structure and function of the nervous system: Update on dietary requirements for brain: Part 1. Micronutrients. *Journal of Nutrition, Health and Aging, 10,* 377–385.

Bourre, J. M. (2006b). Effects of nutrients (in food) on the structure and function of the nervous system: Update on dietary requirements for brain: Part 2. Macronutrients. *Journal of Nutrition, Health and Aging, 10,* 386–399.

Breen, R., & Goldthorpe, J. H. (1999). Class inequality and meritocracy: A critique of Saunders and an alternative analysis. *British Journal of Sociology, 50,* 1–27.

Breen, R., & Goldthorpe, J. H. (2001). Class, mobility and merit: The experience of two British birth cohorts. *European Sociological Review, 17,* 81–101.

Breland, H. M. (1974). Birth order, family configuration, and verbal achievement. *Child Development, 45,* 1011–1049.

Buss, D. M. (2000). Desires in human mating. In D. LeCroy & P. Moller (Eds.), *Annals of the New York Academy of Sciences: Vol. 907. Evolutionary perspectives on human reproductive behavior* (pp. 39–49). New York: New York Academy of Sciences.

Carroll, J. B. (1993). *Human cognitive abilities: A survey of factor analytic studies.* Cambridge, England: Cambridge University Press.

Carstairs, V., & Morris, R. (1991). *Deprivation and health in Scotland*. Aberdeen, Scotland: Aberdeen University Press.

Cervilla, J. A., Prince, M., & Mann, A. (2000). Smoking, drinking, and incident cognitive impairment: A cohort community based study included in the Gospel Oak project. *Journal of Neurology, Neurosurgery and Psychiatry, 68*, 622–626.

Chamorro-Premuzic, T., & Furnham, A. (2004). A possible model for understanding the personality–intelligence interface. *British Journal of Psychology, 95*, 249–264.

Chandola, T., Deary, I. J., Blane, D., & Batty, G. D. (2006). Childhood IQ in relation to obesity and weight gain in adult life: The National Child Development Study. *International Journal of Obesity, 30*, 1422–1432.

Christensen, H., MacKinnon, A. J., Korten, A., & Jorm, A. F. (2001). The "common cause hypothesis" of cognitive ageing: Evidence for not only a common factor but also specific associations of age with vision and grip strength in a cross-sectional analysis. *Psychology and Aging, 16*, 588–599.

Christensen, K., Petersen, I., Skytthe, A., Herskind, A. M., McGue, M., & Bingley, P. (2006, September 29). Comparison of academic performance of twins and singletons in adolescence: Follow-up study. *BMJ, 333*, 1095–1097.

Collin, C., Wade, D. T., Davies, S., & Horne, V. (1988). The Barthel ADL Index: A reliability study. *International Disability Studies, 10*, 61–63.

Corder, E. H., Saunders, A. M., Strittmatter, W. J., Schmechel, D. E., Gaskell, P. C., Small, G. W., et al. (1993, August 13). Gene dose of apolipoprotein type E allele and the risk of Alzheimers's disease in late-onset families. *Science, 261*, 921–923.

Costa, P. T., Jr., & McCrae, R. R. (1992). *Revised NEO Personality Inventory (NEO PI-R) and NEO Five-Factor Inventory (NEO-FFI) professional manual*. Odessa, FL: Psychological Assessment Resources.

Cox, D. R. (1972). Regression models and life tables. *Journal of the Royal Statistical Society: Series B. Statistical Methodology, 34*, 187–220.

Craigie, J. (1972). *The Scottish Council for Research in Education 1928–1972*. Unpublished monograph.

*Crawford, J. R., Deary, I. J., Starr, J. M., & Whalley, L. J. (2001). The NART as an index of prior intellectual functioning: A retrospective validity study covering a 66-year interval. *Psychological Medicine, 31*, 451–458.

Crawford, J. R., Stewart, L. E., Parker, D. M., Besson, J. A., & De Lacey, G. (1989). Prediction of the WAIS IQ with the National Adult Reading Test: Cross-validation and extension. *British Journal of Clinical Psychology, 28*, 267–273.

Davey Smith, G., Hart, C., Blane, D., & Hole, D. (1998, May 30). Adverse socioeconomic conditions in childhood and cause specific adult mortality: Prospective observational study. *BMJ, 316*, 1631–1635.

David, A. S., Malmberg, A., Brandt, L., Allebeck, P., & Lewis, G. (1997). IQ and risk for schizophrenia: A population-based cohort study. *Psychological Medicine, 27*, 1311–1323.

Davis, C., Ho, M.-Y., Bradshaw, C. M., & Szaba, E. (2000). Estimation of premorbid performance on Raven's Standard Progressive Matrices using reading-test performance: New normative data. *Clinical Neuropsychological Assessment, 2,* 113–123.

Deary, I. J. (2006, November 25). Educational performance in twins: Is no different from that seen in singletons by adolescence. *BMJ, 333,* 1080–1081.

*Deary, I. J., Bastin, M. E., Pattie, A., Clayden, J. D., Whalley, L. J., Starr, J. M., & Wardlaw, J. M. (2006). White matter integrity and cognition in childhood and old age. *Neurology, 66,* 505–512.

Deary, I. J., & Batty, G. D. (2007). Cognitive epidemiology: A glossary of terms. *Journal of Epidemiology and Community Health, 61,* 378–384.

Deary, I. J., Batty, G. D., & Gottfredson, L. S. (2005, July 29). Human hierarchies, health, and IQ. *Science, 309,* 703.

Deary, I. J., & Der, G. (2005). Reaction time explains IQ's association with death. *Psychological Science, 16,* 64–69.

Deary, I. J., Der, G., & Shenkin, S. D. (2005). Does mother's IQ explain the association between birth weight and cognitive ability in childhood? *Intelligence, 33,* 445–454.

*Deary, I. J., Gow, A. J., Taylor, M. D., Corley, J., Brett, C., Wilson, V., et al. (2007). The Lothian Birth Cohort 1936: A study to examine influences on cognitive ageing from age 11 to age 70 and beyond. *BMC Geriatrics, 7,* 28.

*Deary, I. J., Hamilton, G., Hayward, C., Whalley, L. J., Powell, J., Starr, J. M., & Lovestone, S. (2005). Nicastrin gene polymorphisms, cognitive ability level and cognitive ageing. *Neuroscience Letters, 373,* 110–114.

*Deary, I. J., Harris, S. E., Fox, H. C., Hayward, C., Wright, A. F., Starr, J. M., & Whalley, L. J. (2005). *KLOTHO* genotype and cognitive ability in childhood and old age in the same individuals. *Neuroscience Letters, 378,* 22–27.

*Deary, I. J., Hayward, C., Permana, P. A., Nair, S., Whalley, L. J., Starr, J. M., et al. (2006). Polymorphisms in the gene encoding 11B-hydroxysteroid dehydrogenase type 1 (HSD11B1) and lifetime cognitive change. *Neuroscience Letters, 393,* 74–77.

Deary, I. J., Irwing, P., Der, G., & Bates, T. C. (2007). Brother–sister differences in the *g* factor in intelligence: Analysis of full, opposite-sex siblings from the NLSY1979. *Intelligence, 35,* 451–456.

*Deary, I. J., Leaper, S. A., Murray, A. D., Staff, R. T., & Whalley, L. J. (2003). Cerebral white matter abnormalities and lifetime cognitive change: A 67-year follow-up of the Scottish Mental Survey of 1932. *Psychology and Aging, 18,* 140–148.

*Deary, I. J., Pattie, A., Taylor, M. D., Whiteman, M. C., Starr, J. M., & Whalley, L. J. (2003). Smoking and cognitive change from age 11 to age 80. *Journal of Neurology, Neurosurgery and Psychiatry, 74,* 1006–1007.

*Deary, I. J., Pattie, A., Wilson, V., & Whalley, L. J. (2005). The cognitive cost of being a twin: Two whole-population surveys. *Twin Research and Human Genetics, 8,* 376–383.

Deary, I. J., Spinath, F. M., & Bates, T. C. (2006). Genetics of intelligence. *European Journal of Human Genetics, 14,* 690–700.

Deary, I. J., Starr, J. M., & MacLennan, W. J. (1998). Is age kinder to the initially more able? Differential aging of verbal ability in the HOPE study. *Intelligence, 26*, 357–375.

*Deary, I. J., Taylor, M. D., Hart, C. L., Wilson, V., Davey Smith, G., Blane, D., & Starr, J. M. (2005). Intergenerational social mobility and mid-life status attainments: Influences of childhood intelligence, childhood social factors, and education. *Intelligence, 33*, 455–472.

*Deary, I. J., Thorpe, G., Wilson, V., Starr, J. M., & Whalley, L. J. (2003). Population sex differences in IQ at age 11: The Scottish Mental Survey 1932. *Intelligence, 31*, 533–542.

*Deary, I. J., Whalley, L. J., Batty, G. D., & Starr, J. M. (2006). Physical fitness and lifetime cognitive change. *Neurology, 67*, 1195–1200.

*Deary, I. J., Whalley, L. J., & Crawford, J. R. (2004). An "instantaneous" estimate of a lifetime's cognitive change. *Intelligence, 32*, 113–119.

*Deary, I. J., Whalley, L. J., Lemmon, H., Crawford, J. R., & Starr, J. M. (2000). The stability of individual differences in mental ability from childhood to old age: Follow-up of the 1932 Scottish Mental Survey. *Intelligence, 28*, 49–55.

*Deary, I. J., Whalley, L. J., St. Clair, D., Breen, G., Leaper, S., Lemmon, H., et al. (2003). The influence of the e4 allele of the apolipoprotein E gene on childhood IQ, nonverbal reasoning in old age, and lifetime cognitive change. *Intelligence, 31*, 85–92.

*Deary, I. J., Whalley, L. J., & Starr, J. M. (2003). IQ at age 11 and longevity, results from a follow-up of the Scottish Mental Survey 1932. In C. E. Finch, J.-M. Robine, & Y. Christen (Eds.), *Brain and longevity* (pp. 153–164). Berlin, Germany: Springer.

*Deary, I. J., Whiteman, M. C., Pattie, A., Starr, J. M., Hayward, C., Wright, A. F., et al. (2002, August 29). Cognitive change and the *APOE* e4 allele. *Nature, 418*, 932.

*Deary, I. J., Whiteman, M. C., Pattie, A., Starr, J. M., Hayward, C., Wright, A. F., et al. (2004). Apolipoprotein E gene variability and cognitive functions at age 79: A follow-up of the Scottish Mental Survey of 1932. *Psychology and Aging, 19*, 367–371.

*Deary, I. J., Whiteman, M. C., Starr, J. M., Whalley, L. J., & Fox, H. C. (2004). The impact of childhood intelligence on later life: Following up the Scottish Mental Surveys of 1932 and 1947. *Journal of Personality and Social Psychology, 86*, 130–147.

Deary, I. J., Wright, A. F., Harris, S. E., Whalley, L. J., & Starr, J. M. (2004). Searching for genetic influences on normal cognitive ageing. *Trends in Cognitive Sciences, 8*, 178–184.

Del Bo, R., Scarlato, M., Ghezzi, S., Martinelli-Boneschi, F., Fenoglio, C., Galimberti, G., et al. (2006). Is M129V of PRNP gene associated with Alzheimer's disease? A case control study and a meta-analysis [Electronic version]. *Neurobiology of Aging, 27*, 770.e1–770.e5.

Der, G., & Deary, I. J. (2006). Reaction time age changes and sex differences in adulthood. Results from a large, population based study: The UK Health and Lifestyle Survey. *Psychology and Aging, 21*, 62–73.

Devine, T. M. (2006). *The Scottish nation: 1700–2007* (2nd ed.). Harmondsworth, England: Penguin.

Diener, E. (1984). Subjective well-being. *Psychological Bulletin, 95*, 542–575.

Diener, E., Emmons, R. A., Larsen, R. J., & Griffin, S. (1985). The Satisfaction With Life Scale. *Journal of Personality Assessment, 49*, 71–75.

*Duthie, S. J., Whalley, L. J., Collins, A. R., Leaper, S., Berger, K., & Deary, I. J. (2002). Homocysteine, B vitamin status, and cognitive function in the elderly. *American Journal of Clinical Nutrition, 75*, 908–913.

Egan, M. F., Goldberg, T. E., Kolachana, B. S., Callicott, J. H., Mazzanti, C. M., Straub, R. E., et al. (2001). Effect of COMT Val108/158Met genotype on frontal lobe function and risk for schizophrenia. *Proceedings of the National Academy of Sciences of the USA, 98*, 6917–6922.

Egan, M. F., Kojima, M., Callicott, J. H., Goldberg, T. E., Kolachana, B. S., Bertolino, A., et al. (2003). The BDNF val66met polymorphism affects activity-dependent secretion of BDNF and human memory and hippocampal function. *Cell, 112*, 257–269.

Emslie, C., Hunt, K., & Macintyre, S. (1999). Problematizing gender, work and health: The relationship between gender, occupational grade, working conditions and minor morbidity in full-time bank employees. *Social Science & Medicine, 48*, 33–48.

Fillit, H. M., Butler, R, N., O'Connell, A. W., Albert, M. S., Birren, J. E., Cotman, C. W., et al. (2002). Achieving and maintaining cognitive vitality with aging. *Mayo Clinic Proceedings, 77*, 681–696.

Finch, C. E., Robine, J.-M., & Christen, Y. (2003). (Eds.), *Brain and longevity*. Berlin, Germany: Springer.

Flynn, J. R. (1999). Searching for justice: The discovery of IQ gains over time. *American Psychologist, 54*, 5–20.

Folstein, M. F., Folstein, S. E., & McHugh, P. R. (1975). Mini-Mental State: A practical method for grading the cognitive state of patients for the clinician. *Journal of Psychiatric Research, 12*, 189–198.

Freeman, J., & Godfrey, H. (2000). The validity of the NART–RSPM index in detecting intellectual decline following traumatic brain injury: A controlled study. *British Journal of Clinical Psychology, 39*, 95–103.

Fukunishi, I., Kitaoka, T., Shirai, T., Kino, K., Kanematsu, E., & Sato, Y. (2002). Psychiatric disorders among patients undergoing hemodialysis therapy. *Nephron, 91*, 344–347.

Furu, M., Lingärde, F., Ljung, B.-O., Munck, I., & Kristenson, H. (1984). *Premature death, cognitive ability and socioeconomic background*. Stockholm: AVEBE Grafiska.

Gale, C. R., Deary, I. J., Schoon, I., & Batty, G. D. (2007, February 3). IQ in childhood and vegetarianism in adulthood: 1970 British Cohort Study. *BMJ, 334,* 245–248.

Goff, M., & Ackerman, P. L. (1992). Personality–intelligence relations: Assessment of typical intellectual engagement. *Journal of Educational Psychology, 84,* 537–552.

Gottfredson, L. (2004). Intelligence: Is it the epidemiologists' elusive "fundamental cause" of social class inequalities in health? *Journal of Personality and Social Psychology, 86,* 174–199.

Gove, W. R. (1973). Sex, marital status and mortality. *American Journal of Sociology, 79,* 45–67.

*Gow, A. J., Pattie, A., Whiteman, M. C., Whalley, L. J., & Deary, I. J. (2007). Social support and successful aging: Investigating the relationships between lifetime cognitive change and life satisfaction. *Journal of Individual Differences, 28,* 103–115.

*Gow, A. J., Whiteman, M. C., Pattie, A., & Deary, I. J. (2005a). Goldberg's "IPIP" Big-Five markers: Internal consistency and concurrent validation in Scotland. *Personality and Individual Differences, 39,* 317–329.

*Gow, A. J., Whiteman, M. C., Pattie, A., & Deary, I. J. (2005b). The personality–intelligence interface: Insights from an ageing cohort. *Personality and Individual Differences, 39,* 751–761.

*Gow, A. J., Whiteman, M. C., Pattie, A., Whalley, L. J., Starr, J. M., & Deary, I. J. (2005, July 6). Lifetime intellectual function and satisfaction with life in old age: Longitudinal cohort study. *BMJ, 331,* 141–142.

*Gray, J., McPherson, A. F., & Raffe, D. (1983). *Reconstructions of secondary education: Theory, myth and practice since the war.* London: Routledge & Kegan Paul.

Gunning-Dixon, F. M., & Raz, N. (2000). The cognitive correlates of white matter abnormalities in normal aging: A quantitative review. *Neuropsychology, 14,* 224–232.

Halliwell, B. (2006). Oxidative stress and neurodegeneration: Where are we now? *Journal of Neurochemistry, 97,* 1634–1658.

*Harris, S. E., Deary, I. J., MacIntyre, A., Lamb, K. J., Radhakrishnan, K., Starr, J. M., et al. (2006). The association between telomere length, physical health, cognitive ageing, and mortality in non-demented older people. *Neuroscience Letters, 406,* 260–264.

*Harris, S. E., Fox, H., Wright, A. F., Hayward, C., Starr, J. M., Whalley, L. J., & Deary, I. J. (2006). The brain-derived neurotrophic factor Val66Met polymorphism is associated with age-related change in reasoning skills. *Molecular Psychiatry, 11,* 505–513.

*Harris, S. E., Fox, H., Wright, A. F., Hayward, C., Starr, J. M., Whalley, L. J., & Deary, I. J. (2007). A genetic association analysis of cognitive ability and cognitive ageing using 325 markers for 109 genes associated with oxidative stress or cognition. *BMC Genetics, 8,* 43.

*Harris, S. E., Wright, A. F., Hayward, C., Starr, J. M., Whalley, L. J., & Deary, I. J. (2005). The functional COMT polymorphism, Val158Met, is associated with logical memory and the personality trait intellect/imagination in a cohort of healthy 79 year olds. *Neuroscience Letters, 385*, 1–6.

*Hart, C. L., Deary, I. J., Taylor, M. D., MacKinnon, P. L., Davey Smith, G., Whalley, L. J., et al. (2003). The Scottish Mental Survey 1932 linked to the Midspan Studies: A prospective investigation of childhood intelligence and future health. *Public Health, 117*, 187–195.

Hart, C. L., MacKinnon, P. L., Watt, G. C. M., Upton, M. N., McConnachie, A., Hole, D. J., et al. (2005). The Midspan Studies. *International Journal of Epidemiology, 34*, 28–34.

*Hart, C. L., Taylor, M. D., Davey Smith, G., Whalley, L. J., Starr, J. M., Hole, D. J., et al. (2003). Childhood IQ, social class, deprivation, and their relationships with mortality and morbidity risk in later life: Prospective observational study linking the Scottish Mental Survey 1932 and the Midspan Studies. *Psychosomatic Medicine, 65*, 877–883.

*Hart, C. L., Taylor, M. D., Davey Smith, G., Whalley, L. J., Starr, J. M., Hole, D. J., et al. (2004). Childhood IQ and cardiovascular disease in adulthood: Prospective observational study linking the Scottish Mental Survey 1932 and the Midspan studies. *Social Science & Medicine, 59*, 2131–2138.

*Hart, C. L., Taylor, M. D., Davey Smith, G., Whalley, L. J., Starr, J. M., Hole, D. J., et al. (2005). Childhood IQ and all-cause mortality before and after age 65: Prospective observational study linking the Scottish Mental Survey 1932 and the Midspan Studies. *British Journal of Health Psychology, 10*, 153–165.

Hayflick, L. (2007). Biological aging is no longer an unsolved problem. In S. I. S. Rattern & S. Akman (Eds.,) *Annals of the New York Academy of Sciences: Vol. 1100. Biogerontology: Mechanisms and interventions* (pp. 1–13). New York: New York Academy of Sciences.

Heasman, M. A., & Clarke, J. A. (1979). Medical record linkage and Scotland. *Health Bulletin, 37*, 97–103.

Hedden, T., & Gabrieli, J. D. E. (2004). Insights into the ageing mind: A view from cognitive neuroscience. *Nature Reviews Neuroscience, 5*, 87–97.

Hedges, L. V., & Nowell, A. (1995, July 7). Sex differences in mental test scores, variability, and numbers of high-scoring individuals. *Science, 269*, 41–45.

Heim, A. (1970). *Intelligence and personality*. Harmondsworth, England: Penguin.

Hemmingsson, T., Melin, B., Allebeck, P., & Lundberg, I. (2006). The association between cognitive ability at ages 18–20 and mortality during 30 years of follow-up: A prospective study among Swedish males born 1949–1951. *International Journal of Epidemiology, 35*, 665–670.

Her Majesty's Stationery Office. (1946). *Education (Scotland) Act, 1946*. London: Author.

Herrmann, W. (2006). Significance of hyperhomocysteinemia. *Clinical Laboratory, 52*, 367–374.

Herrnstein, R. J., & Murray, C. (1994). *The bell curve: Intelligence and class structure in American life*. New York: Free Press.

Hobbes, T. (1885). *Leviathan*. London: Routledge. (Original work published 1651)

Hoddings, N. (1992). Variability: A pernicious hypothesis. *Review of Educational Hypothesis, 62*, 85–88.

*Hope, K. (1984). *As others see us: Schooling and social mobility in Scotland and the United States*. Cambridge, England: Cambridge University Press.

Horn, J. L., & Cattell, R. B. (1966). Refinement and test of the theory of fluid and crystallised intelligences. *Journal of Educational Psychology, 57*, 253–270.

Huang, Y., Weisgraber, K. H., Mucke, L., & Mahley, R. W. (2004). Apolipoprotein E: Diversity of cellular origins, structural and biophysical properties, and effects in Alzheimer's disease. *Journal of Molecular Neuroscience, 23*, 189–204.

Isohanni, I., Jarvelin, M. R., Nieminen, P., Jones, P., Rantakillio, P., Jokelainen, J., & Isohanni, M. (1998). School performance as a predictor of psychiatric hospitalization in adult life: A 28-year follow-up in the Northern Finland 1966 Birth Cohort. *Psychological Medicine, 28*, 967–974.

Jencks, C. (1979). *Who gets ahead? The determinants of economic success in America*. New York: Basic Books.

Jensen, A. R. (1969). How much can we boost IQ and scholastic achievement? *Harvard Educational Review, 39*, 1–123.

*Johnson, W., Harris, S. E., Collins, P., Starr, J. M., Whalley, L. J., & Deary, I. J. (2007). No association of *CETP* genotype with cognitive function or age-related cognitive change. *Neuroscience Letters, 420*, 189–192.

*Kachiwala, S. J., Harris, S. E., Wright, A. F., Hayward, C., Starr, J. M., Whalley, L. J., & Deary, I. J. (2005). Genetic influences on oxidative stress and their association with normal cognitive ageing. *Neuroscience Letters, 386*, 116–120.

Katzman, R. (1993). Education and the prevalence of dementia and Alzheimer's disease. *Neurology, 43*, 13–20.

Keller, J. N., Schmitt, F. A., Scheff, S. W., Ding, Q., Chen, Q., Butterfield, D. A., & Markesbery, W. R. (2005). Evidence of increased oxidative damage in subjects with mild cognitive impairment. *Neurology, 64*, 1152–1156.

Kenrick, D. T., Sadala, E. K., Groth, G., & Trost, M. R. (1990). Evolution, traits, and the stages of human courtship: Qualifying the parental investment model. *Journal of Personality, 58*, 97–116.

Kurella, M., Yaffe, K., Shlipak, M. G., Wenger, N. K., & Chertow, G. M. (2005). Chronic kidney disease and cognitive impairment in menopausal women. *American Journal of Kidney Diseases, 45*, 66–76.

Kuro-o, M. (2006). Klotho as a regulator of fibroblast growth factor signalling and phosphate/calcium metabolism. *Current Opinion in Nephrology and Hypertension, 15*, 437–441.

Lawlor, D. A., Sterne, J. A., Tylenius, P., Davey Smith, G., & Rasmussen, F. (2006). Association of childhood socioeconomic position with cause-specific mortality in a prospective record linkage study of 1,839,384 individuals. *American Journal of Epidemiology, 164*, 907–915.

*Leaper, S. A., Murray, A. D., Lemmon, H. A., Staff, R. T., Deary, I. J., Crawford, J. R., & Whalley, L. J. (2001). Neuropsychologic correlates of brain white matter lesions depicted on MR images: 1921 Aberdeen Birth Cohort. *Radiology, 221*, 51–55.

Lezak, M. (1995). *Neuropsychological testing*. Oxford, England: Oxford University Press.

Li, K. Z. H., & Lindenberger, U. (2002). Relations between ageing sensory/sensorimotor and cognitive functions. *Neuroscience and Biobehavioral Reviews, 26*, 777–783.

Lin, M. T., & Beal, M. F. (2006, October 19). Mitochondrial dysfunction and oxidative stress in neurodegenerative diseases. *Nature, 443*, 787–795.

Lynch, M. (1992). *Scotland: A new history*. London: Pimlico.

Lynn, R. (1996). *Dysgenics*. Westport, CT: Praeger Publishers.

Mackintosh, N. J. (1998a). *IQ and human intelligence*. Oxford, England: Oxford University Press.

Mackintosh, N. J. (1998b). Reply to Lynn. *Journal of Biosocial Science, 30*, 533–539.

*MacPherson, J. S. (1958). *Eleven-year-olds grow up* (Publications of the Scottish Council for Research in Education XLII). London: University of London Press.

Maller, J. B. (1933). Vital indices and their relation to psychological and social factors. *Human Biology, 5*, 94–121.

Malmstrom, T. K., Wolinsky, F. D., Andresen, E. M., Miller, J. P., & Miller, D. K. (2005). Cognitive ability and physical performance in middle-aged African Americans. *Journal of the American Geriatrics Society, 53*, 997–1001.

Marang-van de Mheen, P., Shipley, M. J., Witteman, J., Marmot, M. G., & Gunning-Schepers, L. J. (2001). Decline of the relative risk of death associated with low employment grade at older age: The impact of age related differences in smoking, blood pressure, and plasma cholesterol. *Journal of Epidemiology and Community Health, 55*, 24–28.

Marmot, M. G., Davey Smith, G., Stansfeld, S., Patel, C., North, F., Head, J., et al. (1991). Health inequalities among British civil servants: The Whitehall II study. *The Lancet, 337*, 1387–1393.

Martinez-Vea, A., Salvadó, E., Bardají, A. Guitierrez, C., Ramos, A., García, C., et al. (2006). Silent cerebral white mater lesions and their relationship with vascular risk factors in middle-aged predialysis patients with CKD. *American Journal of Kidney Diseases, 47*, 241–250.

Martin, L., & Kubzansky, L. D. (2005). Childhood cognitive performance and risk of mortality: A prospective cohort study of gifted individuals. *American Journal of Epidemiology, 162*, 887–890.

*Maxwell, J. (1961). *The level and trend of national intelligence: The contribution of the Scottish Mental Surveys* (Publications of the Scottish Council for Research in Education XLVI). London: University of London Press.

*Maxwell, J. (1969a). Intelligence, education and fertility: A comparison between the 1932 and 1947 Scottish Surveys. *Journal of Biosocial Science, 1,* 247–271.

*Maxwell, J. (1969b). *Sixteen years on: A follow-up of the 1949 Scottish Survey* (Publications of the Scottish Council for Research in Education LVIII). London: University of London Press.

*Maxwell, J., & Pilliner, A. E. G. (1960). The intellectual resemblances between sibs. *Annals of Human Genetics, 24,* 23–32.

McClelland, W. (1942). *Selection for secondary education* (Publications of the Scottish Council for Research in Education XIX). London: University of London Press.

McDaniel, M. A. (2005). Big-brained people are smarter: A meta-analysis of the relationship between *in vivo* brain volume and intelligence. *Intelligence, 33,* 337–346.

McEwen, B. S. (2006). Protective and damaging effects of stress mediators: Central role of the brain. *Dialogues in Clinical Neurosciences, 8,* 367–381.

McGonigal, G., Thomas, B., McQuade, C., Starr, J. M., MacLennan, W. J., & Whalley, L. J. (1993, March 13). Epidemiology of Alzheimer's presenile dementia in Scotland, 1974–1988. *BMJ, 306,* 680–683.

McGuffin, P., Farmer, A., & Harvey, I. (1991). A polydiagnostic application of operational criteria in studies of psychotic illness: Development ad reliability of the OPCRIT system. *Archives of General Psychiatry, 48,* 764–770.

*McGurn, B., Starr, J. M., Topfer, J. A., Pattie, A., Whiteman, M. C., Lemmon, H. A., et al. (2004). Pronunciation of irregular words is preserved in dementia, validating premorbid IQ estimation. *Neurology, 62,* 1184–1186.

Meador, K. J. (1998). Cognitive effects of medications. *Neurologic Clinics of North America, 16,* 141–155.

*Mehrotra, S. N., & Maxwell, J. (1949). The intelligence of twins: A comparative study of eleven-year-old twins. *Population Studies, 3,* 295–302.

*Mekel-Bobrov, N., Posthuma, D., Gilbert, S. L., Lind, P., Gosso, M. F., Luciano, M., et al. (2007). The ongoing adaptive evolution of ASPM and Microcephalin is not explained by increased intelligence. *Human Molecular Genetics, 16,* 600–608.

Mesulam, M. M. (1990). Large-scale, neurocognitive networks and distributed processing for attention, language, and memory. *Annals of Neurology, 28,* 597–613.

Miller, A. L. (2003). The methionine–homocysteine cycle and its effects on cognitive diseases. *Alternative Medicine Review, 8,* 7–19.

Miller, D. B., & O'Callaghan, J. P. (2005). Aging, stress and the hippocampus. *Ageing Research Reviews, 4,* 123–140.

Miller, G. (2000). Sexual selection for indicators of intelligence. In G. R. Bock, J. A. Goode, & K. Webb (Eds.), *The nature of intelligence* (pp. 260–275). New York: Wiley.

*Munang, L., Starr, J. M., Whalley, L. J., & Deary, I. J. (2007). Renal function and cognition in the 1932 Scottish Mental Survey Lothian cohort. *Age and Ageing, 36,* 323–325.

*Murray, A. D., Staff, R. T., Shenkin, S. D., Deary, I. J., Starr, J. M., & Whalley, L. J. (2005). Brain white matter hyperintensities: Relative importance of vascular risk factors in non-demented elderly people. *Radiology, 237,* 251–257.

Neale, M. C. (2003). A finite mixture distribution model for data collected from twins. *Twin Research, 6,* 235–239.

Neisser, U., Boodoo, G., Bouchard, T. J., Boykin, A. W., Brody, N., Ceci, S. J., et al. (1996). Intelligence: Knowns and unknowns. *American Psychologist, 51,* 77–101.

Nelson, H. E., & Willison, J. R. (1991). *National Adult Reading Test (NART) test manual* (Part II). Windsor, England: Nfer-Nelson.

O'Boyle, C. A., Browne, J., Hickey, A., McGhee, H. M., & Joyce, C. R. B. (1995). *Schedule for the Evaluation of Individual Quality of Life (SEIQoL): A direct weighting procedure for quality of life domains (SEIQoL-DW).* Unpublished questionnaire, Department of Psychology, Royal College of Surgeons in Ireland, Dublin.

O'Brien, J. T., Erkinjuntti, T., Reisberg, B., Roman, G., Sawada, T., Pantoni, L., et al. (2003). Vascular cognitive impairment. *Lancet Neurology, 2,* 89–98.

O'Sullivan, M., Jones, D. K., Summers, P. E., Morris, R. G., Williams, S. C., & Markus, H. S. (2001). Evidence for cortical "disconnection" as a mechanism of age-related cognitive decline. *Neurology, 57,* 632–638.

O'Toole, B. I., Adena, M. A., & Jones, M. P. (1988). Risk factors for mortality in Australian Vietnam-era national servicemen: A case-control study. *Community Health Studies, 12,* 408–417.

Paterson, L. (2003). *Scottish education in the twentieth century.* Edinburgh, Scotland: Edinburgh University Press.

Patton, N., Aslam, T. M., MacGillivray, T., Deary, I. J., Dhillon, B., Eikelboom, R. H., et al. (2006). Retinal image analysis: Concepts, applications and potential. *Progress in Retinal and Eye Research, 25,* 99–127.

Patton, N., Aslam, T. M., MacGillivray, T., Pattie, A., Deary, I. J., & Dhillon, B. (2005). Retinal vascular image analysis as a potential screening tool for cerebrovascular disease: A rationale based on homology between cerebral and retinal microvasaculatures. *Journal of Anatomy, 206,* 319–348.

*Patton, N., Pattie, A., MacGillivray, T., Aslam, T., Dhillon, B., Gow, A., et al. (2007). The association between retinal vascular geometry and cognitive ability in an elderly population. *Investigative Ophthalmology and Visual Science, 48,* 1995–2000.

Pearce, M. S., Deary, I. J., Young, A. H., & Parker, L. (2006). Childhood IQ and deaths up to middle age: The Newcastle Thousand Families Study. *Public Health, 120,* 1020–1026.

Plomin, R., & Spinath, F. (2004). Intelligence: Genetics, genes, and genomics. *Journal of Personality and Social Psychology, 86,* 112–129.

Porteous, D. J., Thomson, P., Brandon, N. J., & Millar, J. K. (2006). The genetics and biology of DISC1: An emerging role in psychosis and cognition. *Biological Psychiatry, 60,* 123–131.

Rutter, M., MacDonald, H., Lecouteur, A., Harrington, R., Bolton, P., & Bailey, A. (1990). Genetic factors in child psychiatric disorders: Part 2. Empirical findings. *Journal of Child Psychology and Psychiatry and Allied Disciplines, 31*, 38–83.

Salthouse, T. A. (1996). The processing-speed theory of adult age differences in cognition. *Psychological Review, 103*, 403–428.

Salthouse, T. A. (2000). Aging and measures of processing speed. *Biological Psychology, 54*, 35–54.

Salthouse, T. A., & Ferrer-Caja, E. (2003). What needs to be explained to account for the age-related effects on multiple cognitive variables? *Psychology and Aging, 18*, 91–110.

Sapolsky, R. M. (2005, April 29). The influence of social hierarchy on primate health. *Science, 308*, 648–652.

Satz, P. (1993). Brain reserve capacity and symptom onset after brain injury: A formulation and a review of evidence for threshold theory. *Neuropsychology, 7*, 273–295.

Saunders, P. (1997). Social mobility in Britain: An empirical evaluation of two competing theories. *Sociology, 31*, 261–288.

Saunders, P. (2002). Reflections on the meritocracy debate in Britain: A response to Richard Breen and John Goldthorpe. *British Journal of Sociology, 53*, 559–574.

Savitz, J., Solms, M., & Ramesar, R. (2006). The molecular genetics of cognition: Dopamine, COMT and BDNF. *Genes, Brain and Behavior, 5*, 311–328.

Sawrie, S. M., Marson, D. C., Boothe, A. L., & Harrell, L. E. (1999). A method for assessing clinically relevant individual cognitive change in older adult populations. *Journal of Gerontology: Series B. Psychological Sciences, 54*, 116–124.

Scheier, M. F., Carver, C. S., & Bridges, M. W. (1994). Distinguishing optimism from neuroticism (and trait anxiety, self-mastery, and self esteem): A re-evaluation of the Life Orientation Test. *Journal of Personality and Social Psychology, 67*, 1063–1078.

Schwartzman, A. E., Gold, D., Andres, D., Arbuckle, T. Y., & Chaikelson, J. (1987). Stability of intelligence: A 40-year follow-up. *Canadian Journal of Psychology, 41*, 244–256.

*Scottish Council for Research in Education. (1933). *The intelligence of Scottish children: A national survey of an age-group* (Publications of the Scottish Council for Research in Education V). London: University of London Press.

Scottish Council for Research in Education. (1937). *Ninth annual report 1936–1937.* London: University of London Press.

*Scottish Council for Research in Education. (1949). *The trend of Scottish intelligence: A comparison of the 1947 and 1932 surveys of the intelligence of eleven-year-old pupils* (Publications of the Scottish Council for Research in Education XXX). London: University of London Press.

Scottish Council for Research in Education. (1953a). *The Scottish Council for Research in Education: Its aims and activities* (revised ed.). London: University of London Press.

Posthuma, D., Baaré, W. F. C., Hulshoff Pol, H. E., Kahn, R. S., Boomsma, D. I., & De Geus, E. J. C. (2003). Genetic correlations between brain volumes and the WAIS–III dimensions of verbal comprehension, working memory, perceptual organisation, and processing speed. *Twin Research, 6,* 131–139.

Posthuma, D., De Geus, E. J. C., Bleichrodt, N., & Boomsma, D. I. (2000). Twin–singleton differences in intelligence? *Twin Research, 3,* 83–87.

Rafnsson, S. B., Deary, I. J., Smith, F. B., Whiteman, M. C., Rumley, A., Lowe, G. D., & Fowkes, G. D. (2007). Cognitive decline and markers of inflammation and hemostasis: The Edinburgh Artery Study. *Journal of the American Geriatrics Society, 55,* 700–707.

Raven, J. C., Court, J. H., & Raven, J. (1977). *Manual for Raven's Progressive Matrices and Vocabulary Scales.* London: H. K. Lewis.

Raz, N., & Rodrique, K. M. (2006). Differential aging of the brain: Patterns, cognitive correlates and modifiers. *Neuroscience and Biobehavioral Reviews, 30,* 730–748.

Record, R. G., McKeown, T., & Edwards, J. H. (1970). An investigation of the differences in measured intelligence between twins and single births. *Annals Human Genetics, 34,* 11–120.

Registrar General for Scotland. (2001). *Registrar General for Scotland Annual Re 2000.* Retrieved June 7, 2008, from http://www.gro-scotland.gov.uk/statis publications-and-data/annual-report-publications/00annrep/index.html

Richards, M., & Deary, I. J. (2005). A life course approach to cognitive reserv model for cognitive ageing and development? *Annals of Neurology, 58,* 617–

Richards, M., Hardy, R., Kuh, D., & Wadsworth, M. E. (2001, January 27). weight and cognitive function in the British 1946 birth cohort: Longit population based study. *BMJ, 322,* 199–203.

Richards, M., Kuh, D., Hardy, R., & Wadsworth, M. E. (1999). Lifetime co function and timing of the natural menopause. *Neurology, 53,* 308–314.

Richards, M., & Sacker, A. (2003). Lifetime antecedents of cognitive reserv nal of Clinical and Experimental Psychology, 25, 614–624.

Richards, M., Strachan, D., Hardy, R., Kuh, D., & Wadsworth, M. (200 function and cognitive ability in a longitudinal birth cohort study. *Psyc Medicine, 67,* 602–608.

Riggs, K. M., Spiro, A. III, Tucker, K., & Rush, D. (1996). Relations of vita vitamin B-6, folate, and homocysteine to cognitive performance in th tive Ageing Study. *American Journal of Clinical Nutrition, 63,* 306–31

Ronalds, G. A., De Stavola, B. L., & Leon, D. A. (2005, November 18). tive cost of being a twin: Evidence from comparisons within fam Aberdeen Children of the 1950s Cohort Study. *BMJ, 331,* 1306–1

Royle, E. (1997). *Modern Britain: A social history, 1750–1997* (2nd e Hodder Arnold.

Rujescu, D., Hartmann, A. M., Gonnermann, C., Moller, H. J., & (2003). M129V variation in the prion protein may influence cogn ance. *Molecular Psychiatry, 8,* 937–941.

*Scottish Council for Research in Education. (1953b). *Social implications of the 1947 Scottish Mental Survey* (Publications of the Scottish Council for Research in Education XXXV). London: University of London Press.

*Scottish Council for Research in Education. (1958). *Educational and other aspects of the 1947 Scottish Mental Survey* (Publications of the Scottish Council for Research in Education XLI). London: University of London Press.

Scottish Council for Research in Education. (1963). *Scottish Council for Research in Education twenty-fifth annual report.* London: University of London Press.

Sharp, S. (1997). Much more at home with 3.999 pupils than with four: The contributions to psychometrics of Sir Godfrey Thomson. *British Journal of Mathematical and Statistical Psychology, 50,* 163–174.

*Shenkin, S. D., Bastin, M. E., MacGillivray, T. J., Deary, I. J., Starr, J. M., & Wardlaw, J. M. (2003). Childhood and current cognitive function in healthy 80-year-olds: A DT–MRI study. *NeuroReport, 14,* 345–349.

Shenkin, S. D., Starr, J. M., & Deary, I. J. (2004). Birth weight and cognitive ability in childhood: A systematic review. *Psychological Bulletin, 130,* 989–1013.

*Shenkin, S. D., Starr, J. M., Pattie, A., Rush, M. A., Whalley, L. J., & Deary, I. J. (2001). Birth weight and cognitive function at age 11 years: The Scottish Mental Survey 1932. *Archives of Disease in Childhood, 85,* 189–197.

Shields, S. A. (1982). The variability hypothesis: The history of a biological model of sex differences in intelligence. *Signs, 7,* 769–797.

Shipley, B. A., Der, G., Taylor, M. D., & Deary, I. J. (2006). Cognition and all-cause mortality across the entire adult age range: Health and lifestyle survey. *Psychosomatic Medicine, 68,* 17–24.

*Sisodiya, S. M., Thompson, P. J., Need, A., Harris, S. E., Weale, M. E., Wilkie, S. E., et al. (2007). Genetic enhancement of cognition in a kindred with cone-rod dystrophy due to *RIMS1* mutation. *Journal of Medical Genetics, 44,* 373–380.

Small, B. J., Rosnick, C. B., Fratiglioni, L., & Backman, L. (2004). Apolipoprotein E and cognitive performance: A meta-analysis. *Psychology and Aging, 19,* 592–600.

Smith, J. D. (2002). Apolipoproteins and aging: Emerging mechanisms. *Ageing Research Reviews, 1,* 345–365.

Smout, T. C. (1997). *A century of the Scottish people, 1830–1950.* London: Fontana.

Snowdon, D. A., Greiner, L. H., Kemper, S. J., Nanayakkara, N., & Mortimer, J. A. (1999). Linguistic ability in early life and longevity: Findings from the Nun Study. In J. Robine, B. Forette, C. Franceschi, & M. Allard (Eds.), *The paradoxes of longevity* (pp. 103–113). New York: Springer-Verlag.

Snowdon, D. A., Kemper, S. J., Mortimer, J. A., Greiner, L. H., Wekstein, D. R., & Markesbery, W. R. (1996). Linguistic ability in early life and cognitive function and Alzheimer's disease in late life: Findings from the Nun Study. *Journal of the American Medical Association, 275,* 528–532.

*Staff, R. T., Murray, A. D., Deary, I. J., & Whalley, L. J. (2004). What provides cerebral reserve? *Brain, 127,* 1191–1199.

*Staff, R. T., Murray, A. D., Deary, I. J., & Whalley, L. J. (2006). Generality and specificity in cognitive ageing: A volumetric brain analysis. *NeuroImage, 30,* 1433–1440.

Starr, J. M. (1999). Blood pressure and cognitive decline in the elderly. *Current Opinion in Nephrology and Hypertension, 8,* 347–351.

*Starr, J. M., Deary, I. J., Fox, H. C., & Whalley, L. J. (2007). Smoking and cognitive change from age 11 to age 66 years: A confirmatory investigation. *Addictive Behaviors, 32,* 63–68.

*Starr, J. M., Deary, I. J., Lemmon, H., & Whalley, L. J. (2000). Mental ability age 11 years and health status age 77 years. *Age and Ageing, 29,* 523–528.

*Starr, J. M., Fox, H., Harris, S. E., Deary, I. J., & Whalley, L. J. (2007). COMT genotype and cognitive ability: A longitudinal aging study. *Neuroscience Letters, 421,* 57–61.

*Starr, J. M., Leaper, S. A., Murray, A. D., Lemmon, H. A., Staff, R. T., Deary, I. J., & Whalley, L. J. (2003). Brain white matter lesions detected by magnetic resonance imaging are associated with balance and gait speed. *Journal of Neurology, Neurosurgery and Psychiatry, 74,* 94–98.

*Starr, J. M., McGurn, B., Harris, S. E., Whalley, L. J., Deary, I. J., & Shiels, P. G. (2007). Association between telomere length and heart disease in a narrow age cohort of older people. *Experimental Genrontology, 42,* 571–573.

*Starr, J. M., McGurn, B., Whiteman, M., Pattie, A., Whalley, L. J., & Deary, I. J. (2004). Life long changes in cognitive ability are associated with prescribed medications in old age. *International Journal of Geriatric Psychiatry, 19,* 327–332.

*Starr, J. M., Pattie, A., Whiteman, M. C., Deary, I. J., & Whalley, L. J. (2005). Vitamin B-12, serum folate, and cognitive change between 11 and 79 years. *Journal of Neurology, Neurosurgery and Psychiatry, 76,* 291–292.

*Starr, J. M., Taylor, M. D., Hart, C. L., Davey Smith, G. D., Whalley, L. J., Hole, D. J., et al. (2004). Childhood mental ability and blood pressure at midlife: Linking the Scottish Mental Survey 1932 and the Midspan Studies. *Journal of Hypertension, 22,* 893–897.

Starr, J. M., Whalley, L. J., Inch, S., & Schering, P. A. (1992). The quantification of the relative effects of age and NART-predicted IQ on cognitive function in healthy old people. *International Journal of Geriatric Psychiatry, 7,* 153–157.

Stern, Y. (2002). What is cognitive reserve? Theory and research application of the reserve concept. *Journal of the International Neuropsychological Society, 8,* 448–460.

Strand, S., Deary, I. J., & Smith, P. (2006). Sex differences in cognitive ability test score: A UK national picture. *British Journal of Educational Psychology, 76,* 463–480.

Tabbarah, M., Crimmins, E. M., & Seeman, T. E. (2002). The relationship between physical and cognitive performance. *Journal of Gerontology: Series A. Medical Sciences, 57,* 228–235.

Tang, Y., Nyengaard, J. R., Pakkenberg, B., & Gundersen, H. J. G. (1997). Age-induced white matter changes in the human brain: A stereological investigation. *Neurobiology of Aging, 18,* 609–615.

*Taylor, M. D., Hart, C. L., Davey Smith, G. D., Starr, J. M., Hole, D. J., Whalley, L. J., et al. (2003). Childhood mental ability and smoking cessation in adulthood: Prospective observational study linking the Scottish Mental Survey 1932 and the Midspan Studies. *Journal of Epidemiology and Community Health, 57,* 464–465.

*Taylor, M. D., Hart, C. L., Davey Smith, G. D., Starr, J. M., Hole, D. J., Whalley, L. J., et al. (2005). Childhood IQ and social factors on smoking behavior, lung function and smoking-related outcomes in adulthood: Linking the Scottish Mental Survey 1932 and the Midspan Studies. *British Journal of Health Psychology, 10,* 399–410.

*Taylor, M. D., Hart, C. L., Davey Smith, G. D., Whalley, L. J., Hole, D. J., Wilson, V., & Deary, I. J. (2005). Childhood IQ and marriage by mid-life: The Scottish Mental Survey 1932 and the Midspan Studies. *Personality and Individual Differences, 38,* 1621–1630.

Terman, L. M. (1916). *The measurement of intelligence.* Boston: Houghton Mifflin.

Terman, L. M., & Ogden, M. H. (1947). *The gifted child grows up: Twenty-five years follow-up of a superior group* (Genetic Studies of Genius IV). Stanford, CA: Stanford University Press.

Thomson, G. H. (1936). *Intelligence and civilisation.* Edinburgh, Scotland: Edinburgh University Press.

Thomson, G. H. (1940). *What are Moray House Tests?* London: University of London Press.

Thomson, G. H. (1969). *The education of an Englishman: An autobiography.* Edinburgh, Scotland: Moray House College of Education.

*Thomson, P. A., Harris, S. E., Starr, J. M., Whalley, L. J., Porteous, D. J., & Deary, I. J. (2005). Association between genotype at an exonic SNP in *DISC1* and normal cognitive aging. *Neuroscience Letters, 389,* 41–45.

Tisserand, D. J., & Jolles, J. (2003). On the involvement of prefrontal networks in cognitive ageing. *Cortex, 39,* 1107–1128.

Townsend, P. (1979). *Poverty in the United Kingdom.* Harmondsworth, England: Penguin.

Turic, D., Fisher, P. J., Plomin, R., & Owen, M. J. (2001). No association between apolipoprotein E polymorphisms and general cognitive ability in children. *Neuroscience Letters, 299,* 97–100.

*Visscher, P. M., Tynan, M., Whiteman, M. C., Pattie, A., White, I., Hayward, C., et al. (2003). Lack of association between polymorphisms in angiotensin-converting-enzyme and methylenetetrahydrofolate reductase genes and normal cognitive ageing in humans. *Neuroscience Letters, 347,* 175–178.

Wadsworth, M., Kuh, D., Richards, M., & Hardy, R. (2006). Cohort profile: The 1946 National Birth Cohort (MRC National Survey of Health and Development). *International Journal of Epidemiology, 35,* 49–54.

*Walker, N. P., McConville, P. M., Hunter, D., Deary, I. J., & Whalley, L. J. (2002). Childhood mental ability and lifetime psychiatric contact: A 66-year follow-up study of the 1932 Scottish Mental Ability Survey. *Intelligence, 30,* 233–245.

Webbink, D., Roeleveld, J., & Visscher, P. M. (2006). Identification of twin pairs from large population-based samples. *Twin Research and Human Genetics, 9,* 496–500.

Wechsler, D. (1981). *Wechsler Adult Intelligence Scale—Revised.* New York: Psychological Corporation.

Wechsler, D. (1987). *Wechsler Memory Scale—Revised.* New York: Psychological Corporation.

Wechsler, D. (1997). *Wechsler Adult Intelligence Scale—III.* New York: Psychological Corporation.

Werneke, U., Turner, T., & Priebe, S. (2006). Complementary medicines in psychiatry: Review of effectiveness and safety. *British Journal of Psychiatry, 188,* 109–121.

*Whalley, L. J., & Deary, I. J. (2001, April 7). Longitudinal cohort study of childhood IQ and survival up to age 76. *BMJ, 322,* 819–822.

*Whalley, L. J., Fox, H. C., Deary, I. J., & Starr, J. M. (2005). Childhood IQ, smoking, and cognitive change from age 11 to 64 years. *Addictive Behaviors, 30,* 77–88.

*Whalley, L. J., Fox, H. C., Lemmon, H. A., Duthie, S. J., Collins, A. R., Peace, H., et al. (2003). Dietary supplement use in old age: Associations with childhood IQ, current cognition and health. *International Journal of Geriatric Psychiatry, 18,* 769–776.

*Whalley, L. J., Fox, H. C., Starr, J. M., & Deary, I. J. (2004). Age at natural menopause and cognition. *Maturitas, 49,* 148–156.

*Whalley, L. J., Fox, H. C., Wahle, K. W., Starr, J. M., & Deary, I. J. (2004). Cognitive aging, childhood intelligence, and the use of food supplements: Possible involvement of n-3 fatty acids. *American Journal of Clinical Nutrition, 80,* 1650–1657.

*Whalley, L. J., Staff, R. T., Murray, A. D., Duthie, S. J., Collins, A. R., Lemmon, H. A., et al.(2003). Plasma vitamin C, cholesterol and homocysteine are associated with grey matter volume determined by MRI in non-demented older people. *Neuroscience Letters, 341,* 173–176.

*Whalley, L. J., Starr, J. M., Athawes, R., Hunter, D., Pattie, A., & Deary, I. J. (2000). Childhood mental ability and dementia. *Neurology, 55,* 1455–1459.

Winblad, B., Jelic, V., Kershaw, P., & Amatniek, J. (2007). Effects of statins on cognitive function in patients with Alzheimer's disease in galantamine clinical trials. *Drugs and Aging, 24,* 57–61.

Wong, T. Y., Klein, R., Sharrett, A. R., Nieto, F. J., Boland, L. L., Couper, D. J., et al. (2002). Retinal microvascular abnormalities and cognitive impairment in middle-aged persons: The Atherosclerosis Risk in Communities Study. *Stroke, 33,* 1487–1492.

World Health Organization. (1994). *International classification of diseases* (10th ed.). Geneva: Author.

Xiong, G. L., Benson, A., & Doraiswamy, P. M. (2005). Statins and cognition: What can we learn from existing randomized trials? *CNS Spectrums, 10,* 867–874.

Yaffe, K., Barrett-Connor, E., Lin, F., & Grady, D. (2002). Serum lipoprotein levels, statin use, and cognitive function in older women. *Archives of Neurology, 59,* 378–384.

Zenderland, L. (1998). *Measuring minds: Henry Herbert Goddord and the origins of American intelligence testing.* Cambridge, England: Cambridge University Press.

Zigmond, A. S., & Snaith, R. P. (1983). The Hospital Anxiety and Depression Scale. *Acta Psychiatrica Scandinavica, 67,* 361–370.

Zipp, F., & Aktas, O. (2006). The brain as a target of inflammation: Common pathways link inflammatory and neurodegenerative diseases. *Trends in Neurosciences, 29,* 518–527.

AUTHOR INDEX

David, A. S., 89, 92
Davies, S., 106
Davis, C., 222
Deary, I. J., 12, 14, 39, 48–59, 62,
    65–70, 74, 77, 79–83, 85, 87–89,
    91, 92, 99, 101, 102, 106,
    109–113, 116–124, 126–129,
    132–134, 136–138, 141–148,
    150, 151, 154, 156, 158,
    160–165, 167, 168, 170, 172,
    173, 182–192, 194, 195, 198,
    201, 202, 204–209, 211, 218,
    219, 222–225
De Geus, E. J. C., 188
De Lacey, G., 218
Del Bo, R., 125
Der, G., 83, 143, 184, 195
De Stavola, B. L., 191
Devine, T. M., 229, 243
Dhillon, B., 156
Diener, E., 200
Doraiswamy, P. M., 175
Duthie, S. J., 166–169

Edwards, J. H., 187
Egan, M. F., 127, 130, 131
Eikelboom, R. H., 156
Emmons, R. A., 200
Emslie, C., 198

Farmer, A., 90
Ferrer-Caja, E., 120, 142, 151
Fillit, H. M., 160
Finch, C. E., 53, 71
Fisher, P. J., 117
Flynn, J. R., 24
Folstein, M. F., 103, 104, 118, 200, 218
Folstein, S. E., 103, 118, 200, 218
Fox, H., 65, 67, 74, 79–81, 101n, 112,
    113, 124, 129–133, 161–163,
    170–174, 211
Fratiglioni, L., 120
Freeman, J., 222
Fukunishi, I., 158
Furnham, A., 202
Furu, M., 46

Gabrieli, J. D. E., 151
Gale, C. R., 83
Giegling, I., 125
Godfrey, H., 222
Goff, M., 202, 203
Gold, D., 109
Goldthorpe, J. H., 205
Gonnermann, C., 125
Gottfredson, L., 68, 82, 83
Gove, W. R., 199
Gow, A. J., 101, 102, 128, 200–204,
    212, 225
Grady, D., 175
Gray, J., 39
Greiner, L. H., 48, 86
Griffin, S., 200
Groth, G., 199
Gundersen, H. J., 139
Gunning-Dixon, F. M., 135
Gunning-Schepers, L. J., 74

Halliwell, B., 125, 157
Hamilton, G., 121
Hardy, R., 38, 77, 79, 164, 192
Harrell, L. E., 222
Harris, S. E., 116, 122–134
Hart, C., 54–64, 70–78, 198, 199, 205,
    207–209
Hartmann, A. M., 125
Harvey, I., 90
Hayflick, L., 123
Hayward, C., 117, 120, 124, 126, 129,
    132–134
Heasman, M. A., 65
Hedden, T., 151
Hedges, L. V., 182
Heim, A., 181, 184
Hemmingsson, T., 82
Her Majesty's Stationery Office, 17
Herrmann, W., 168
Herrnstein, R. J., 197, 205
Hickey, A., 210
Ho, M.-Y., 222
Hobbes, T., 201
Hoddings, N., 182
Hole, D., 70

Hole, D. J., 58, 60–64, 75, 76, 78
Hope, K., xii
Horn, J. L., 202
Horne, V., 106
Huang, Y., 119
Hunt, K., 198
Hunter, D., 88, 89, 91, 92

Inch, S., 218
Irwing, P., 184
Isohanni, I., 89

Jelic, V., 175
Jencks, C., 46, 205
Jensen, A. R., 38
Johnson, W., 134
Jolles, J., 142
Jones, M. P., 46
Jorm, A. F., 68, 165
Joyce, C. R. B., 210

Kachiwala, S. J., 125, 126
Katzman, R., 86
Keller, J. N., 125, 157
Kemper, S. J., 48, 86
Kendrick, D. T., 199
Kershaw, P., 175
Korten, A., 68, 165
Kristenson, H., 46
Kubzansky, L. D., 82
Kuh, D., 38, 77, 79, 164, 192
Kurella, M., 158

Larsen, R. J., 200
Lawlor, D. A., 46
Leaper, S., 101n, 135–138, 146, 147,
    167
Lemmon, H., 12, 68, 74, 77, 106, 109,
    136, 137, 146, 147, 211, 220, 221
Leon, D. A., 191
Lewis, G., 89
Lezak, M., 105, 108
Li, K. Z. H., 165
Lin, F., 175
Lin, M. T., 165
Lindenberger, U., 165

Lingärde, F., 46
Ljung, B.-O., 46
Lundberg, I., 82
Lynch, M., 243
Lynn, R., x

MacGillivray, T., 141, 156
Macintyre, S., 83, 198
MacKinnon, A. J., 68, 165
MacKinnon, P. L., 54, 55, 57, 58
Mackintosh, N. J., 182
MacLennan, W. J., 85
MacPherson, J. S., 28–32
Mahley, R. W., 119
Maller, J. B., 46, 47
Malmberg, A., 89
Malmstrom, T. K., 163
Mann, A., 159
Marang-van de Mheen, P., 74
Markesbery, W. R., 86
Marmot, M. G., 74, 198, 199
Marson, D. C., 222
Martin, L., 82
Martinez-Vea, A., 158
Maxwell, J., 15, 32–38, 40, 185, 188
McClelland, W., 8
McConville, P. M., 89, 91, 92
McCrae, R. R., 203
McDaniel, M. A., 151
McEwen, B. S., 165
McGhee, H. M., 210
McGonigal, G., 86
McGue, M., 185
McGuffin, P., 90
McGurn, B., 134, 174, 220–222
McHugh, P. R., 103, 118, 200, 218
McKeown, T., 187
McPherson, A. F., 39
Meador, K. J., 174
Mehrotra, S. N., 185, 188
Mekel-Bobrov, N., 134
Melin, B., 82
Mesulam, M. M., 142
Millar, J. K., 126
Miller, A. L., 168
Miller, D. B., 165

SUBJECT INDEX

Cereal fiber, 171
Cerebral reserve, 148–151
CETP (cholesteryl ester transfer protein),
    134
Charitable organizations, 233
Cholesterol, 169, 175
Cholesteryl ester transfer protein
    (CETP), 134
Christian moral values, 236, 238
Chronic obstructive pulmonary disease,
    77
Church building, 232
CI (confidence interval), 47
Cities
    IQ and residence in, 31
    overcrowding of, 232–233
    of Scotland, 231–232
    slum dwellings in, 232
Civil Service entrance examinations, 7
Classics, classes in the, 236
Class size, 27
Clean water, 232
Coalfields, 234
Coats, Archibald, 230
Cognitive ability, 122
Cognitive aging, 43
    causes of, 97–98
    common-cause hypothesis of, 68
    estimating, 215
    gene studies of, 99
    and hypertension, 78, 79
    and menopause, 79–81
    and technology, 98–100
    testing of, 98
Cognitive aging studies, 101–114
    Aberdeen Birth Cohort 1921,
        102–106
    Aberdeen Birth Cohort 1936, 106
    Lothian Birth Cohort 1921, 106–109
    recruitment for, 101–102
    and stability of intelligence over life-
        time, 109–114
Cognitive change, 222–224
Cognitive epidemiology
    defined, 43
    explanatory model of, 82
    and physical illness, 81–83
    studies of, 43–44

Cognitive reserve capacity, 89
Cognitive tests
    Digit Symbol, 105
    health outcomes testing, 106
    Hospital Anxiety Depression Scale,
        106
    Logical Memory, 107–108
    Mini-Mental State Examination, 104
    Moray House Test. *See* Moray House
        Test
    National Adult Reading Test, 105–106
    Raven's Standard Progressive
        Matrices, 104
    Rey Auditory Verbal Learning Test,
        105
    Uses of Common Objects, 105
    Verbal Fluency, 108
Collaborative Study, 54
Colon cancer, 71
Common-cause hypothesis, of cognitive
    aging, 68
Community Health Index
    Aberdeen, 45, 49
    Edinburgh, 107
    Grampian, 89, 103
    Scotland's, 43–44
Compliance, with medical advice, 242
Composition (class subject), 236
Comprehensive education, 239
Compulsory education, 236, 238, 239
COMT gene. *See Catechol-O-*
    methyltransferase gene
Concordia study, 109, 110
Confidence interval (CI), 47
Conscientiousness, 29
Contagious disease, 232
Coordinated movement, 146
Copper uptake, 125
Copy number variations, 116
Coronary heart disease, 72, 73, 122
Cortical disconnection syndrome, 139
Cost of living, 233
Cox's proportional hazards regression
    analysis, 47, 50, 60, 76
Criminal offenses, 35
Crystallized stores, 202

Deaf children, 7
Deary, Ann, x
Deary, Ian, x, xi
Deary, Richard, 10
Deep/subcortical white matter, 136–138, 146
Dementia, 85–89
  in ABC1921, 103
  early-onset, 86–87, 121–122
  late-onset, 87–88, 121
  and NART validation, 218–222
  screening test for, 104
Democratic ideals, 238
Depression, 106, 147, 212
Deprivation, 55, 57, 58, 60–63, 209
Developmental origins of health and adult disease hypothesis, 192
Diener, E., 200
Dietary supplements, 170–174
Diffusion tensor magnetic resonance imaging, 139–141
Digit Symbol, 105
DISC1 gene. See Disrupted in schizophrenia 1 gene
Disease, 232
Disease outcome, 73–74
Disrupted in schizophrenia 1 (DISC1) gene, 126–127
Distaste for school, 33
Distribution, of test, 9
Diuretics, 174
Divorced parents, 31
Dizygotic twins, 186, 187
Docosahexaenoic acid, 173
Doctor–patient relationship, 240, 242
Doctors, 36, 240–242
Dopamine, 168
Dopamine signaling, 128, 129
Douglas, J. W. B., 38
Drever, James, 6–9
Dundee, Scotland, 230, 231, 234

e2 allele of APOE, 117, 119–121
e3 allele of APOE, 117, 119–121
e4 allele of APOE, 117–121
Early-onset dementia, 86–87, 121–122
Economy, Scottish, 231, 238

Edinburgh, Scotland, 25, 107, 229, 231–232
Edinburgh Hospitals, 179
Edinburgh Royal Maternity Hospital, 193
Education
  and cerebral reserve, 150
  compulsory, 236, 239
  and occupational class/intelligence, 38
  parents' level of, 28, 35
  and social mobility, 206, 210
Education Act of 1946 (Scotland), 17
Educational and Other Aspects of the 1947 Scottish Mental Survey (SCRE), 25–27
Educational Institute of Scotland (EIS), 6, 19, 238–239
Educational outcomes, of SMS1947 cohort, 29
Educational system, 229, 235–240
  curriculum of, 236
  mandates for, 235–236
  secondary-level, 237–240
  state support of, 239
  university, 236–237
Education Health Service of Glasgow, 24
EIS. See Educational Institute of Scotland
Eleven-Year-Olds Grow Up (MacPherson), 27–32
Emigration, from Scotland, 33, 35, 49, 230, 235, 238
Endophenotypes, 143
English public school model, 239
Entrance examinations, 236
Epidemics, 232
Epidemiology, cognitive. See Cognitive epidemiology
Esophageal cancer, 77
Eugenics, 17
Eugenics Society, 17
Evictions, 233
Excitatory neuroreceptor activation, 168
Executive function, 105, 108, 145
Expectations, low, 233
Exports, 231

Family, and quality of life, 210–212
Family Doctor Committee, 103

father's. *See* Paternal occupation
of SMS1947 cohort, 30
of sons/fathers, 34–36
Occupational class(es)
and cerebral reserve, 149–150
and childhood IQ, 32
and education/intelligence, 38
and marriage studies, 199
in midlife, 56–57
and social mobility, 206–210
types of, 55
in west-of-Scotland mortality study,
61–63
Occupational mobility, 35
OPCRIT system, 90
Openness, 202, 203
Optimism, 212
Orr, A. M., 38
Overcrowding, 30n2, 31, 52, 232–233
Overmatching, 86–87
Oxidative stress, 116, 123, 125–126,
165, 168

Pack years of smoking, 163
Pancreatic cancer, 71, 77
Parents
death of, 31
educational involvement of, 34
marriage of, 28
Parkinson's disease, 125
Passive cerebral reserve, 148–150, 154
Past smokers, 75–77
Paternal occupation
and cancer, 70
data gathering about, 24, 28
on death certificates, 52
and educational attainment, 39–40
and IQ, 31, 32
Path analysis, 60, 61, 194
Patient Centred Management System,
89
Penmanship, 236
People, of Scotland, 233–234
Periventricular white matter, 135, 136,
146, 147
Perseverance, 29
Personality disorders, 91

Personality ratings, by teachers, 28, 29, 32
Personality traits, 202–204
Pharyngeal cancer, 77
Philosophy classes, 236
Physical fitness, 163–166
Physical tests, 108
Physiological measures, 106
Pictish people, 234
Pictorial Classification (SCRE), 12
Poland, immigration from, 231
Pons, 146
Poor law relief, 233
Population density, 27, 31
Population Investigation Committee,
16, 17
Poverty, 233
Preliminary Practice Test, 12
Premature birth, 192
Premature death, 230
Presbyterianism, 232
Preventable outcomes, 73
Preventive medicine, 241
Primary school, 237
Prion protein (PRNP) gene, 125–126
Private schools, 8, 29, 238, 239
PRNP gene. *See Prion protein* gene
Professional-class occupations, 35
Protestant Reformation, 235
Psychiatric illness, 89–93
Public housing, 233
Public schools, 238
Puerperal sepsis, 241
Pulmonary disease, 77
Purposive action, 105

Quality of life, 210–212
Queen's Institute of District Nursing, 18

Railways, 232
Raven's Standard Progressive Matrices
(Raven), 104, 222–224
Raw data, 5, 9
Reaction times, 83, 143–144
Recreational activities, 28
Rectal cancer, 71
Regional groups, 26
Register House, 86

Register of Deaths, 48–49
Register of Marriages, 49
Regression path model, 194
Religious education, 236
Remethylation, 168
Renal function, 158
Renfrew–Paisley Study, 54
Residential institutions, 8
Respiratory disease, 72
Retinal vascular network geometry,
    155–157
Reverse causation, 135, 136
Rey Auditory Verbal Learning Test
    (AVLT), 105
RIMS1 gene, 134
Rockefeller Foundation, 28
Roman Catholics, 234, 238
Rowett Research Institute, 114
Royal College, 237
Rural areas, residing in, 31

S-Adenosylmethionine, 168
Safe environments, 68
Sanitation, 233
Satisfaction with life, 200–201
Scandinavian people, 234
Schedule for the Evaluation of Individual
    Quality of Life—Direct Weight-
    ing (SEIQoL–DW), 210–212
Schizophrenia, 89, 91, 126
School attendance, 32, 239
School curriculum, 236
School placement, 8
Schools, separate, 234, 238
School Sisters of Notre Dame, 48
School size, 27
Scoring, of tests, 9, 10
Scotland, 229–243
    education in, 235–240
    emigration from, 235
    illness/health in, 240–242
    IQ related to geography of, 25–26
    in 1900, 230–232
    people of, 233–234
    population of, 229, 230
    social inequalities in, 232–233
Scott, Sir Walter, 232

Scottish Cancer Registry, 66
Scottish Council for Research in Educa-
    tion (SCRE), ix, 5–6, 16, 39, 65,
    239
Scottish Education Department, 238–240
Scottish Heart Health/MONICA ques-
    tionnaire, 170, 171
Scottish-history classes, 236
Scottish Mental Survey of 1932
    (SMS1932), 6–16. *See also*
    Aberdeen Birth Cohort 1921;
    Lothian Birth Cohort 1921
  age of test takers, 8
  birth-weight studies, 193–195
  components of, 11–12
  conclusions of, 14
  and dementia, 85–89
  distribution of test for, 9
  evaluating, 14–16
  example page of, 10
  First Picture Test portion of, 12
  gender studies, 181–185
  lasting value of, 15–16
  marriage studies, 198–199
  and Midspan Studies, 55–57
  planning for, 6–10
  Preliminary Practice Test portion of,
    12
  results of, 13–14
  scope of, 6
  scoring of, 9, 10
  Second Picture Test portion of, 12–13
  social mobility/attainment studies,
    205–210
  test selection for, 8
  timing of, 8
  twin studies, 186–189
  validation of scores, 9, 11
  Verbal Test portion of, 13
Scottish Mental Survey of 1947
    (SMS1947), 16–40. *See also*
    Aberdeen Birth Cohort 1936;
    Lothian Birth Cohort 1936
  aims of, 16
  comparison with SMS1932, 19–21
  educational aspects of, 25–27
  and family position, 21, 22

and mortality, 65–67
objections to, 17
potential uses of, 23
scoring of, 19
7-year follow-up to, 27–32
6-Day Sample of, 18–19
16-year follow-up to, 32–39
and social class, 39–40
social implications of, 23–25
sociological schedule with, 18
36-Day Sample of, 18
twin studies, 185–191
validation of scores, 22
Scottish Mental Surveys (SMSs), x–xiii
comparison of, 19–21
raw data of, 5
timelessness of, xiii
Scottish Morbidity Records 1, 65–66
Scottish Morbidity Records 4, 66
Scottish National Health Service, 58, 65
Scottish Record Linkage System, 65
SCRE. *See* Scottish Council for
Research in Education
SCRE Centre at the University of
Glasgow, 5
Secondary school
Scottish system of, 237–240
selection for, 13
SMS1947 cohort in, 29
social factors in completion of, 31–32
Second Picture Test, 12–13
Sectarian conflict, 234
SEIQoL–DW. *See* Schedule for the
Evaluation of Individual Quality
of Life—Direct Weighting
Self-employed traders, 232
Separated parents, 31
Separate schools, 234, 238
Serotonin, 168
Sewer construction, 232
Sex hormones, 79
Shale oil, 230
Short-term memory, 105
Siblings
number of younger, 28
of parents, 28
testing of, 29, 33, 37

Simpson's Memorial Hospital, 193
Single-nucleotide polymorphism (SNP),
116, 133
6-Day Sample
extent of, 18–19
and mortality/morbidity, 65–67
7-year follow-up studies on, 27, 28
16-year follow-up studies on, 32–37,
39
twins in, 188–191
Sixteen Years On (Maxwell), 32–39
Skilled manual workers, 30
Slum dwellings, 232, 238
Smoking
and cardiovascular disease, 74, 75
as health factor, 159–163
and lung function, 75–78
and mortality, 65
SMS1932. *See* Scottish Mental Survey
of 1932
SMS1947. *See* Scottish Mental Survey
of 1947
SMSs. *See* Scottish Mental Surveys
SNP. *See* Single-nucleotide polymorphism
Social class, 36–37
Social factors, 52–53
*Social Implications of the 1947 Scottish
Mental Survey* (SCRE), 23–25
Social inequalities, 232–233
Socialist thinking, 240–241
Social mobility, 35, 204–210
Socioeconomic status, 197–198
Sociological schedule, 18, 23
Sociological survey, 17
Soundex code, 65
Speed of information processing, 105,
143–145
St. Andrew's Societies, 235
Stability of intelligence over lifetime,
109–114
Standard deviation, 19–21
Stanford–Binet Scale, 11, 109
State-run schools, 8
Statins, 174, 175
Status attainment, 204–210
Stomach cancer, 70, 71
Stroke, 71–74

Vegetables, 171
Verbal Fluency task, 108
Verbal memory, 120
Verbal Test, 12, 13. *See also Moray House Test*
Vietnam veterans, 46, 47
Vitamin B6, 166
Vitamin B12, 166–169
Vitamin C, 169, 171
Vitamin supplements, 170–172
Voxel-based morphometry, 151–153
Voxels, 153

Wages, 230, 233
WAIS–R. *See* Wechsler Adult Intelligence Scale—Revised
Walker, David A., 39
Walker, Norman T., 25
Walking speed, 146, 147, 164
"Wastage," 8, 29, 37
Water, clean, 232
Watt, James, 230
Wealthier families, 233
Wechsler Adult Intelligence Scale—Revised (WAIS–R), 222–224
Wechsler Digit Symbol-Coding test, 12, 105
Wechsler Memory Scale—Revised, 107
Weight, of child, 24
Wellcome Trust Clinical Research Facility, 108
Well-fitting model, 61, 62
West-of-Scotland mortality study, 57–65
    analysis used in, 60–62
    and cancer, 70, 71
    and deprivation, 60–63
    gender differences found in, 59–61

and occupational class, 61–63
    risk factors found in, 64–65
    standard deviation in, 63
Whalley, Lawrence J., x, xi
Whalley, Patricia, x
Whisky production, 231
White matter
    disconnection of, 139–145
    effects on mood/balance/walking speed, 145–147
    function of, 135
    importance of, 153
    mechanisms of association between cognition and, 147–155
    volume of, 152
White matter abnormalities, 135
White matter–cognition association mechanisms, 147–155
    brain volume, 151–155
    cerebral reserve, 148–151
White matter hyperintensities, 135–139
White matter lesions, 135
Will to do well, 29
Women
    in Aberdeen study, 49
    occupational class of, 57
    social class of, 37
    in universities, 237
    with university degrees, 35, 36
Women's occupations, 30, 35, 36
Work patterns, 231
"Workshop of the World," 231
World War I, 7, 229, 237
World War II, 50, 53, 109, 110, 199, 229

Young, James, 230

ABOUT THE AUTHORS

Ian J. Deary, PhD, is professor of differential psychology at the University of Edinburgh and director of the Medical Research Council Centre for Cognitive Ageing and Cognitive Epidemiology.

Lawrence J. Whalley, MD, is professor of mental health at the University of Aberdeen.

John M. Starr, MD, is a consultant physician in geriatric medicine at the Royal Victoria Hospital in Edinburgh and honorary professor in health and aging at the University of Edinburgh.